THE MEMOIRS
OF JACQUES CASANOVA
DE SEINGALT

THE RARE UNABRIDGED LONDON EDITION OF
1894 TRANSLATED BY ARTHUR MACHEN TO
WHICH HAS BEEN ADDED THE CHAPTERS DIS-
COVERED BY ARTHUR SYMONS, A SUPPLEMENT
AND BIBLIOGRAPHY.

VOLUME FIVE

The Memoirs of
JACQUES
CASANOVA
DE SEINGALT

IN LONDON
AND MOSCOW

---

*Volume Five of the first complete and
unabridged English translation*

BY

ARTHUR MACHEN

Illustrated with Old Engravings

G. P. PUTNAM'S SONS, NEW YORK

ELEK BOOKS, LONDON

Published in England by
ELEK BOOKS LIMITED
14 Great James Street
London, W.C.1

Published in the United States of America by
G. P. PUTNAM'S SONS
210 Madison Avenue
New York City 16
New York

Published in Canada by
LONGMANS, GREEN AND COMPANY
Toronto

Printed in the United States of America

CONTENTS

v

CONTENTS

vii

The Memoirs of
JACQUES CASANOVA

CHAPTER I

I Find Rosalie Happy—The Signora Isola-Bella—The Cook—Biribi—Irene—Possano in Prison—My Niece Proves to be an Old Friend of Rosalie's

AT GENOA, where he was known to all, Pogomas called himself Possano. He introduced me to his wife and daughter, but they were so ugly and disgusting in every respect that I left them on some trifling pretext, and went to dine with my new niece. Afterwards I went to see the Marquis Grimaldi, for I longed to know what had become of Rosalie. The marquis was away in Venice, and was not expected back till the end of April; but one of his servants took me to Rosalie, who had become Madame Paretti six months after my departure.

My heart beat fast as I entered the abode of this woman, of whom I had such pleasant recollections. I first went to M. Paretti in his shop, and he received me with a joyful smile, which shewed me how happy he was. He took me to his wife directly, who cried out with delight, and ran to embrace me.

1

M. Paretti was busy, and begged me to excuse him, saying his wife would entertain me.

Rosalie shewed me a pretty little girl of six months old, telling me that she was happy, that she loved her husband, and was loved by him, that he was industrious and active in business, and under the patronage of the Marquis Grimaldi had prospered exceedingly.

The peaceful happiness of marriage had improved her wonderfully; she had become a perfect beauty in every sense of the word.

"My dear friend," she said, "you are very good to call on me directly you arrive, and I hope you will dine with us to-morrow. I owe all my happiness to you, and that is even a sweeter thought than the recollection of the passionate hours we have spent together. Let us kiss, but no more; my duty as an honest wife forbids me from going any further, so do not disturb the happiness you have given."

I pressed her hand tenderly, to shew that I assented to the conditions she laid down.

"Oh! by the way," she suddenly exclaimed, "I have a pleasant surprise for you."

She went out, and a moment afterward returned with Véronique, who had become her maid. I was glad to see her and embraced her affectionately, asking after Annette. She said her sister was well, and was working with her mother.

"I want her to come and wait on my niece while we are here," said I.

At this Rosalie burst out laughing.

"What! another niece? You have a great many relations! But as she is your niece, I hope you will bring her with you to-morrow."

"Certainly, and all the more willingly as she is from Marseilles."

"From Marseilles? Why, we might know each other. Not that that would matter, for all your nieces are discreet young persons. What is her name?"

"Crosin."

"I don't know it."

"I daresay you don't. She is the daughter of a cousin of mine who lived at Marseilles."

"Tell that to someone else; but, after all, what does it matter? You choose well, amuse yourself, and make them happy. It may be wisdom after all, and at any rate I congratulate you. I shall be delighted to see your niece, but if she knows me you must see that she knows her part as well."

On leaving Madame Paretti I called on the Signora Isola-Bella, and gave her the Marquis Triulzi's letter. Soon after she came into the room and welcomed me, saying that she had been expecting me, as Triulzi had written to her on the subject. She introduced me to the Marquis Augustino Grimaldi della Pietra, her *cicisbeo-in-chief* during the long absence of her husband, who lived at Lisbon.

The signora's apartments were very elegant. She was pretty with small though regular features, her manner was pleasant, her voice sweet, and her figure well shaped, though too thin. She was nearly thirty. I say nothing of her complexion, for her face was plastered with white and red, and so coarsely, that these patches of paint were the first things that caught my attention. I was disgusted at this, in spite of her fine expressive eyes. After an hour spent in question and reply, in which both parties were feeling their way, I accepted her invitation to come to supper on the following day.

When I got back I complimented my niece on the
way in which she had arranged her room, which was
only separated from mine by a small closet which I intended for her maid, who, I told her, was coming the
next day. She was highly pleased with this attention,
and it paved the way for my success. I also told her
that the next day she was to dine with me at a sub-
stantial merchant's as my niece, and this piece of news
made her quite happy.

This girl whom Croce had infatuated and deprived
of her senses was exquisitely beautiful, but more charming than all her physical beauties were the nobleness of
her presence and the sweetness of her disposition. I
was already madly in love with her, and I repented not
having taken possession of her on the first day of our
journey. If I had taken her at her word I should have
been a steadfast lover, and I do not think it would have
taken me long to make her forget her former admirer.

I had made but a small dinner, so I sat down to
supper famishing with hunger; and as my niece had an
excellent appetite we prepared ourselves for enjoyment,
but instead of the dishes being delicate, as we had expected, they were detestable. I told Clairmont to send
for the landlady, and she said that she could not help
it, as everything had been done by my own cook.

"My cook?" I repeated.

"Yes, sir, the one your secretary, M. Possano, engaged for you. I could have got a much better one and
a much cheaper one myself."

"Get one to-morrow."

"Certainly; but you must rid yourself and me of the
present cook, for he has taken up his position here with
his wife and children. Tell Possano to send for him."

"I will do so, and in the meanwhile do you get me a fresh cook. I will try him the day after to-morrow."

I escorted my niece into her room, and begged her to go to bed without troubling about me, and so saying I took up the paper and began to read it. When I had finished, I went up to bed, and said,——

"You might spare me the pain of having to sleep by myself."

She lowered her eyes but said nothing, so I gave her a kiss and left her.

In the morning my fair niece came into my room just as Clairmont was washing my feet, and begged me to let her have some coffee as chocolate made her hot. I told my man to go and fetch some coffee, and as soon as he was gone she went down on her knees and would have wiped my feet.

"I cannot allow that, my dear young lady."

"Why not? it is a mark of friendship."

"That may be, but such marks cannot be given to any-one but your lover without your degrading yourself."

She got up and sat down on a chair quietly, but saying nothing.

Clairmont came back again, and I proceeded with my toilette.

The landlady came in with our breakfast, and asked my niece if she would like to buy a fine silk shawl made in the Genoese fashion. I did not let her be confused by having to answer, but told the landlady to let us see it. Soon after the milliner came in, but by that time I had given my young friend twenty Genoese sequins, tell-ing her that she might use them for her private wants. She took the money, thanking me with much grace, and letting me imprint a delicious kiss on her lovely lips.

I had sent away the milliner after having bought the

shawl, when Possano took it upon himself to remonstrate with me in the matter of the cook.

"I engaged the man by your orders," said he, "for the whole time you stayed at Genoa, at four francs a day, with board and lodging."

"Where is my letter?"

"Here it is: 'Get me a good cook; I will keep him while I stay in Genoa.'"

"Perhaps you did not remark the expression, *a good cook?* Well, this fellow is a very bad cook; and, at all events, I am the best judge whether he is good or bad."

"You are wrong, for the man will prove his skill. He will cite you in the law courts, and win his case."

"Then you have made a formal agreement with him?"

"Certainly; and your letter authorized me to do so."

"Tell him to come up; I want to speak to him."

While Possano was downstairs I told Clairmont to go and fetch me an advocate. The cook came upstairs, I read the agreement, and I saw that it was worded in such a manner that I should be in the wrong legally; but I did not change my mind for all that.

"Sir," said the cook, "I am skilled in my business, and I can get four thousand Genoese to swear as much."

"That doesn't say much for their good taste; but whatever they may say, the execrable supper you gave me last night proves that you are only fit to keep a low eating-house."

As there is nothing more irritable than the feelings of a culinary artist, I was expecting a sharp answer; but just then the advocate came in. He had heard the end of our dialogue, and told me that not only would the man find plenty of witnesses to his skill, but that I should find a very great difficulty in getting anybody at all to swear to his want of skill.

"That may be," I replied, "but as I stick to my own opinion, and think his cooking horrible, he must go, for I want to get another, and I will pay that fellow as if he had served me the whole time."

"That won't do," said the cook; "I will summon you before the judge and demand damages for defamation of character."

At this my bile overpowered me, and I was going to seize him and throw him out of the window, when Don Antonio Grimaldi came in. When he heard what was the matter, he laughed and said, with a shrug of his shoulders,——

"My dear sir, you had better not go into court, or you will be cast in costs, for the evidence is against you. Probably this man makes a slight mistake in believing himself to be an excellent cook, but the chief mistake is in the agreement, which ought to have stipulated that he should cook a trial dinner. The person who drew up the agreement is either a great knave or a great fool."

At this Possano struck in in his rude way, and told the nobleman that he was neither knave nor fool.

"But you are cousin to the cook," said the landlady.

This timely remark solved the mystery. I paid and dismissed the advocate, and having sent the cook out of the room I said,——

"Do I owe you any money, Possano?"

"On the contrary, you paid me a month in advance, and there are ten more days of the month to run."

"I will make you a present of the ten days and send you away this very moment, unless your cousin does not leave my house to-day, and give you the foolish engagement which you signed in my name."

"That's what I call cutting the Gordian knot," said M. Grimaldi.

He then begged me to introduce him to the lady he had seen with me, and I did so, telling him she was my niece.

"Signora Isola-Bella will be delighted to see her."

"As the marquis did not mention her in his letter, I did not take the liberty of bringing her."

The marquis left a few moments afterwards, and soon after Annette came in with her mother. The girl had developed in an incredible manner while I was away. Her cheeks blossomed like the rose, her teeth were white as pearls, and her breasts, though modestly concealed from view, were exquisitely rounded. I presented her to her mistress, whose astonishment amused me.

Annette, who looked pleased to be in my service again, went to dress her new mistress; and, after giving a few sequins to the mother I sent her away, and proceeded to make my toilette.

Towards noon, just as I was going out with my niece to dine at Rosalie's, my landlady brought me the agreement Possano had made, and introduced the new cook. I ordered the next day's dinner, and went away much pleased with my comic victory.

A brilliant company awaited us at the Paretti's, but I was agreeably surprised on introducing my niece to Rosalie to see them recognize each other. They called each other by their respective names, and indulged in an affectionate embrace. After this they retired to another room for a quarter of an hour, and returned looking very happy. Just then Paretti entered, and on Rosalie introducing him to my niece under her true name he welcomed her in the most cordial manner. Her father was a correspondent of his, and drawing a letter he had just received from him from his pocket, he gave it to her to read. My niece read it eagerly, with tears in her eyes, and gave the signature a respectful pressure with her lips. This expression of filial love, which displayed all the feelings of her heart, moved me to such an extent that I burst into tears. Then taking Rosalie aside, I begged her to ask her husband not to mention the fact to his correspondent that he had seen his daughter.

The dinner was excellent, and Rosalie did the honours with that grace which was natural to her. However, the guests did not by any means pay her all their attentions, the greater portion of which was diverted in the direction of my supposed niece. Her father, a prosperous merchant of Marseilles, was well known in the commercial circles of Genoa, and besides this her wit and beauty captivated everybody, and one young gentleman fell madly in love with her. He was an extremely good match, and proved to be the husband whom Heaven had destined for my charming friend. What a happy thought it was for me that I had been the means of rescuing her from the gulf of shame, misery, and despair, and placing her on the high road to happiness. I own that I have always felt a keener pleasure in doing good than in anything else, though, perhaps, I may not always have done good from strictly disinterested motives.

When we rose from the table in excellent humour with ourselves and our surroundings, cards were proposed, and Rosalie, who knew my likings, said it must be trente-quarante. This was agreed to, and we played till supper, nobody either winning or losing to any extent. We did not go till midnight, after having spent a very happy day.

When we were in our room I asked my niece how she had known Rosalie.

"I knew her at home; she and her mother used

to bring linen from the wash. I always liked her."

"You must be nearly the same age."

"She is two years older than I am. I recognized her directly."

"What did she tell you?"

"That it was you who brought her from Marseilles and made her fortune."

"She has not made you the depositary of any other confidences?"

"No, but there are some things which don't need telling."

"You are right. And what did you tell her?"

"Only what she could have guessed for herself. I told her that you were not my uncle, and if she thought you were my lover I was not sorry. You do not know how I have enjoyed myself to-day, you must have been born to make me happy."

"But how about La Croix?"

"For heaven's sake say nothing about him."

This conversation increased my ardour. She called Annette, and I went to my room.

As I had expected, Annette came to me as soon as her mistress was in bed.

"If the lady is really your niece," said she, "may I hope that you still love me?"

"Assuredly, dear Annette, I shall always love you. Undress, and let us have a little talk."

I had not long to wait, and in the course of two voluptuous hours I quenched the flames that another woman had kindled in my breast.

Next morning Possano came to tell me that he had arranged matters with the cook with the help of six sequins. I gave him the money, and told him to be more careful for the future.

I went to Rosalie's for my breakfast, which she was delighted to give me; and I asked her and her husband to dinner on the following day, telling her to bring any four persons she liked.

"Your decision," said I, "will decide the fate of my cook; it will be his trial dinner."

She promised to come, and then pressed me to tell her the history of my amours with her fair country-woman.

"Alas!" I said, "you may not believe me, but I assure you I am only beginning with her."

"I shall certainly believe you, if you tell me so, though it seems very strange."

"Strange but true. You must understand, however, that I have only known her for a very short time; and, again, I would not be made happy save through love, mere submission would kill me."

"Good! but what did she say of me?"

I gave her a report of the whole conversation I had had with my niece the night before, and she was delighted."

"As you have not yet gone far with your niece, would you object if the young man who shewed her so much attention yesterday were of the party to-morrow?"

"Who is he? I should like to know him."

"M. N——, the only son of a rich merchant."

"Certainly, bring him with you."

When I got home I went to my niece, who was still in bed, and told her that her fellow-countryman would dine with us to-morrow. I comforted her with the assurance that M. Paretti would not tell her father that she was in Genoa. She had been a good deal tormented with the idea that the merchant would inform her father of all.

As I was going out to supper I told her that she could

go and sup with Rosalie, or take supper at home if she preferred it.

"You are too kind to me, my dear uncle. I will go to Rosalie's."

"Very good. Are you satisfied with Annette?"

"Oh! by the way, she told me that you spent last night with her, and that you had been her lover and her sister's at the same time."

"It is true, but she is very indiscreet to say anything about it."

"We must forgive her, though. She told me that she only consented to sleep with you on the assurance that I was really your niece. I am sure she only made this confession out of vanity, and in the hope of gaining my favour, which would be naturally bestowed on a woman you love."

"I wish you had the right to be jealous of her; and I swear that if she does not comport herself with the utmost obedience to you in every respect, I will send her packing, in despite of our relations. As for you, you may not be able to love me, and I have no right to complain; but I will not have you degrade yourself by becoming my submissive victim."

I was not sorry for my niece to know that I made use of Annette, but my vanity was wounded at the way she took it. It was plain that she was not at all in love with me, and that she was glad that there was a safeguard in the person of her maid, and that thus we could be together without danger, for she could not ignore the power of her charms.

We dined together, and augured well of the skill of the new cook. M. Paretti had promised to get me a good man, and he presented himself just as we were finishing dinner, and I made a present of him to my niece. We went for a drive together, and I left my niece at Rosalie's, and I then repaired to Isola-Bella's, where I found a numerous and brilliant company had assembled consisting of all the best people in Genoa.

Just then all the great ladies were mad over biribi, a regular cheating game. It was strictly forbidden at Genoa, but this only made it more popular, and besides, the prohibition had no force in private houses, which are outside of the jurisdiction of the Government; in short, I found the game in full swing at the Signora Isola-Bella's. The professional gamesters who kept the bank went from house to house, and the amateurs were advised of their presence at such a house and at such a time.

Although I detested the game, I began to play—to do as the others did.

In the room there was a portrait of the mistress of the house in harlequin costume, and there happened to be the same picture on one of the divisions of the biribi-table. I chose this one out of politeness, and did not play on any other. I risked a sequin each time. The board had thirty-six compartments, and if one lost, one paid thirty-two times the amount of the stake; this, of course, was an enormous advantage for the bank.

Each player drew three numbers in succession, and there were three professionals; one kept the bag, another the bank, and the third the board, and the last took care to gather in the winnings as soon as the result was known, and the bank amounted to two thousand sequins or thereabouts. The table, the cloth, and four silver candlesticks belonged to the players.

I sat at the left of Madame Isola-Bella, who began to play, and as there were fifteen or sixteen of us I had lost about fifty sequins when my turn came, for my harlequin had not appeared once. Everybody pitied me, or pretended to do so, for selfishness is the predominant passion of gamesters.

My turn came at last. I drew my harlequin and received thirty-two sequins. I left them on the same figure, and got a thousand sequins. I left fifty still on the board, and the harlequin came out for the third time. The bank was broken, and the table, the cloth, the candlesticks, and the board all belonged to me. Everyone congratulated me, and the wretched bankrupt gamesters were hissed, hooted, and turned out of doors.

After the first transports were over, I saw that the ladies were in distress; for as there could be no more gaming they did not know what to do. I consoled them by declaring that I would be banker, but with equal stakes, and that I would pay winning cards thirty-six times the stake instead of thirty-two. This was pronounced charming of me, and I amused everybody till supper-time, without any great losses or gains on either side. By dint of entreaty I made the lady of the house accept the whole concern as a present, and a very handsome one it was.

The supper was pleasant enough, and my success at play was the chief topic of conversation. Before leaving I asked Signora Isola-Bella and her marquis to dine with me, and they eagerly accepted the invitation. When I got home I went to see my niece, who told me she had spent a delightful evening.

"A very pleasant young man," said she, "who is coming to dine with us to-morrow, paid me great attention."

"The same, I suppose, that did so yesterday?"

"Yes. Amongst other pretty things he told me that if I liked he would go to Marseilles and ask my hand of my father. I said nothing, but I thought to myself that if the poor young man gave himself all this trouble he would be woefully misled, as he would not see me."

"Why not?"

"Because I should be in a nunnery. My kind good father will forgive me, but I must punish myself."

"That is a sad design, which I hope you will abandon. You have all that would make the happiness of a worthy husband. The more I think it over, the more I am convinced of the truth of what I say."

We said no more just then, for she needed rest. Annette came to undress her, and I was glad to see the goodness of my niece towards her, but the coolness with which the girl behaved to her mistress did not escape my notice. As soon as she came to sleep with me I gently remonstrated with her, bidding her to do her duty better for the future. Instead of answering with a caress, as she ought to have done, she began to cry.

"My dear child," said I, "your tears weary me. You are only here to amuse me, and if you can't do that, you had better go."

This hurt her foolish feelings of vanity, and she got up and went away without a word, leaving me to go to sleep in a very bad temper.

In the morning I told her, in a stern voice, that if she played me such a trick again I would send her away. Instead of trying to soothe me with a kiss the little rebel burst out crying again. I sent her out of the room impatiently, and proceeded to count my gains.

I thought no more about it, but presently my niece came in and asked me why I had vexed poor Annette.

"My dear niece," said I, "tell her to behave better or else I will send her back to her mother's."

She gave me no reply, but took a handful of silver and fled. I had not time to reflect on this singular conduct, for Annette came in rattling her crowns in her pocket, and promised, with a kiss, not to make me angry any more.

Such was my niece. She knew I adored her, and she loved me; but she did not want me to be her lover, though she made use of the ascendancy which my passion gave her. In the code of feminine coquetry such cases are numerous.

Possano came uninvited to see me, and congratulated me on my victory of the evening before.

"Who told you about it?"

"I have just been at the coffee-house, where everybody is talking of it. It was a wonderful victory, for those *biribanti* are knaves of the first water. Your adventure is making a great noise, for everyone says that you could not have broken their bank unless you had made an agreement with the man that kept the bag."

"My dear fellow, I am tired of you. Here, take this piece of money for your wife and be off."

The piece of money I had given him was a gold coin worth a hundred Genoese livres, which the Government had struck for internal commerce; there were also pieces of fifty and twenty-five livres.

I was going on with my calculations when Clairmont brought me a note. It was from Irene, and contained a tender invitation to breakfast with her. I did not know that she was in Genoa, and the news gave me very great pleasure. I locked up my money, dressed in haste, and started out to see her. I found her in good and well-furnished rooms, and her old father, Count Rinaldi, embraced me with tears of joy.

After the ordinary compliments had been passed, the old man proceeded to congratulate me on my winnings of the night before.

"Three thousand sequins!" he exclaimed, "that is a grand haul indeed."

"Quite so."

"The funny part of it is that the man who keeps the bag is in the pay of the others."

"What strikes you as funny in that?"

"Why, he gained half without any risk, otherwise he would not have been likely to have entered into an agreement with you."

"You think, then, that it was a case of connivance?"

"Everybody says so; indeed what else could it be? The rascal has made his fortune without running any risk. All the Greeks in Genoa are applauding him and you."

"As the greater rascal of the two?"

"They don't call you a rascal; they say you're a great genius; you are praised and envied."

"I am sure I ought to be obliged to them."

"I heard it all from a gentleman who was there. He says that the second and the third time the man with the bag gave you the office."

"And you believe this?"

"I am sure of it. No man of honour in your position could have acted otherwise. However, when you come to settle up with the fellow I advise you to be very careful, for there will be spies on your tracks. If you like, I will do the business for you."

I had enough self-restraint to repress the indignation and rage I felt. Without a word I took my hat and marched out of the room, sternly repulsing Irene who tried to prevent me from going as she had done once before. I resolved not to have anything more to do with the wretched old count.

This calumnious report vexed me extremely, although

I knew that most gamesters would consider it an honour. Possano and Rinaldi had said enough to shew me that all the town was talking over it, and I was not surprised that everyone believed it; but for my part I did not care to be taken for a rogue when I had acted honourably.

I felt the need of unbosoming myself to someone, and walked towards the Strada Balbi to call on the Marquis Grimaldi, and discuss the matter with him. I was told he was gone to the courts, so I followed him there and was ushered into a vast hall, where he waited on me. I told him my story, and he said,——

"My dear chevalier, you ought to laugh at it, and I should not advise you to take the trouble to refute the calumny."

"Then you advise me to confess openly that I am a rogue?"

"No, for only fools will think that of you. Despise them, unless they tell you you are a rogue to your face."

"I should like to know the name of the nobleman who was present and sent this report about the town."

"I do not know who it is. He was wrong to say anything, but you would be equally wrong in taking any steps against him, for I am sure he did not tell the story with any intention of giving offence; quite the contrary."

"I am lost in wonder at his course of reasoning. Let us suppose that the facts were as he told them, do you think they are to my honour?"

"Neither to your honour nor shame. Such are the morals and such the maxims of gamesters. The story will be laughed at, your skill will be applauded, and you will be admired, for each one will say that in your place he would have done likewise."

"Would you?"

"Certainly. If I had been sure that the ball would

have gone to the harlequin, I would have broken the rascal's bank, as you did. I will say honestly that I do not know whether you won by luck or skill, but the most probable hypothesis, to my mind, is that you knew the direction of the ball. You must confess that there is something to be said in favour of the supposition."

"I confess that there is, but it is none the less a dishonourable imputation on me, and you in your turn must confess that those who think that I won by sleight of hand, or by an agreement with a rascal, insult me grievously."

"That depends on the way you look at it. I confess they insult you, if you think yourself insulted; but they are not aware of that, and their intention being quite different there is no insult at all in the matter. I promise you no one will tell you to your face that you cheated, but how are you going to prevent them thinking so?"

"Well, let them think what they like, but let them take care not to tell me their thoughts."

I went home angry with Grimaldi, Rinaldi, and everyone else. My anger vexed me, I should properly have only laughed, for in the state of morals at Genoa, the accusation, whether true or false, could not injure my honour. On the contrary I gained by it a reputation for being a genius, a term which the Genoese prefer to that Methodistical word, "a rogue," though the meaning is the same. Finally I was astonished to find myself reflecting that I should have had no scruple in breaking the bank in the way suggested, if it had only been for the sake of making the company laugh. What vexed me most was that I was credited with an exploit I had not performed.

When dinner-time drew near I endeavoured to overcome my ill temper for the sake of the company I was going to receive. My niece was adorned only with her native charms, for the rascal Croce had sold all her jewels; but she was elegantly dressed, and her beautiful hair was more precious than a crown of rubies.

Rosalie came in richly dressed and looking very lovely. Her husband, her uncle, and her aunt were with her, and also two friends, one of whom was the aspirant for the hand of my niece.

Madame Isola-Bella and her shadow, M. Grimaldi, came late, like great people.

Just as we were going to sit down, Clairmont told me that a man wanted to speak to me.

"Shew him in."

As soon as he appeared M. Grimaldi exclaimed:

"The man with the bag!"

"What do you want?" I said, dryly.

"Sir, I am come to ask you to help me. I am a family man, and it is thought that . . ."

I did not let him finish.

"I have never refused to aid the unfortunate," said I. "Clairmont, give him ten sequins. Leave the room."

This incident spoke in my favour, and made me in a better temper.

We sat down to table, and a letter was handed to me. I recognized Possano's writing, and put it in my pocket without reading it.

The dinner was delicious, and my cook was pronounced to have won his spurs. Though her exalted rank and the brilliance of her attire gave Signora Isola-Bella the first place of right, she was nevertheless eclipsed by my two nieces. The young Genoese was all attention for the fair Marseillaise, and I could see that she was not displeased. I sincerely wished to see her in love with someone, and I liked her too well to bear the idea of her burying herself in a convent. She could never be happy till she found someone who would make her forget the rascal who had brought her to the brink of ruin.

I seized the opportunity, when all my guests were engaged with each other, to open Possano's letter. It ran as follows:

"I went to the bank to change the piece of gold you gave me. It was weighed, and found to be ten carats under weight. I was told to name the person from whom I got it, but of course I did not do so. I then had to go to prison, and if you do not get me out of the scrape I shall be prosecuted, though of course I am not going to get myself hanged for anybody."

I gave the letter to Grimaldi, and when we had left the table he took me aside, and said,——

"This is a very serious matter, for it may end in the gallows for the man who clipped the coin."

"Then they can hang the *biribanti!* That won't hurt me much."

"No, that won't do; it would compromise Madame Isola-Bella, as biribi is strictly forbidden. Leave it all to me, I will speak to the State Inquisitors about it. Tell Possano to persevere in his silence, and that you will see him safely through. The laws against coiners and clippers are only severe with regard to these particular coins, as the Government has special reasons for not wishing them to be depreciated."

I wrote to Possano, and sent for a pair of scales. We weighed the gold I had won at biribi, and every single piece had been clipped. M. Grimaldi said he would have them defaced and sold to a jeweller.

When we got back to the dining-room we found everybody at play. M. Grimaldi proposed that I should play at quinze with him. I detested the game, but as he was my guest I felt it would be impolite to refuse, and in four hours I had lost five hundred sequins.

Next morning the marquis told me that Possano was out of prison, and that he had been given the value of the coin. He brought me thirteen hundred sequins which had resulted from the sale of the gold. We agreed that I was to call on Madame Isola-Bella the next day, when he would give me my revenge at quinze.

I kept the appointment, and lost three thousand sequins. I paid him a thousand the next day, and gave him two bills of exchange, payable by myself, for the other two thousand. When these bills were presented I was in England, and being badly off I had to have them protested. Five years later, when I was at Barcelona, M. de Grimaldi was urged by a traitor to have me imprisoned, but he knew enough of me to be sure that if I did not meet the bills it was from sheer inability to do so. He even wrote me a very polite letter, in which he gave the name of my enemy, assuring me that he would never take any steps to compel me to pay the money. This enemy was Possano, who was also at Barcelona, though I was not aware of his presence. I will speak of the circumstance in due time, but I cannot help remarking that all who aided me in my pranks with Madame d'Urfé proved traitors, with the exception of a Venetian girl, whose acquaintance the reader will make in the following chapter.

In spite of my losses I enjoyed myself, and had plenty of money, for after all I had only lost what I had won at biribi. Rosalie often dined with us, either alone or with her husband, and I supped regularly at her home with my niece, whose love affair seemed quite promising. I congratulated her upon the circumstance, but she persisted in her determination to take refuge from the world

"First of all, answer my questions. How long have you been here?"

"Since yesterday."

"Who told you that I was here?"

"Count B——, at Milan."

"Who told you that the count knew me?"

"I found out by chance. I was at M. de Bragadin's a month ago, and on his table I saw a letter from the count to you."

"Did you tell him you were my brother?"

"I had to when he said how much I resembled you."

"He made a mistake, for you are a blockhead."

"He did not think so, at all events, for he asked me to dinner."

"You must have cut a pretty figure, if you were in your present state."

"He gave me four sequins to come here; otherwise, I should never have been able to do the journey."

"Then he did a very foolish thing. You're a mere beggar, then; you take alms. Why did you leave Venice? What do you want with me? I can do nothing for you."

"Ah! do not make me despair, or I shall kill myself."

"That's the very best thing you could do; but you are too great a coward. I ask again why you left Venice, where you could say mass, and preach, and make an honest living, like many priests much better than you?"

"That is the kernel of the whole matter. Let us go in and I will tell you."

"No; wait for me here. We will go somewhere where you can tell me your story, if I have patience to listen to it. But don't tell any of my people that you are my brother, for I am ashamed to have such a relation. Come, take me to the place where you are staying."

in a cloister. Women often do the most idiotic things out of sheer obstinacy; possibly they deceive even themselves, and act in good faith; but unfortunately, when the veil falls from before their eyes, they see but the profound abyss into which their folly had plunged them.

In the meanwhile, my niece had become so friendly and familiar that she would often come and sit on my bed in the morning when Annette was still in my arms. Her presence increased my ardour, and I quenched the fires on the blonde which the brunette was kindling. My niece seemed to enjoy the sight, and I could see that her senses were being pleasantly tortured. Annette was short-sighted, and so did not perceive my distractions, while my fair niece caressed me slightly, knowing that it would add to my pleasures. When she thought I was exhausted she told Annette to get up and leave me alone with her, as she wanted to tell me something. She then began to jest and toy, and though her dress was extremely disordered she seemed to think that her charms would exercise no power over me. She was quite mistaken, but I was careful not to undeceive her for fear of losing her confidence. I watched the game carefully, and noting how little by little her familiarity increased, I felt sure that she would have to surrender at last, if not at Genoa, certainly on the journey, when we would be thrown constantly in each other's society with nobody to spy upon our actions, and with nothing else to do but to make love. It is the weariness of a journey, the constant monotony, that makes one do something to make sure of one's existence; and when it comes to the reckoning there is usually more joy than repentance.

But the story of my journey from Genoa to Marseilles was written in the book of fate, and could not be read by me. All I knew was that I must soon go as Madame d'Urfé was waiting for me at Marseilles. I knew not that in this journey would be involved the fate of a Venetian girl of whom I had never heard, who had never seen me, but whom I was destined to render happy. My fate seemed to have made me stop at Genoa to wait for her.

I settled my accounts with the banker, to whom I had been accredited, and I took a letter of credit on Marseilles, where, however, I was not likely to want for funds, as my high treasurer, Madame d'Urfé was there. I took leave of Madame Isola-Bella and her circle that I might be able to devote all my time to Rosalie and her friends.

CHAPTER II

Disgraceful Behaviour of My Brother, the Abbé—I Re-
lieve Him of His Mistress—Departure from Genoa—
The Prince of Monaco—My Niece Overcome—O
Arrival at Antibes

ON THE Tuesday in Holy Week I was just getting when Clairmont came to tell me that a priest would not give his name wanted to speak to me. I w out in my night-cap, and the rascally priest rushed at and nearly choked me with his embraces. I did not so much affection, and as I had not recognized him at on account of the darkness of the room, I took him b arm and led him to the window. It was my you brother, a good-for-nothing fellow, whom I had a disliked. I had not seen him for ten years, but I so little about him that I had not even enquired w he were alive or dead in the correspondence I mai with M. de Bragadin, Dandolo, and Barbaro.

As soon as his silly embraces were over, I coldl him what chance had brought him to Genoa in gusting state of dirt, rags, and tatters. He w twenty-nine, his complexion was fresh and heal he had a splendid head of hair. He was a pos son, born like Mahomet, three months after the his father.

"The story of my misfortunes would be only Take me into your room, and I will sit down at the whole story."

25

"I must tell you that at my inn I am not alone, and I want to have a private interview with you."

"Who is with you?"

"I will tell you presently, but let us go into a coffee-house."

"Are you in company with a band of brigands? What are you sighing at?"

"I must confess it, however painful it may be to my feelings. I am with a woman."

"A woman! and you a priest!"

"Forgive me. I was blinded by love, and seduced by my senses and her beauty, so I seduced her under a promise to marry her at Geneva. I can never go back to Venice, for I took her away from her father's house."

"What could you do at Geneva? They would expel you after you had been there three or four days. Come, we will go to the inn and see the woman you have deceived. I will speak to you afterwards."

I began to trace my steps in the direction he had pointed out, and he was obliged to follow me. As soon as we got to the inn, he went on in front, and after climbing three flights of stairs I entered a wretched den where I saw a tall young girl, a sweet brunette, who looked proud and not in the least confused. As soon as I made my appearance she said, without any greeting,——

"Are you the brother of this liar and monster who has deceived me so abominably?"

"Yes," said I. "I have the honour."

"A fine honour, truly. Well, have the kindness to send me back to Venice, for I won't stop any longer with this rascal whom I listened to like the fool I was, who turned my head with his lying tales. He was going to meet you

at Milan, and you were to give us enough money to go to
Geneva, and there we were to turn Protestants and get
married. He swore you were expecting him at Milan, but
you were not there at all, and he contrived to get money
in some way or another, and brought me here miserably
enough. I thank Heaven he has found you at last, for if
he had not I should have started off by myself and
begged my way. I have not a single thing left; the
wretch sold all I possessed at Bergamo and Verona. I
don't know how I kept my senses through it all. To
hear him talk, the world was a paradise outside Venice,
but I have found to my cost that there is no place like
home. I curse the hour when I first saw the miserable
wretch. He's a beggarly knave; always whining. He
wanted to enjoy his rights as my husband when we got
to Padua, but I am thankful to say I gave him nothing.
Here is the writing he gave me; take it, and do what you
like with it. But if you have any heart, send me back
to Venice or I will tramp there on foot."

I had listened to this long tirade without interrupting
her. She might have spoken at much greater length, so
far as I was concerned; my astonishment took my breath
away. Her discourse had all the fire of eloquence, and
was heightened by her expressive face and the flaming
glances she shot from her eyes.

My brother, sitting down with his head between his
hands, and obliged to listen in silence to this long cata-
logue of well-deserved reproaches, gave something of a
comic element to the scene. In spite of that, however,
I was much touched by the sad aspects of the girl's story.
I felt at once that I must take charge of her, and put an
end to this ill-assorted match. I imagined that I should
not have much difficulty in sending her back to Venice,
which she might never have quitted if it had not been for

her trust in me, founded on the fallacious promises of her seducer.

The true Venetian character of the girl struck me even more than her beauty. Her courage, frank indignation, and the nobility of her aspect made me resolve not to abandon her. I could not doubt that she had told a true tale, as my brother continued to observe a guilty silence.

I watched her silently for some time, and, my mind being made up, said,——

"I promise to send you back to Venice with a respectable woman to look after you; but you will be unfortunate if you carry back with you the results of your amours."

"What results? Did I not tell you that we were going to be married at Geneva?"

"Yes, but in spite of that . . ."

"I understand you, sir, but I am quite at ease on that point, as I am happy to say that I did not yield to any of the wretch's desires."

"Remember," said the abbé, in a plaintive voice, "the oath you took to be mine for ever. You swore it upon the crucifix."

So saying he got up and approached her with a supplicating gesture, but as soon as he was within reach she gave him a good hearty box on the ear. I expected to see a fight, in which I should not have interfered, but nothing of the kind. The humble abbé gently turned away to the window, and casting his eyes to heaven began to weep.

"You are too malicious, my dear," I said; "the poor devil is only unhappy because you have made him in love with you."

"If he is it's his own fault. I should never have thought of him but for his coming to me and fooling me.

I shall never forgive him till he is out of my sight. That's not the first blow I have given him; I had to begin at Padua."

"Yes," said the abbé, "but you are excommunicated, for I am a priest."

"It's little I care for the excommunication of a scoundrel like you, and if you say another word I will give you some more."

"Calm yourself, my child," said I; "you have cause to be angry, but you should not beat him. Take up your things and follow me."

"Where are you going to take her?" said the foolish priest.

"To my own house, and I should advise you to hold your tongue. Here, take these twenty sequins and buy yourself some clean clothes and linen, and give those rags of yours to the beggars. I will come and talk to you to-morrow, and you may thank your stars that you found me here. As for you, mademoiselle, I will have you conducted to my lodging, for Genoa must not see you in my company after arriving here with a priest. We must not have any scandal. I shall place you under the charge of my landlady, but whatever you do don't tell her this sad story. I will see that you are properly dressed, and that you want for nothing."

"May Heaven reward you!"

My brother, astonished at the sight of the twenty sequins, let me go away without a word. I had the fair Venetian taken to my lodging in a sedan-chair, and putting her under the charge of my landlady I told the latter to see that she was properly dressed. I wanted to see how she would look in decent clothes, for her present rags and tatters detracted from her appearance. I warned Annette that a girl who had been placed in my care

would eat and sleep with her, and then having to entertain a numerous company of guests I proceeded to make
my toilette.

Although my niece had no rights over me, I valued her
esteem, and thought it best to tell her the whole story
lest she should pass an unfavourable judgment on me.
She listened attentively and thanked me for my confidence in her, and said she should very much like to see
the girl and the abbé too, whom she pitied, though she
admitted he was to be blamed for what he had done. I
had got her a dress to wear at dinner, which became her
exquisitely. I felt only too happy to be able to please
her in any way, for her conduct towards myself and the
way she treated her ardent lover commanded my admiration. She saw him every day either at my house or at
Rosalie's. The young man had received an excellent
education, though he was of the mercantile class, and
wrote to her in a business-like manner, that, as they were
well suited to each other in every way, there was nothing
against his going to Marseilles and obtaining her father's
consent to the match, unless it were a feeling of aversion
on her side. He finished by requesting her to give him
an answer. She shewed me the letter, and I congratulated her, and advised her to accept, if there was nothing
about the young man which displeased her.

"There is nothing of the kind," she said, "and Rosalie
thinks with you."

"Then tell him by word of mouth that you give your
consent, and will expect to see him at Marseilles."

"Very good; as you think so, I will tell him to-
morrow."

When dinner was over a feeling of curiosity made me
go into the room where Annette was dining with the
Venetian girl, whose name was Marcoline. I was struck

with astonishment on seeing her, for she was completely
changed, not so much by the pretty dress she had on as
by the contented expression of her face, which made her
look quite another person. Good humour had vanquished
unbecoming rage, and the gentleness born of happiness
made her features breathe forth love. I could scarcely
believe that this charming creature before me was the
same who had dealt such a vigorous blow to my brother,
a priest, and a sacred being in the eyes of the common
people. They were eating, and laughing at not being
able to understand each other, for Marcoline only spoke
Venetian, and Annette Genoese, and the latter dialect
does not resemble the former any more than Bohemian
resembles Dutch.

I spoke to Marcoline in her native tongue, which was
mine too, and she said,——

"I seem to have suddenly passed from hell to Paradise."

"Indeed, you look like an angel."

"You called me a little devil this morning. But here
is a fair angel," said she, pointing to Annette; "we don't
see such in Venice."

"She is my treasure."

Shortly after my niece came in, and seeing me talking
and laughing with the two girls began to examine the
new-comer. She told me in French that she thought
her perfectly beautiful, and repeating her opinion to the
girl in Italian gave her a kiss. Marcoline asked her
plainly in the Venetian manner who she was.

"I am this gentleman's niece, and he is taking me back
to Marseilles, where my home is."

"Then you would have been my niece too, if I
had married his brother. I wish I had such a pretty
niece."

This pleasant rejoinder was followed by a storm of kisses given and returned with ardour which one might pronounce truly Venetian, if it were not that this would wound the feelings of the almost equally ardent Provençals.

I took my niece for a sail in the bay, and after we had enjoyed one of those delicious evenings which I think can be found nowhere else—sailing on a mirror silvered by the moon, over which float the odours of the jasmine, the orange-blossom, the pomegranates, the aloes, and all the scented flowers which grow along the coasts—we returned to our lodging, and I asked Annette what had become of Marcoline. She told me that she had gone to bed early, and I went gently into her room, with no other intention than to see her asleep. The light of the candle awoke her, and she did not seem at all frightened at seeing me. I sat by the bed, and fell to making love to her, and at last made as if I would kiss her, but she resisted, and we went on talking.

When Annette had put her mistress to bed, she came in and found us together.

"Go to bed, my dear," said I. "I will come to you directly."

Proud of being my mistress, she gave me a fiery kiss and went away without a word.

I began to talk about my brother, and passing from him to myself I told her of the interest I felt for her, saying that I would either have her taken to Venice, or bring her with me when I went to France.

"Do you want to marry me?"

"No, I am married already."

"That's a lie, I know, but it doesn't matter. Send me back to Venice, and the sooner the better. I don't want to be anybody's concubine."

"I admire your sentiments, my dear, they do you honour."

Continuing my praise I became pressing, not using any force, but those gentle caresses which are so much harder for a woman to resist than a violent attack. Marcoline laughed, but seeing that I persisted in spite of her resistance, she suddenly glided out of the bed and took refuge in my niece's room and locked the door after her. I was not displeased; the thing was done so easily and gracefully. I went to bed with Annette, who lost nothing by the ardour with which Marcoline had inspired me. I told her how she had escaped from my hands, and Annette was loud in her praises.

In the morning I got up early and went into my niece's room to enjoy the sight of the companion I had involuntarily given her, and the two girls were certainly a very pleasant sight. As soon as my niece saw me, she exclaimed,——

"My dear uncle, would you believe it? This sly Venetian has violated me."

Marcoline understood her, and far from denying the fact proceeded to give my niece fresh marks of her affection, which were well received, and from the movements of the sheets which covered them I could make a pretty good guess as to the nature of their amusement.

"This is a rude shock to the respect which your uncle has had for your prejudices," said I.

"The sports of two girls cannot tempt a man who has just left the arms of Annette."

"You are wrong, and perhaps you know it, for I am more than tempted."

With these words I lifted the sheets of the bed. Marcoline shrieked but did not move, but my niece earnestly begged me to replace the bed-clothes. However, the picture before me was too charming to be concealed.

At this point Annette came in, and in obedience to her mistress replaced the coverlet over the two Bacchantes. I felt angry with Annette, and seizing her threw her on the bed, and then and there gave the two sweethearts such an interesting spectacle that they left their own play to watch us. When I had finished, Annette, who was in high glee, said I was quite right to avenge myself on their prudery. I felt satisfied with what I had done, and went to breakfast. I then dressed, and visited my brother.

"How is Marcoline?" said he, as soon as he saw me.

"Very well, and you needn't trouble yourself any more about her. She is well lodged, well dressed, and well fed, and sleeps with my niece's maid."

"I didn't know I had a niece."

"There are many things you don't know. In three or four days she will return to Venice."

"I hope, dear brother, that you will ask me to dine with you to-day."

"Not at all, dear brother. I forbid you to set foot in my house, where your presence would be offensive to Marcoline, whom you must not see any more."

"Yes, I will; I will return to Venice, if I have to hang for it."

"What good would that be? She won't have you."

"She loves me."

"She beats you."

"She beats me because she loves me. She will be as gentle as a lamb when she sees me so well dressed. You do not know how I suffer."

"I can partly guess, but I do not pity you, for you are an impious and cruel fool. You have broken your vows, and have not hesitated to make a young girl endure misery and degradation to satisfy your caprice. What would you have done, I should like to know, if I had given you the cold shoulder instead of helping you?"

"I should have gone into the street, and begged for my living with her."

"She would have beaten you, and would probably have appealed to the law to get rid of you."

"But what will you do for me, if I let her go back to Venice without following her."

"I will take you to France, and try to get you employed by some bishop."

"Employed! I was meant by nature to be employed by none but God."

"You proud fool! Marcoline rightly called you a whiner. Who is your God? How do you serve Him? You are either a hypocrite or an idiot. Do you think that you, a priest, serve God by decoying an innocent girl away from her home? Do you serve Him by profaning the religion you do not even understand? Unhappy fool! do you think that with no talent, no theological learning, and no eloquence, you can be a Protestant minister. Take care never to come to my house, or I will have you expelled from Genoa."

"Well, well, take me to Paris, and I will see what my brother Francis can do for me; his heart is not so hard as yours."

"Very good! you shall go to Paris, and we will start from here in three or four days. Eat and drink to your heart's content, but remain indoors; I will let you know when we are going. I shall have my niece, my secretary, and my valet with me. We shall travel by sea."

"The sea makes me sick."

"That will purge away some of your bad humours."

When I got home I told Marcoline what had passed between us.

"I hate him!" said she; " but I forgive him, since it is through him I know you."

"And I forgive him, too, because unless it had been for him I should never have seen you. But I love you, and I shall die unless you satisfy my desires."

"Never; for I know I should be madly in love with you, and then you would leave me, and I should be miserable again."

"I will never leave you."

"If you will swear that, take me into France and make me all your own. Here you must continue living with Annette; besides, I have got your niece to make love to."

The pleasant part of the affair was that my niece was equally taken with her, and had begged me to let her take meals with us and sleep with her. As I had a prospect of being at their lascivious play, I willingly consented, and henceforth she was always present at the table. We enjoyed her company immensely, for she told us side-splitting tales which kept us at table till it was time to go to Rosalie's, where my niece's adorer was certain to be awaiting us.

The next day, which was Holy Thursday, Rosalie came with us to see the processions. I had Rosalie and Marcoline with me, one on each arm, veiled in their mezzaros, and my niece was under the charge of her lover. The day after we went to see the procession called at Genoa *Caracce,* and Marcoline pointed out my brother who kept hovering round us, though he pretended not to see us. He was most carefully dressed, and the stupid fop seemed to think he was sure to find favour in Marcoline's eyes, and make her regret having despised him; but he was woefully deceived, for Marcoline knew how to manage her mezzaro so well that, though he was both seen and laughed at, the poor devil could not be certain that she had noticed him at all, and in addition the sly girl held me so closely by the arm that he must have concluded we were very intimate.

My niece and Marcoline thought themselves the best friends in the world, and could not bear my telling them that their amorous sports were the only reason for their attachment. They therefore agreed to abandon them as soon as we left Genoa, and promised that I should sleep between them in the felucca, all of us to keep our clothes on. I said I should hold them to their word, and I fixed our departure for Thursday. I ordered the felucca to be in readiness and summoned my brother to go on board.

It was a cruel moment when I left Annette with her mother. She wept so bitterly that all of us had to shed tears. My niece gave her a handsome dress and I thirty sequins, promising to come and see her again on my return from England. Possano was told to go on board with the abbé; I had provisioned the boat for three days. The young merchant promised to be at Marseilles, telling my niece that by the time he came everything would be settled. I was delighted to hear it; it assured me that her father would give her a kind reception. Our friends did not leave us till the moment we went on board.

The felucca was very conveniently arranged, and was propelled by the twelve oarsmen. On the deck there were also twenty-four muskets, so that we should have been able to defend ourselves against a pirate. Clairmont had arranged my carriage and my trunks so cleverly, that by stretching five mattresses over them we had an excellent bed, where we could sleep and undress ourselves in perfect comfort; we had good pillows and plenty of sheets. A long awning covered the deck, and two lanterns were hung up, one at each end. In the evening they were lighted and Clairmont brought in supper. I had warned my brother that at the slightest presumption on his part he should be flung into the sea, so I allowed him and Possano to sup with us.

I sat between my two nymphs and served the company merrily, first my niece, then Marcoline, then my brother, and finally Possano. No water was drunk at table, so we each emptied a bottle of excellent Burgundy, and when we had finished supper the rowers rested on their oars, although the wind was very light. I had the lamps put out and went to bed with my two sweethearts, one on each side of me.

The light of dawn awoke me, and I found my darlings still sleeping in the same position. I could kiss neither of them, since one passed for my niece, and my sense of humanity would not allow me to treat Marcoline as my mistress in the presence of an unfortunate brother who adored her, and had never obtained the least favour from her. He was lying near at hand, overwhelmed with grief and seasickness, and watching and listening with all his might for the amorous encounter he suspected us of engaging in. I did not want to have any unpleasantness, so I contented myself with gazing on them till the two roses awoke and opened their eyes.

When this delicious sight was over, I got up and found that we were only opposite Final, and I proceeded to reprimand the master.

"The wind fell dead at Savona, sir"; and all the seamen chorused his excuse.

"Then you should have rowed instead of idling."

"We were afraid of waking you. You shall be at Antibes by to-morrow."

After passing the time by eating a hearty meal, we

took a fancy to go on shore at St. Remo. Everybody was delighted. I took my two nymphs on land, and after forbidding any of the others to disembark I conducted the ladies to an inn, where I ordered coffee. A man accosted us, and invited us to come and play biribi at his house.

"I thought the game was forbidden in Genoa," said I.

I felt certain that the players were the rascals whose bank I had broken at Genoa, so I accepted the invitation. My niece had fifty louis in her purse, and I gave fifteen to Marcoline. We found a large assemblage, room was made for us, and I recognized the knaves of Genoa. As soon as they saw me they turned pale and trembled. I should say that the man with the bag was not the poor devil who had served me so well without wanting to.

"I play harlequin," said I.

"There isn't one."

"What's the bank?"

"There it is. We play for small stakes here, and those two hundred louis are quite sufficient. You can bet as low as you like, and the highest stake is of a louis."

"That's all very well, but my louis is full weight."

"I think ours are, too."

"Are you sure?"

"No."

"Then I won't play," said I, to the keeper of the rooms.

"You are right; bring the scales."

The banker then said that when play was over he would give four crowns of six livres for every louis that the company had won, and the matter was settled. In a moment the board was covered with stakes.

We each punted a louis at a time, and I and my niece

lost twenty louis, but Marcoline, who had never possessed two sequins in her life before, won two hundred
and forty louis. She played on the figure of an abbé
which came out fifth twenty times. She was given a bag
full of crown pieces, and we returned to the felucca.

The wind was contrary, and we had to row all night,
and in the morning the sea was so rough that we had to
put in at Mentone. My two sweethearts were very sick,
as also my brother and Possano, but I was perfectly
well. I took the two invalids to the inn, and allowed my
brother and Possano to land and refresh themselves.
The innkeeper told me that the Prince and Princess of
Monaco were at Mentone, so I resolved to pay them a
visit. It was thirteen years since I had seen the prince
at Paris, where I had amused him and his mistress Caroline at supper. It was this prince who had taken me to
see the horrible Duchess of Rufec; then he was un-
married, and now I met him again in his principality
with his wife, of whom he had already two sons. The
princess had been a Duchess de Borgnoli, a great heiress,
and a delightful and pretty woman. I had heard all
about her, and I was curious to verify the facts for myself.

I called on the prince, was announced, and after a
long wait they introduced me to his presence. I gave
him his title of highness, which I had never done at Paris,
where he was not known under his full style and title.
He received me politely, but with that coolness which
lets one know that one is not an over-welcome visitor.

"You have put in on account of the bad weather, I
suppose?" said he.

"Yes, prince, and if your highness will allow me I will
spend the whole day in your delicious villa." (It is far
from being delicious.)

"As you please. The princess as well as myself likes it better than our place at Monaco, so we live here by preference."

"I should be grateful if your highness would present me to the princess."

Without mentioning my name he ordered a page in waiting to present me to the princess.

The page opened the door of a handsome room and said, "The Princess," and left me. She was singing at the piano, but as soon as she saw me she rose and came to meet me. I was obliged to introduce myself, a most unpleasant thing, and no doubt the princess felt the position, for she pretended not to notice it, and addressed me with the utmost kindness and politeness, and in a way that shewed that she was learned in the maxims of good society. I immediately became very much at my ease, and proceeded in a lordly manner to entertain her with pleasant talk, though I said nothing about my two lady friends.

The princess was handsome, clever, and good-natured. Her mother, who knew that a man like the prince would never make her daughter happy, opposed the marriage, but the young marchioness was infatuated, and the mother had to give in when the girl said,——

"*O Monaco o monaca.*" (Either Monaco or a convent.)

We were still occupied in the trifles which keep up an ordinary conversation, when the prince came in running after a waiting-maid, who was making her escape, laughing. The princess pretended not to see him, and went on with what she was saying. The scene displeased me, and I took leave of the princess, who wished me a pleasant journey. I met the prince as I was going out, and he invited me to come and see him whenever I passed that way.

"Certainly," said I; and made my escape without saying any more.

I went back to the inn and ordered a good dinner for three.

In the principality of Monaco there was a French garrison, which was worth a pension of a hundred thousand francs to the prince—a very welcome addition to his income.

A curled and scented young officer, passing by our room, the door of which was open, stopped short, and with unblushing politeness asked us if we would allow him to join our party. I replied politely, but coldly, that he did us honour—a phrase which means neither yes nor no; but a Frenchman who has advanced one step never retreats.

He proceeded to display his graces for the benefit of the ladies, talking incessantly, without giving them time to get in a word, when he suddenly turned to me and said that he wondered how it was that the prince had not asked me and my ladies to dinner. I told him that I had not said anything to the prince about the treasure I had with me.

I had scarcely uttered the words, when the kindly blockhead rose and cried enthusiastically,——

"Parbleu! I am no longer surprised. I will go and tell his highness, and I shall soon have the honour of dining with you at the castle."

He did not wait to hear my answer, but went off in hot haste.

We laughed heartily at his folly, feeling quite sure that we should neither dine with him nor the prince, but in a quarter of an hour he returned in high glee, and invited us all to dinner on behalf of the prince.

"I beg you will thank his highness, and at the same time ask him to excuse us. The weather has improved, and I want to be off as soon as we have taken a hasty morsel."

The young Frenchman exerted all his eloquence in vain, and at length retired with a mortified air to take our answer to the prince.

I thought I had got rid of him at last, but I did not know my man. He returned a short time after, and addressing himself in a complacent manner to the ladies, as if I was of no more account, he told them that he had given the prince such a description of their charms that he had made up his mind to dine with them.

"I have already ordered the table to be laid for two more, as I shall have the honour of being of the party. In a quarter of an hour, ladies, the prince will be here."

"Very good," said I, "but as the prince is coming I must go to the felucca and fetch a capital pie of which the prince is very fond, I know. Come, ladies."

"You can leave them here, sir. I will undertake to keep them amused."

"I have no doubt you would, but they have some things to get from the felucca as well."

"Then you will allow me to come too."

"Certainly with pleasure."

As we were going down the stairs, I asked the innkeeper what I owed him.

"Nothing, sir, I have just received orders to serve you in everything, and to take no money from you."

"The prince is really magnificent!" During this short dialogue, the ladies had gone on with the fop. I hastened to rejoin them, and my niece took my arm, laughing heartily to hear the officer making love to Marcoline, who did not understand a word he said. He did not notice it in the least, for his tongue kept going like the wheel of a mill, and he did not pause for any answers.

"We shall have some fun at dinner," said my niece, "but what are we going to do on the felucca?"

"We are leaving. Say nothing."

"Leaving?"

"Immediately."

"What a jest! it is worth its weight in gold."

We went on board the felucca, and the officer, who was delighted with the pretty vessel, proceeded to examine it. I told my niece to keep him company, and going to the master, whispered to him to let go directly.

"Directly?"

"Yes, this moment."

"But the abbé and your secretary are gone for a walk, and two of my men are on shore, too."

"That's no matter; we shall pick them up again at Antibes; it's only ten leagues, and they have plenty of money. I must go, and directly. Make haste."

"All right."

He tripped the anchor, and the felucca began to swing away from the shore. The officer asked me in great astonishment what it meant.

"It means that I am going to Antibes and I shall be very glad to take you there for nothing."

"This is a fine jest! You are joking, surely?"

"Your company will be very pleasant on the journey."

"Pardieu! put me ashore, for with your leave, ladies, I cannot go to Antibes."

"Put the gentleman ashore," said I to the master, "he does not seem to like our company."

"It's not that, upon my honour. These ladies are

charming, but the prince would think that I was in the plot to play this trick upon him, which you must confess is rather strong."

"I never play a weak trick."

"But what will the prince say?"

"He may say what he likes, and I shall do as I like."

"Well, it's no fault of mine. Farewell, ladies! farewell, sir!"

"Farewell, and you may thank the prince for me for paying my bill."

Marcoline who did not understand what was passing gazed in astonishment, but my niece laughed till her sides ached, for the way in which the poor officer had taken the matter was extremely comic.

Clairmont brought us an excellent dinner, and we laughed incessantly during its progress, even at the astonishment of the abbé and Possano when they came to the quay and found the felucca had flown. However, I was sure of meeting them again at Antibes, and we reached that port at six o'clock in the evening.

The motion of the sea had tired us without making us feel sick, for the air was fresh, and our appetites felt the benefits of it, and in consequence we did great honour to the supper and the wine. Marcoline whose stomach was weakened by the sickness she had undergone soon felt the effects of the Burgundy, her eyes were heavy, and she went to sleep. My niece would have imitated her, but I reminded her tenderly that we were at Antibes, and said I was sure she would keep her word. She did not answer me, but gave me her hand, lowering her eyes with much modesty.

Intoxicated with her submission which was so like love, I got into bed beside her, exclaiming,——

"At last the hour of my happiness has come!"

"And mine too, dearest."

"Yours? Have you not continually repulsed me?"

"Never! I always loved you, and your indifference has been a bitter grief to me."

"But the first night we left Milan you preferred being alone to sleeping with me."

"Could I do otherwise without passing in your eyes for one more a slave to sensual passion than to love? Besides you might have thought I was giving myself to you for the benefits I had received; and though gratitude be a noble feeling, it destroys all the sweet delights of love. You ought to have told me that you loved me and subdued me by those attentions which conquer the hearts of us women. Then you would have seen that I loved you too, and our affection would have been mutual. On my side I should have known that the pleasure you had of me was not given out of a mere feeling of gratitude. I do not know whether you would have loved me less the morning after, if I had consented, but I am sure I should have lost your esteem."

She was right, and I applauded her sentiments, while giving her to understand that she was to put all notions of benefits received out of her mind. I wanted to make her see that I knew that there was no more need for gratitude on her side than mine.

We spent a night that must be imagined rather than described. She told me in the morning that she felt all had been for the best, as if she had given way at first she could never have made up her mind to accept the young Genoese, though he seemed likely to make her happy.

Marcoline came to see us in the morning, caressed us, and promised to sleep by herself the rest of the voyage.

"Then you are not jealous?" said I.

"No, for her happiness is mine too, and I know she will make you happy."

She became more ravishingly beautiful every day.

Possano and the abbé came in just as we were sitting down to table, and my niece having ordered two more plates I allowed them to dine with us. My brother's face was pitiful and yet ridiculous. He could not walk any distance, so he had been obliged to come on horseback, probably for the first time in his life.

"My skin is delicate," said he, "so I am all blistered. But God's will be done! I do not think any of His servants have endured greater torments than mine during this journey. My body is sore, and so is my soul."

So saying he cast a piteous glance at Marcoline, and we had to hold our sides to prevent ourselves laughing. My niece could bear it no more, and said,——

"How I pity you, dear uncle!"

At this he blushed, and began to address the most absurd compliments to her, styling her "my dear niece." I told him to be silent, and not to speak French till he was able to express himself in that equivocal language without making a fool of himself. But the poet Pogomas spoke no better than he did.

I was curious to know what had happened at Mentone after we had left, and Pogomas proceeded to tell the story.

"When we came back from our walk we were greatly astonished not to find the felucca any more. We went to the inn, where I knew you had ordered dinner; but the inn-keeper knew nothing except that he was expecting the prince and a young officer to dine with you. I told him he might wait for you in vain, and just then the prince came up in a rage, and told the inn-keeper that now you were gone he might look to you for his payment. 'My lord,' said the inn-keeper, 'the gentleman wanted to pay me, but I respected the orders I had received from your highness and would not take the money.' At this the prince flung him a louis with an ill grace, and asked us who we were. I told him that we belonged to you, and that you had not waited for us either, which put us to great trouble. 'You will get away easily enough,' said he; and then he began to laugh, and swore the jest was a pleasant one. He then asked me who the ladies were. I told him that the one was your niece, and that I knew nothing of the other; but the abbé interfered, and said she was your *cuisine*. The prince guessed he meant to say 'cousin,' and burst out laughing, in which he was joined by the young officer. 'Greet him from me,' said he, as he went away, 'and tell him that we shall meet again, and that I will pay him out for the trick he has played me.'

"The worthy host laughed, too, when the prince had gone, and gave us a good dinner, saying that the prince's louis would pay for it all. When we had dined we hired two horses, and slept at Nice. In the morning we rode on again, being certain of finding you here."

Marcoline told the abbé in a cold voice to take care not to tell anyone else that she was his *cuisine,* or his cousin, or else it would go ill with him, as she did not wish to be thought either the one or the other. I also advised him seriously not to speak French for the future, as the absurd way in which he had committed himself made everyone about him ashamed.

Just as I was ordering post-horses to take us to Fréjus, a man appeared, and told me I owed him ten louis for the storage of a carriage which I had left on his hands

nearly three years ago. This was when I was taking
Rosalie to Italy. I laughed, for the carriage itself was
not worth five louis. "Friend," said I, "I make you a
present of the article."

"I don't want your present. I want the ten louis you
owe me."

"You won't get the ten louis. I will see you further
first."

"We will see about that"; and so saying he took his
departure.

I sent for horses that we might continue our journey.

A few moments after, a sergeant summoned me to the
governor's presence. I followed him, and was politely
requested to pay the ten louis that my creditor demanded. I answered that, in the agreement I had entered into for six francs a month, there was no mention
of the length of the term, and that I did not want to
withdraw my carriage.

"But supposing you were never to withdraw it?"

"Then the man could bequeath his claim to his heir."

"I believe he could oblige you to withdraw it, or to
allow it to be sold to defray expenses."

"You are right, sir, and I wish to spare him that
trouble. I make him a present of the carriage."

"That's fair enough. Friend, the carriage is yours."

"But sir," said the plaintiff, "it is not enough; the
carriage is not worth ten louis, and I want the surplus."

"You are in the wrong. I wish you a pleasant journey,
sir, and I hope you will forgive the ignorance of these
poor people, who would like to shape the laws according
to their needs."

All this trouble had made me lose a good deal of
time, and I determined to put off my departure till the
next day. However, I wanted a carriage for Possano

and the abbé, and I got my secretary to buy the one
I had abandoned for four louis. It was in a deplorable
state, and I had to have it repaired, which kept us till the
afternoon of the next day; however, so far as pleasure
was concerned, the time was not lost.

CHAPTER III

*My Arrival at Marseilles—Madame d'Urfé—My Niece
Is Welcomed by Madame Audibert—I Get Rid of My
Brother and Possano—Regeneration—Departure of
Madame d'Urfé—Marcoline Remains Constant*

MY NIECE, now my mistress, grew more dear to me
every day, and I could not help trembling when I
reflected that Marseilles would be the tomb of our love.
Though I could not help arriving there, I prolonged my
happiness as long as I could by travelling by short stages.
I got to Fréjus in less than three hours, and stopped there,
and telling Possano and the abbé to do as they liked
during our stay, I ordered a delicate supper and choice
wine for myself and my nymphs. Our repast lasted till
midnight, then we went to bed, and passed the time in
sweet sleep and sweeter pleasures. I made the same
arrangements at Lucca, Brignoles, and Aubayne, where
I passed the sixth and last night of happiness.

As soon as I got to Marseilles I conducted my niece
to Madame Audibert's, and sent Possano and my brother
to the "Trieze Cantons" inn, bidding them observe the
strictest silence with regard to me, for Madame d'Urfé
had been awaiting me for three weeks, and I wished
to be my own herald to her.

It was at Madame Audibert's that my niece had met
Croce. She was a clever woman, and had known the girl
from her childhood, and it was through her that my
niece hoped to be restored to her father's good graces.

We had agreed that I should leave my niece and Marcoline in the carriage, and should interview Madame Audibert, whose acquaintance I had made before, and with whom I could make arrangements for my niece's lodging till some arrangement was come to.

Madame Audibert saw me getting out of my carriage, and as she did not recognize me her curiosity made her come down and open the door. She soon recognized me, and consented to let me have a private interview with the best grace in the world.

I did not lose any time in leading up to the subject, and after I had given her a rapid sketch of the affair, how misfortune had obliged La Croix to abandon Mdlle. Crosin, how I had been able to be of service to her, and finally, how she had had the good luck to meet a wealthy and distinguished person, who would come to Marseilles to ask her hand in a fortnight, I concluded by saying that I should have the happiness of restoring to her hands the dear girl whose preserver I had been.

"Where is she?" cried Madame Audibert.

"In my carriage. I have lowered the blinds."

"Bring her in, quick! I will see to everything. Nobody shall know that she is in my house."

Happier than a prince, I made one bound to the carriage and, concealing her face with her cloak and hood, I led my niece to her friend's arms. This was a dramatic scene full of satisfaction for me. Kisses were given and received, tears of happiness and repentance shed, I wept myself from mingled feelings of emotion, happiness, and regret.

In the meanwhile Clairmont had brought up my niece's luggage, and I went away promising to return and see her another day.

I had another and as important an arrangement to conclude, I mean with respect to Marcoline. I told the postillions to take me to the worthy old man's where I had lodged Rosalie so pleasantly. Marcoline was weeping at this separation from her friend. I got down at the house, and made my bargain hastily. My new mistress was, I said, to be lodged, fed, and attended on as if she had been a princess. He shewed me the apartment she was to occupy; it was fit for a young marchioness, and he told me that she should be attended by his own niece, that she should not leave the house, and that nobody but myself should visit her.

Having made these arrangements I made the fair Venetian come in. I gave her the money she had won, which I had converted into gold and made up to a thousand ducats.

"You won't want it here," said I, "so take care of it. At Venice a thousand ducats will make you somebody. Do not weep, dearest, my heart is with you, and to-morrow evening I will sup with you."

The old man gave me the latch-key, and I went off to the "Treize Cantons." I was expected, and my rooms were adjacent to those occupied by Madame d'Urfé.

As soon as I was settled, Bourgnole waited on me, and told me her mistress was alone and expecting me impatiently.

I shall not trouble my readers with an account of our interview, as it was only composed of Madame d'Urfé's mad flights of fancy, and of lies on my part which had not even the merit of probability. A slave to my life of happy profligacy, I profited by her folly; she would have found someone else to deceive her, if I had not done so, for it was really she who deceived herself. I naturally preferred to profit by her rather than that a stranger should do so; she was very rich, and I did myself a great deal of good, without doing anyone any harm.

The first thing she asked me was, "Where is Querilinthos?" And she jumped with joy when I told her that he was under the same roof.

" 'Tis he, then, who shall make me young again. So has my genius assured me night after night. Ask Paralis if the presents I have prepared are good enough for Semiramis to present to the head of the Fraternity of the Rosy Cross."

I did not know what these presents were, and as I could not ask to see them, I answered that, before consulting Paralis, it would be necessary to consecrate the gifts under the planetary hours, and that Querilinthos himself must not see them before the consecration. Thereupon she took me to her closet, and shewed me the seven packets meant for the Rosicrucian in the form of offerings to the seven planets.

Each packet contained seven pounds of the metal proper to the planet, and seven precious stones, also proper to the planets, each being seven carats in weight; there were diamonds, rubies, emeralds, sapphires, chrysolites, topazes, and opals.

I made up my mind that nothing of this should pass into the hands of the Genoese, and told the mad woman that we must trust entirely in Paralis for the method of consecration, which must be begun by our placing each packet in a small casket made on purpose. One packet, and one only, could be consecrated in a day, and it was necessary to begin with the sun. It was now Friday, and we should have to wait till Sunday, the day of the sun. On Saturday I had a box with seven niches made for the purpose.

For the purposes of consecration I spent three hours every day with Madame d'Urfé, and we had not finished till the ensuing Saturday. Throughout this week I made Possano and my brother take their meals with us, and as the latter did not understand a word the good lady said, he did not speak a word himself, and might have passed for a mute of the seraglio. Madame d'Urfé pronounced him devoid of sense, and imagined we were going to put the soul of a sylph into his body that he might engender some being half human, half divine.

It was amusing to see my brother's despair and rage at being taken for an idiot, and when he endeavoured to say something to shew that he was not one, she only thought him more idiotic than ever. I laughed to myself, and thought how ill he would have played the part if I had asked him to do it. All the same the rascal did not lose anything by his reputation, for Madame d'Urfé clothed him with a decent splendour that would have led one to suppose that the abbé belonged to one of the first families in France. The most uneasy guest at Madame d'Urfé's table was Possano, who had to reply to questions of the most occult nature, and, not knowing anything about the subject, made the most ridiculous mistakes.

I brought Madame d'Urfé the box, and having made all the necessary arrangements for the consecrations, I received an order from the oracle to go into the country and sleep there for seven nights in succession, to abstain from intercourse with all mortal women, and to perform ceremonial worship to the moon every night, at the hour of that planet, in the open fields. This would make me fit to regenerate Madame d'Urfé myself in case Querilinthos, for some mystic reasons, might not be able to do so.

Through this order Madame d'Urfé was not only not vexed with me for sleeping away from the hotel, but was grateful for the pains I was taking to ensure the success of the operation.

The day after my arrival I called on Madame Audibert, and had the pleasure of finding my niece well pleased with the efforts her friend was making in her favour. Madame Audibert had spoken to her father, telling him that his daughter was with her, and that she hoped to obtain his pardon and to return to his house, where she would soon become the bride of a rich Genoese, who wished to receive her from her father's hands. The worthy man, glad to find again the lost sheep, said he would come in two days and take her to her aunt, who had a house at St. Louis, two leagues from the town. She might then quietly await the arrival of her future husband, and avoid all occasion of scandal. My niece was surprised that her father had not yet received a letter from the young man, and I could see that she was anxious about it; but I comforted her and assured her that I would not leave Marseilles till I had danced at her wedding.

I left her to go to Marcoline, whom I longed to press to my heart. I found her in an ecstasy of joy, and she said that if she could understand what her maid said her happiness would be complete. I saw that her situation was a painful one, especially as she was a woman, but for the present I saw no way out of the difficulty; I should have to get an Italian-speaking servant, and this would have been a troublesome task. She wept with joy when I told her that my niece desired to be remembered to her, and that in a day she would be on her father's hearth. Marcoline had found out that she was not my real niece when she found her in my arms.

The choice supper which the old man had procured us, and which shewed he had a good memory for my favorite tastes, made me think of Rosalie. Marcoline heard me tell the story with great interest, and said that it seemed to her that I only went about to make unfortunate girls happy, provided I found them pretty.

"I almost think you are right," said I; "and it is certain that I have made many happy, and have never brought misfortune to any girl."

"God will reward you, my dear friend."

"Possibly I am not worth His taking the trouble."

Though the wit and beauty of Marcoline had charmed me, her appetite charmed me still more; the reader knows that I have always liked women who eat heartily. And in Marseilles they make an excellent dish of a common fowl, which is often so insipid.

Those who like oil will get on capitally in Provençe, for it is used in everything, and it must be confessed that if used in moderation it makes an excellent relish.

Marcoline was charming in bed. I had not enjoyed the Venetian vices for nearly eight years, and Marcoline was a beauty before whom Praxiteles would have bent the knee. I laughed at my brother for having let such a treasure slip out of his hands, though I quite forgave him for falling in love with her. I myself could not take her about, and as I wanted her to be amused I begged my kind old landlord to send her to the play every day, and to prepare a good supper every evening. I got her some rich dresses that she might cut a good figure, and this attention redoubled her affection for me.

The next day, which was the second occasion on which I had visited her, she told me that she had enjoyed the play though she could not understand the dialogues; and the day after she astonished me by saying that my brother had intruded himself into her box, and had said so many impertinent things that if she had been at Venice she would have boxed his ears.

"I am afraid," she added, "that the rascal has followed me here, and will be annoying me."

"Don't be afraid," I answered, "I will see what I can do."

When I got to the hotel I entered the abbé's room, and by Possano's bed I saw an individual collecting lint and various surgical instruments.

"What's all this? Are you ill?"

"Yes, I have got something which will teach me to be wiser for the future."

"It's rather late for this kind of thing at sixty."

"Better late than never."

"You are an old fool. You stink of mercury."

"I shall not leave my room."

"This will harm you with the marchioness, who believes you to be the greatest of adepts, and consequently above such weaknesses."

"Damn the marchioness! Let me be."

The rascal had never talked in this style before. I thought it best to conceal my anger, and went up to my brother who was in a corner of the room.

"What do you mean by pestering Marcoline at the theatre yesterday?"

"I went to remind her of her duty, and to warn her that I would not be her complaisant lover."

"You have insulted me and her too, fool that you are! You owe all to Marcoline, for if it had not been for her, I should never have given you a second glance; and yet you behave in this disgraceful manner."

"I have ruined myself for her sake, and I can never shew my face in Venice again. What right have you to take her from me?"

"The right of love, blockhead, and the right of luck,

and the right of the strongest! How is it that she is happy with me, and does not wish to leave me?"

"You have dazzled her."

"Another reason is that with you she was dying of misery and hunger."

"Yes, but the end of it will be that you will abandon her as you have done with many others, whereas I should have married her."

"Married her! You renegade, you seem to forget that you are a priest. I do not propose to part with her, but if I do I will send her away rich."

"Well, well, do as you please; but still I have the right to speak to her whenever I like."

"I have forbidden you to do so, and you may trust me when I tell you that you have spoken to her for the last time."

So saying I went out and called on an advocate. I asked him if I could have a foreign abbé, who was indebted to me, arrested, although I had no proof of the debt.

"You can do so, as he is a foreigner, but you will have to pay caution-money. You can have him put under arrest at his inn, and you can make him pay unless he is able to prove that he owes you nothing. Is the sum a large one?"

"Twelve louis."

"You must come with me before the magistrate and deposit twelve louis, and from that moment you will be able to have him arrested. Where is he staying?"

"In the same hotel as I am, but I do not wish to have him arrested there, so I will get him to the 'Ste. Baume,' and put him under arrest. Here are the twelve louis caution-money, so you can get the magistrate's order, and we will meet again to-morrow."

"Give me his name, and yours also."

I returned in haste to the "Treize Cantons," and met the abbé, dressed up to the nines, and just about to go out.

"Follow me," said I, "I am going to take you to Marcoline, and you shall have an explanation in her presence."

"With pleasure."

He got into a carriage with me, and I told the coachman to take us to the "Ste. Baume" inn. When we got there, I told him to wait for me, that I was going to fetch Marcoline, and that I would return with her in a minute.

I got into the carriage again, and drove to the advocate, who gave the order for arrest to a policeman, who was to execute it. I then returned to the "Treize Cantons" and put his belongings into a trunk, and had them transported to his new abode.

I found him under arrest, and talking to the astonished host, who could not understand what it was all about. I told the landlord the mythical history of the abbé debt to me, and handed over the trunk, telling him that he had nothing to fear with regard to the bill, as I would take care that he should be well paid.

I then began my talk with the abbé, telling him that he must get ready to leave Marseilles the next day, and that I would pay for his journey to Paris; but that if he did not like to do so, I should leave him to his fate, and in three days he would be expelled from Marseilles. The coward began to weep and said he would go to Paris.

"You must start for Lyons to-morrow, but you will first write me out an I O U for twelve louis."

"Why?"

"Because I say so. If you do so I will give you twelve louis and tear up the document before your face."

"I have no choice in the matter."

"You are right."

When he had written the I O U, I went to take a place in the diligence for him, and the next morning I went with the advocate to withdraw the arrest and to take back the twelve louis, which I gave to my brother in the diligence, with a letter to M. Bono, whom I warned not to give him any money, and to send him on to Paris by the same diligence. I then tore up his note of hand, and wished him a pleasant journey.

Thus I got rid of this foolish fellow, whom I saw again in Paris in a month's time.

The day I had my brother arrested and before I went to dine with Madame d'Urfé I had an interview with Possano in the hope of discovering the reason of his ill humour.

"The reason is," said he, "that I am sure you are going to lay hands on twenty or thirty thousand crowns in gold and diamonds, which the marchioness meant me to have."

"That may be, but it is not for you to know anything about it. I may tell you that it rests entirely with me to prevent your getting anything. If you think you can succeed go to the marchioness and make your complaints to her. I will do nothing to prevent you."

"Then you think I am going to help you in your imposture for nothing; you are very much mistaken. I want a thousand louis, and I will have it, too."

"Then get somebody to give it you," said I; and I turned my back on him.

I went up to the marchioness and told her that dinner was ready, and that we should dine alone, as I had been obliged to send the abbé away.

"He was an idiot; but how about Querilinthos?"

"After dinner Paralis will tell us all about him. I have strong suspicions that there is something to be cleared up."

"So have I. The man seems changed. Where is he?"

"He is in bed, ill of a disease which I dare not so much as name to you."

"That is a very extraordinary circumstance; I have never heard of such a thing before. It must be the work of an evil genius."

"I have never heard of such a thing, either; but now let us dine. We shall have to work hard to-day at the consecration of the tin."

"All the better. We must offer an expiatory sacrifice to Oromasis, for, awful thought! in three days he would have to regenerate me, and the operation would be performed in that condition."

"Let us eat now," I repeated; "I fear lest the hour of Jupiter be over-past."

"Fear nothing, I will see that all goes well."

After the consecration of the tin had been performed, I transferred that of Oromasis to another day, while I consulted the oracle assiduously, the marchioness translating the figures into letters. The oracle declared that seven salamanders had transported the true Querilinthos to the Milky Way, and that the man in the next room was the evil genius, St. Germain, who had been put in that fearful condition by a female gnome, who had intended to make him the executioner of Semiramis, who was to die of the dreadful malady before her term had expired. The oracle also said that Semiramis should leave to *Paraliseus Galtinardus* (myself) all the charge of getting rid of the evil genius, St. Germain; and that she was not to doubt concerning her regeneration, since the word would be sent me by the true Querilinthos from the Milky Way on the seventh night of my worship of the moon. Finally the oracle declared that I was to embrace Semiramis two days before the end of the ceremonies, after an Undine had purified us by bathing us in the room where we were.

I had thus undertaken to regenerate the worthy Semiramis, and I began to think how I could carry out my undertaking without putting myself to shame. The marchioness was handsome but old, and I feared lest I should be unable to perform the great act. I was thirty-eight, and I began to feel age stealing on me. The Undine, whom I was to obtain of the moon, was none other than Marcoline, who was to give me the necessary generative vigour by the sight of her beauty and by the contact of her hands. The reader will see how I made her come down from heaven.

I received a note from Madame Audibert which made me call on her before paying my visit to Marcoline. As soon as I came in she told me joyously that my niece's father had just received a letter from the father of the Genoese, asking the hand of his daughter for his only son, who had been introduced to her by the Chevalier de Seingalt, her uncle, at the Paretti's.

"The worthy man thinks himself under great obligations to you," said Madame Audibert. "He adores his daughter, and he knows you have cared for her like a father. His daughter has drawn your portrait in very favourable colors, and he would be extremely pleased to make your acquaintance. Tell me when you can sup with me; the father will be here to meet you, though unaccompanied by his daughter."

"I am delighted at what you tell me, for the young man's esteem for his future wife will only be augmented when he finds that I am her father's friend. I cannot come to supper, however; I will be here at six and stop till eight."

As the lady left the choice of the day with me I fixed the day after next, and then I repaired to my fair Venetian, to whom I told my news, and how I had managed to get rid of the abbé.

On the day after next, just as we were sitting down to dinner, the marchioness smilingly gave me a letter which Possano had written her in bad but perfectly intelligible French. He had filled eight pages in his endeavour to convince her that I was deceiving her, and to make sure he told the whole story without concealing any circumstance to my disadvantage. He added that I had brought two girls with me to Marseilles; and though he did not know where I had hidden them, he was sure that it was with them that I spent my nights.

After I had read the whole letter through, with the utmost coolness I gave it back to her, asking her if she had had the patience to read it through. She replied that she had run through it, but that she could not make it out at all, as the evil genius seemed to write a sort of outlandish dialect, which she did not care to puzzle herself over, as he could only have written down lies calculated to lead her astray at the most important moment of her life. I was much pleased with the marchioness's prudence, for it was important that she should have no suspicions about the Undine, the sight and the touch of whom were necessary to me in the great work I was about to undertake.

After dining, and discharging all the ceremonies and oracles which were necessary to calm the soul of my poor victim, I went to a banker and got a bill of a hundred louis on Lyons, to the order of M. Bono, and I advised him of what I had done, requesting him to cash it for Possano if it were presented on the day named thereon.

I then wrote the advice for Possano to take with him, it ran as follows: "M. Bonno, pay to M. Possano, on sight, to himself, and not to order, the sum of one hundred louis, if these presents are delivered to you on the 30th day of April, in the year 1763; and after the day aforesaid my order to become null and void."

With this letter in my hand I went to the traitor who had been lanced an hour before.

"You're an infamous traitor," I began, "but as Madame d'Urfé knows of the disgraceful state you are in she would not so much as read your letter. I have read it, and by way of reward I give you two alternatives which you must decide on immediately. I am in a hurry. You will either go to the hospital—for we can't have pestiferous fellows like you here—or start for Lyons in an hour. You must not stop on the way, for I have only given you sixty hours, which is ample to do forty posts in. As soon as you get to Lyons present this to M. Bono, and he will give you a hundred louis. This is a present from me, and afterwards I don't care what you do, as you are no longer in my service. You can have the carriage I bought for you at Antibes, and there is twenty-five louis for the journey: that is all. Make your choice, but I warn you that if you go to the hospital I shall only give you a month's wages, as I dismiss you from my service now at this instant."

After a moment's reflection he said he would go to Lyons, though it would be at the risk of his life, for he was very ill.

"You must reap the reward of your treachery," said I, "and if you die it will be a good thing for your family, who will come in for what I have given you, but not what I should have given you if you had been a faithful servant."

I then left him and told Clairmont to pack up his trunk. I warned the inn-keeper of his departure and told him to get the post horses ready as soon as possible.

I then gave Clairmont the letter to Bono and twenty-five louis, for him to hand them over to Possano when he was in the carriage and ready to go off.

When I had thus successfully accomplished my designs by means of the all-powerful lever, gold, which I knew how to lavish in time of need, I was once more free for my amours. I wanted to instruct the fair Marcoline, with whom I grew more in love every day. She kept telling me that her happiness would be complete if she knew French, and if she had the slightest hope that I would take her to England with me.

I had never flattered her that my love would go as far as that, but yet I could not help feeling sad at the thought of parting from a being who seemed made to taste voluptuous pleasures, and to communicate them with tenfold intensity to the man of her choice. She was delighted to hear that I had got rid of my two odious companions, and begged me to take her to the theatre, "for," said she, "everybody is asking who and what I am, and my landlord's niece is quite angry with me because I will not let her tell the truth."

I promised I would take her out in the course of the next week, but that for the present I had a most important affair on hand, in which I had need of her assistance.

"I will do whatever you wish, dearest."

"Very good! then listen to me. I will get you a disguise which will make you look like a smart footman, and in that costume you will call on the marchioness with whom I live, at the hour I shall name to you, and you will give her a note. Have you sufficient courage for that?"

"Certainly. Will you be there?"

"Yes. She will speak, but you must pretend to be dumb, as the note you bring with you will tell us; as also that you have come to wait upon us while we are bathing. She will accept the offer, and when she tells you to undress her from head to foot you will do so. When you have done, undress yourself, and gently rub the marchioness from the feet to the waist, but not higher. In the meanwhile I shall have taken off my clothes, and while I hold her in a close embrace you must stand so that I can see all your charms.

"Further, sweetheart, when I leave you you must gently wash her generative organs, and afterwards wipe them with a fine towel. Then do the same to me, and try to bring me to life again. I shall proceed to embrace the marchioness a second time, and when it is over wash her again and embrace her, and then come and embrace me and kiss in your Venetian manner the instrument with which the sacrifice is consummated. I shall then clasp the marchioness to my arms a third time, and you must caress us till the act is complete. Finally, you will wash us for the third time, then dress, take what she gives you and come here, where I will meet you in the course of an hour."

"You may reckon on my following all your instructions, but you must see that the task will be rather trying to my feelings."

"Not more trying than to mine. I could do nothing with the old woman if you were not present."

"Is she very old?"

"Nearly seventy."

"My poor sweetheart! I do pity you. But after this painful duty is over you must sup here and sleep with me."

"Certainly."

On the day appointed I had a long and friendly interview with the father of my late niece. I told him all about his daughter, only suppressing the history of our own amours, which were not suitable for a father's ears. The worthy man embraced me again and again, calling me his benefactor, and saying that I had done more for his daughter than he would have done himself, which in a sense was perhaps true. He told me that he had received another letter from the father, and a letter from the young man himself, who wrote in the most tender and respectful manner possible.

"He doesn't ask anything about the dower," said he, "a wonderful thing these days, but I will give her a hundred and fifty thousand francs, for the marriage is an excellent one, above all after my poor simpleton's escape. All Marseilles knows the father of her future husband, and to-morrow I mean to tell the whole story to my wife, and I am sure she will forgive the poor girl as I have done."

I had to promise to be present at the wedding, which was to be at Madame Audibert's. That lady knowing me to be very fond of play, and there being a good deal of play going on at her house, wondered why she did not see more of me; but I was at Marseilles to create and not to destroy: there is a time for everything.

I had a green velvet jacket made for Marcoline, with

breeches of the same and silver-lace garters, green silk stockings, and fine leather shoes of the same colour. Her fine black hair was confined in a net of green silk, with a silver brooch. In this dress the voluptuous and well-rounded form of Marcoline was displayed to so much advantage, that if she had shewn herself in the street all Marseilles would have run after her, for, in spite of her man's dress, anybody could see that she was a girl. I took her to my rooms in her ordinary costume, to shew her where she would have to hide after the operation was over.

By Saturday we had fiinished all the consecrations, and the oracle fixed the regeneration of Semiramis for the following Tuesday, in the hours of the sun, Venus, and Mercury, which follow each other in the planetary system of the magicians, as also in Ptolemy's. These hours were in ordinary parlance the ninth, tenth, and eleventh of the day, since the day being a Tuesday, the first hour was sacred to Mars. And as at the beginning of May the hours are sixty-five minutes long, the reader, however little of a magician he may be, will understand that I had to perform the great work on Madame d'Urfé, beginning at half-past two and ending at five minutes to six. I had taken plenty of time, as I expected I should have great need of it.

On the Monday night, at the hour of the moon, I had taken Madame d'Urfé to the sea-shore, Clairmont following behind with the box containing the offerings, which weighed fifty pounds.

I was certain that nobody could see us, and I told my companion that the time was come. I told Clairmont to put down the box beside us, and to go and await us at the carriage. When we were alone we addressed a solemn prayer to Selenis, and then to the great satisfaction of the marchioness the box was consigned to the address. My satisfaction however was still greater than hers, for the box contained fifty pounds of lead. The real box, containing the treasure, was comfortably hidden in my room.

When we got back to the "Treize Cantons," I left Madame d'Urfé alone, telling her that I would return to the hotel when I had performed my conjurations to the moon, at the same hour and in the same place in which I had performed the seven consecrations.

I spoke the truth. I went to Marcoline, and while she was putting on her disguise I wrote on a sheet of white paper, in large and odd-looking letters, the following sentences, using, instead of ink, rock-alum:

"I am dumb but not deaf. I am come from the Rhone to bathe you. The hour of Oromasis has begun."

"This is the note you are to give to the marchioness," I said, "when you appear before her."

After supper we walked to the hotel and got in without anyone seeing us. I hid Marcoline in a large cupboard, and then putting on my dressing-gown I went to the marchioness to inform her that Selenis had fixed the next day for the hour of regeneration, and that we must be careful to finish before the hour of the moon began, as otherwise the operation would be annulled or at least greatly enfeebled.

"You must take care," I added, "that the bath be here beside your bed, and that Brougnole does not interrupt us."

"I will tell her to go out. But Selenis promised to send an Undine."

"True, but I have not yet seen such a being."

"Ask the oracle."

"Willingly."

She herself asked the question imploring Paralis not to delay the time of her regeneration, even though the Undine were lacking, since she could very well bathe herself.

"The commands of Oromasis change not," came the reply; "and in that you have doubted them you have sinned."

At this the marchioness arose and performed an expiatory sacrifice, and it appeared, on consulting the oracle, that Oromasis was satisfied.

The old lady did not move my pity so much as my laughter. She solemnly embraced me and said,——

"To-morrow, Galtinardus, you will be my spouse and my father."

When I got back to my room and had shut the door, I drew the Undine out of her place of concealment. She undressed, and as she knew that I should be obliged to husband my forces, she turned her back on me, and we passed the night without giving each other a single kiss, for a spark would have set us all ablaze.

Next morning, before summoning Clairmont, I gave her her breakfast, and then replaced her in the cupboard. Later on, I gave her her instructions over again, telling her to do everything with calm precision, a cheerful face, and, above all, silence.

"Don't be afraid," said she, "I will make no mistakes."

As we were to dine at noon exactly, I went to look for the marchioness, but she was not in her room, though the bath was there, and the bed which was to be our altar was prepared.

A few moments after, the marchioness came out of her dressing-room, exquisitely painted, her hair arranged with the choicest lace, and looking radiant. Her breasts,

which forty years before had been the fairest in all
France, were covered with a lace shawl, her dress was
of the antique kind, but of extremely rich material, her
ear-rings were emeralds, and a necklace of seven aqua-
marines of the finest water, from which hung an enormous emerald, surrounded by twenty brilliants, each
weighing a carat and a half, completed her costume.
She wore on her finger the carbuncle which she thought
worth a million francs, but which was really only a
splendid imitation.

Seeing Semiramis thus decked out for the sacrifice,
I thought it my bounden duty to offer her my homage.
I would have knelt before her and kissed her hand, but
she would not let me, and instead opened her arms and
strained me to her breast.

After telling Brougnole that she could go out till six
o'clock, we talked over our mysteries till the dinner was
brought in.

Clairmont was the only person privileged to see us at
dinner, at which Semiramis would only eat fish. At half-
past one I told Clairmont I was not at home to anyone,
and giving him a louis I told him to go and amuse himself till the evening.

The marchioness began to be uneasy, and I pretended
to be so, too. I looked at my watch, calculated how the
planetary hours were proceeding, and said from time to
time,——

"We are still in the hour of Mars, that of the sun has
not yet commenced."

At last the time-piece struck half-past two, and in
two minutes afterwards the fair and smiling Undine was
seen advancing into the room. She came along with
measured steps, and knelt before Madame d'Urfé, and
gave her the paper she carried. Seeing that I did not

rise, the marchioness remained seated, but she raised the spirit with a gracious air and took the paper from her. She was surprised, however, to find that it was all white.

I hastened to give her a pen to consult the oracle on the subject, and after I had made a pyramid of her question, she interpreted it and found the answer:

"That which is written in water must be read in water."

"I understand now," said she, and going to the bath she plunged the paper into it, and then read in still whiter letters: "I am dumb, but not deaf. I am come from the Rhone to bathe you. The hour of Oromasis has begun."

"Then bathe me, divine being," said Semiramis, putting down the paper and sitting on the bed.

With perfect exactitude Marcoline undressed the marchioness, and delicately placed her feet in the water, and then, in a twinkling she had undressed herself, and was in the bath, beside Madame d'Urfé. What a contrast there was between the two bodies; but the sight of the one kindled the flame which the other was to quench.

As I gazed on the beautiful girl, I, too, undressed, and when I was ready to take off my shirt I spoke as follows: "O divine being, wipe the feet of Semiramis, and be the witness of my union with her, to the glory of the immortal Horomadis, King of the Salamanders."

Scarcely had I uttered my prayer when it was granted, and I consummated my first union with Semiramis, gazing on the charms of Marcoline, which I had never seen to such advantage before.

Semiramis had been handsome, but she was then what I am now, and without the Undine the operation would have failed. Nevertheless, Semiramis was affectionate, clean, and sweet in every respect, and had nothing disgusting about her, so I succeeded.

When the milk had been poured forth upon the altar, I said——

"We must now await the hour of Venus."

The Undine performed the ablutions, embraced the bride, and came to perform the same office for me.

Semiramis was in an ecstasy of happiness, and as she pointed out to me the beauties of the Undine I was obliged to confess that I had never seen any mortal woman to be compared to her in beauty. Semiramis grew excited by so voluptuous a sight, and when the hour of Venus began I proceeded to the second assault, which would be the severest, as the hour was of sixty-five minutes. I worked for half an hour, steaming with perspiration, and tiring Semiramis, without being able to come to the point. Still I was ashamed to trick her. She, the victim, wiped the drops of sweat from my forehead, while the Undine, seeing my exhaustion, kindled anew the flame which the contact of that aged body had destroyed. Towards the end of the hour, as I was exhausted and still unsuccessful, I was obliged to deceive her by making use of those movements which are incidental to success. As I went out of the battle with all the signs of my strength still about me, Semiramis could have no doubts as to the reality of my success, and even the Undine was deceived when she came to wash me. But the third hour had come, and we were obliged to satisfy Mercury. We spent a quarter of the time in the bath, while the Undine delighted Semiramis by caresses which would have delighted the regent of France, if he had ever known of them. The good marchioness, believing these endearments to be peculiar to river-spirits, was pleased with everything, and begged the Undine to shew me the same kindness. Marcoline obeyed, and lavished on me all the resources of the Venetian school of love. She was a perfect Lesbian, and her caresses having soon restored me to all my vigour I was encouraged to undertake to satisfy Mercury. I proceeded to the work, but alas! it was all in vain. I saw how my fruitless efforts vexed the Undine, and perceiving that Madame d'Urfé had had enough, I again took the course of deceiving her by pretended ecstacies and movements, followed by complete rest. Semiramis afterwards told me that my exertions shewed that I was something more than mortal.

I threw myself into the bath, and underwent my third ablution, then I dressed. Marcoline washed the marchioness and proceeded to clothe her, and did so with such a graceful charm that Madame d'Urfé followed the inspiration of her good genius, and threw her magnificent necklace over the Undine's neck. After a parting Venetian kiss she vanished, and went to her hiding place in the cupboard.

Semiramis asked the oracle if the operation had been successful. The answer was that she bore within her the seed of the sun, and that in the beginning of next February she would be brought to bed of another self of the same sex as the creator; but in order that the evil genii might not be able to do her any harm she must keep quiet in her bed for a hundred and seven hours in succession.

The worthy marchioness was delighted to receive this order, and looked upon it as a good omen, for I had tired her dreadfully. I kissed her, saying that I was going to the country to collect together what remained of the substances that I had used in my ceremonies, but I promised to dine with her on the morrow.

I shut myself up in my room with the Undine, and we amused ourselves as best we could till it was night, for she could not go out while it was light in her spiritual costume. I took off my handsome wedding garment, and as soon as it was dusk we crept out, and went away to Marcoline's lodging in a hackney coach, carrying with us the planetary offerings which I had gained so cleverly.

We were dying of hunger, but the delicious supper which was waiting for us brought us to life again. As soon as we got into the room Marcoline took off her green clothes and put on her woman's dress, saying,——

"I was not born to wear the breeches. Here, take the beautiful necklace the madwoman gave me!"

"I will sell it, fair Undine, and you shall have the proceeds."

"Is it worth much?"

"At least a thousand sequins. By the time you get back to Venice you will be worth at least five thousand ducats, and you will be able to get a husband and live with him in a comfortable style."

"Keep it all, I don't want it; I want *you*. I will never cease to love you; I will do whatever you tell me, and I promise never to be jealous. I will care for you—yes, as if you were my son."

"Do not let us say anything more about it, fair Marcoline, but let us go to bed, for you have never inspired me with so much ardour as now."

"But you must be tired."

"Yes, but not exhaustion, for I was only able to perform the distillation once."

"I thought you sacrificed twice on that old altar. Poor

old woman! she is still pretty, and I have no doubt that fifty years ago she was one of the first beauties in France. How foolish of her to be thinking of love at that age."

"You excited me, but she undid your work even more quickly."

"Are you always obliged to have a girl beside you when you make love to her?"

"No; before, there was no question of making a son."

"What? you are going to make her pregnant? That's ridiculous! Does she imagine that she has conceived?"

"Certainly; and the hope makes her happy."

"What a mad idea! But why did you try to do it three times?"

"I thought to shew my strength, and that if I gazed on you I should not fail; but I was quite mistaken."

"I pity you for having suffered so much."

"You will renew my strength."

As a matter of fact, I do not know whether to attribute it to the difference between the old and the young, but I spent a most delicious night with the beautiful Venetian—a night which I can only compare to those I passed at Parma with Henriette, and at Muran with the beautiful nun. I spent fourteen hours in bed, of which four at least were devoted to expiating the insult I had offered to love. When I had dressed and taken my chocolate I told Marcoline to dress herself with elegance, and to expect me in the evening just before the play began. I could see that she was intensely delighted with the prospect.

I found Madame d'Urfé in bed, dressed with care and in the fashion of a young bride, and with a smile of satisfaction on her face which I had never remarked there before.

"To thee, beloved Galtinardus, I owe all my happiness," said she, as she embraced me.

"I am happy to have contributed to it, divine Semiramis, but you must remember I am only the agent of the genii."

Thereupon the marchioness began to argue in the most sensible manner, but unfortunately the foundation of her argument was wholly chimerical.

"Marry me," said she; "you will then be able to be governor of the child, who will be your son. In this manner you will keep all my property for me, including what I shall have from my brother M. de Pontcarré, who is old and cannot live much longer. If you do not care for me in February next, when I shall be born again, into what hands shall I fall! I shall be called a bastard, and my income of twenty-four thousand francs will be lost to me. Think over it, dear Galtinardus. I must tell you that I feel already as if I were a man. I confess I am in love with the Undine, and I should like to know whether I shall be able to sleep with her in fourteen or fifteen years time. I shall be so if Oromasis will it, and then I shall be happy indeed. What a charming creature she is? Have you ever seen a woman like her? What a pity she is dumb!"

"She, no doubt, has a male water-spirit for a lover. But all of them are dumb, since it is impossible to speak in the water. I wonder she is not deaf as well. I can't think why you didn't touch her. The softness of her skin is something wonderful—velvet and satin are not to be compared to it! And then her breath is so sweet! How delighted I should be if I could converse with such an exquisite being."

"Dear Galtinardus, I beg you will consult the oracle to find out where I am to be brought to bed, and if you

won't marry me I think I had better save all I have that
I may have some provision when I am born again, for
when I am born I shall know nothing, and money will
be wanted to educate me. By selling the whole a large
sum might be realized which could be put out at interest. Thus the interest would suffice without the capital being touched."

"The oracle must be our guide," said I. "You will
be my son, and I will never allow anyone to call you a
bastard."

The sublime madwoman was quiet by this assurance.

Doubtless many a reader will say that if I had been
an honest man I should have undeceived her, but I cannot agree with them; it would have been impossible, and
I confess that even if it had been possible I would not
have done so, for it would only have made me unhappy.

I had told Marcoline to dress with elegance, and I
put on one of my handsomest suits to accompany her to
the theatre. Chance brought the two sisters Rangoni,
daughters of the Roman consul, into our box. As I had
made their acquaintance on my first visit to Marseilles,
I introduced Marcoline to them as my niece, who only
spoke Italian. As the two young ladies spoke the tongue
of Tasso also, Marcoline was highly delighted. The
younger sister, who was by far the handsomer of the two,
afterwards became the wife of Prince Gonzaga Solferino.
The prince was a cultured man, and even a genius, but
very poor. For all that he was a true son of Gonzaga,
being a son of Leopold, who was also poor, and a girl of
the Medini family, sister to the Medini who died in
prison at London in the year 1787.

Babet Rangoni, though poor, deserved to become a
princess, for she had all the airs and manners of one.
She shines under her name of Rangoni amongst the

princess and princesses of the almanacs. Her vain husband is delighted at his wife being thought to belong to the illustrious family of Medini—an innocent feeling, which does neither good nor harm. The same publications turn Medini into Medici, which is equally harmless. This species of lie arises from the idiotic pride of the nobles who think themselves raised above the rest of humanity by their titles which they have often acquired by some act of baseness. It is of no use interfering with them on this point, since all things are finally appreciated at their true value, and the pride of the nobility is easily discounted when one sees them as they really are.

Prince Gonzaga Solferino, whom I saw at Venice eighteen years ago, lived on a pension allowed him by the empress. I hope the late emperor did not deprive him of it, as it was well deserved by this genius and his knowledge of literature.

At the play Marcoline did nothing but chatter with Babet Rangoni, who wanted me to bring the fair Venetian to see her, but I had my own reasons for not doing so.

I was thinking how I could send Madame d'Urfé to Lyons, for I had no further use for her at Marseilles, and she was often embarrassing. For instance, on the third day after her regeneration, she requested me to ask Paralis where she was to die—that is, to be brought to bed. I made the oracle reply that she must sacrifice to the water-spirits on the banks of two rivers, at the same hour, and that afterwards the question of her lying-in would be resolved. The oracle added that I must perform three expiatory sacrifices to Saturn, on account of my too harsh treatment of the false Querilinthos, and that Semiramis need not take part in these ceremonies, though she herself must perform the sacrifices to the water-spirits.

As I was pretending to think of a place where two rivers were sufficiently near to each other to fulfil the requirements of the oracle, Semiramis herself suggested that Lyons was watered by the Rhone and the Saone, and that it would be an excellent place for the ceremony. As may be imagined, I immediately agreed with her. On asking Paralis if there were any preparations to be made, he replied that it would be necessary to pour a bottle of sea-water into each river a fortnight before the sacrifice, and that this ceremony was to be performed by Semiramis in person, at the first diurnal hour of the moon.

"Then," said the marchioness, "the bottles must be filled here, for the other French ports are farther off. I will go as soon as ever I can leave my bed, and will wait for you at Lyons; for as you have to perform expiatory sacrifices to Saturn in this place, you cannot come with me."

I assented, pretending sorrow at not being able to accompany her. The next morning I brought her two well-sealed bottles of sea-water, telling her that she was to pour them out into the two rivers on the 15th of May (the current month). We fixed her departure for the 11th, and I promised to rejoin her before the expiration of the fortnight. I gave her the hours of the moon in writing, and also directions for the journey.

As soon as the marchioness had gone I left the "Treize Cantons" and went to live with Marcoline, giving her four hundred and sixty louis, which, with the hundred and forty she had won at biribi, gave her a total of six hundred louis, or fourteen thousand four hundred francs. With this sum she could look the future in the face fearlessly.

The day after Madame d'Urfé's departure, the betrothed of Mdlle. Crosin arrived at Marseilles with a letter from Rosalie, which he handed to me on the day of his arrival. She begged me in the name of our common honour to introduce the bearer in person to the father of the betrothed. Rosalie was right, but as the lady was not my real niece there were some difficulties in the way. I welcomed the young man and told him that I would first take him to Madame Audibert, and that we could then go together to his father-in-law in prospective.

The young Genoese had gone to the "Treize Cantons," where he thought I was staying. He was delighted to find himself so near the goal of his desires, and his ecstacy received a new momentum when he saw how cordially Madame Audibert received him. We all got into my carriage and drove to the father's who gave him an excellent reception, and then presented him to his wife, who was already friendly disposed towards him.

I was pleasantly surprised when this good and sensible man introduced me to his wife as his cousin, the Chevalier de Seingalt, who had taken such care of their daughter. The good wife and good mother, her husband's worthy partner, stretched out her hand to me, and all my trouble was over.

My new cousin immediately sent an express messenger to his sister, telling her that he and his wife, his future son-in-law, Madame Audibert, and a cousin she had not met before, would come and dine with her on the following day. This done he invited us, and Madame Audibert said that she would escort us. She told him that I had another niece with me, of whom his daughter was very fond, and would be delighted to see again. The worthy man was overjoyed to be able to increase his daughter's happiness.

I, too, was pleased with Madame Audibert's tact and
thoughtfulness; and as making Marcoline happy was to
make me happy also, I expressed my gratitude to her in
very warm terms.

I took the young Genoese to the play, to Marcoline's
delight, for she would have liked the French very much
if she could have understood them. We had an excellent
supper together, in the course of which I told Marcoline
of the pleasure which awaited her on the morrow. I
thought she would have gone wild with joy.

The next day we were at Madame Audibert's as punc-
tually as Achilles on the field of battle. The lady spoke
Italian well, and was charmed with Marcoline, reproaching me for not having introduced her before. At eleven
we got to St. Louis, and my eyes were charmed with
the dramatic situation. My late niece had an air of dignity which became her to admiration, and received her
future husband with great graciousness; and then, after
thanking me with a pleasant smile for introducing him
to her father, she passed from dignity to gaiety, and gave
her sweetheart a hundred kisses.

The dinner was delicious, and passed off merrily; but I
alone preserved a tender melancholy, though I laughed
to myself when they asked me why I was sad. I was
thought to be sad because I did not talk in my usual
vivacious manner, but far from being really sad that was
one of the happiest moments of my life. My whole being was absorbed in the calm delight which follows a
good action. I was the author of the comedy which
promised such a happy ending. I was pleased with the
thought that my influence in the world was more for
good than for ill, and though I was not born a king yet
I contrived to make many people happy. Everyone at
table was indebted to me for some part of their hap-

piness, and the father, the mother, and the betrothed pair wholly so. This thought made me feel a peaceful calm which I could only enjoy in silence.

Mdlle. Crosin returned to Marseilles with her father, her mother, and her future husband, whom the father wished to take up his abode with them. I went back with Madame Audibert, who made me promise to bring the delightful Marcoline to sup with her.

The marriage depended on the receipt of a letter from the young man's father, in answer to one from my niece's father. It will be taken for granted that we were all asked to the wedding, and Marcoline's affection for me increased every day.

When we went to sup with Madame Audibert we found a rich and witty young wine merchant at her house. He sat beside Marcoline, who entertained him with her sallies; and as the young man could speak Italian, and even the Venetian dialect (for he had spent a year at Venice), he was much impressed by the charms of my new niece.

I have always been jealous of my mistresses; but when a rival promises to marry them and give them a good establishment, jealousy gives way to a more generous feeling. For the moment I satisfied myself by asking Madame Audibert who he was, and I was delighted to hear that he had an excellent reputation, a hundred thousand crowns, a large business, and complete independence.

The next day he came to see us in our box at the theatre, and Marcoline received him very graciously. Wishing to push the matter on I asked him to sup with us, and when he came I was well pleased with his manners and his intelligence; to Marcoline he was tender but respectful. On his departure I told him I hoped he would come and see us again, and when we were alone I

congratulated Marcoline on her conquest, and shewed
her that she might succeed almost as well as Mdlle.
Crosin. But instead of being grateful she was furiously
angry.

"If you want to get rid of me," said she, "send me
back to Venice, but don't talk to me about marrying."

"Calm yourself, my angel! I get rid of you? What
an idea! Has my behaviour led you to suppose that you
are in my way? This handsome, well-educated, and rich
young man has come under my notice. I see he loves
you and you like him, and as I love you and wish to see
you sheltered from the storms of fortune, and as I think
this pleasant young Frenchman would make you happy,
I have pointed out to you these advantages, but instead
of being grateful you scold me. Do not weep, sweetheart, you grieve my very soul!"

"I am weeping because you think that I can love him."

"It might be so, dearest, and without my honour taking any hurt; but let us say no more about it and get
into bed."

Marcoline's tears changed to smiles and kisses, and
we said no more about the young wine merchant. The
next day he came to our box again, but the scene had
changed; she was polite but reserved, and I dared not
ask him to supper as I had done the night before. When
we had got home Marcoline thanked me for not doing
so, adding that she had been afraid I would.

"What you said last night is a sufficient guide for me
for the future."

In the morning Madame Audibert called on behalf
of the wine merchant to ask us to sup with him. I
turned towards the fair Venetian, and guessing my
thoughts she hastened to reply that she would be happy

to go anywhere in company with Madame Audibert. That lady came for us in the evening, and took us to the young man's house, where we found a magnificent supper, but no other guests awaiting us. The house was luxuriously furnished, it only lacked a mistress. The master divided his attention between the two ladies, and Marcoline looked ravishing. Everything convinced me that she had kindled the ardour of the worthy young wine merchant.

The next day I received a note from Madame Audibert, asking me to call on her. When I went I found she wanted to give my consent to the marriage of Marcoline with her friend.

"The proposal is a very agreeable one to me," I answered, "and I would willingly give her thirty thousand francs as a dowry, but I can have nothing to do with the matter personally. I will send her to you; and if you can win her over you may count on my word, but do not say that you are speaking on my behalf, for that might spoil everything."

"I will come for her, and if you like she shall dine with me, and you can take her to the play in the evening."

Madame Audibert came the following day, and Marcoline went to dinner with her. I called for her at five o'clock, and finding her looking pleased and happy I did not know what to think. As Madame Audibert did not take me aside I stifled my curiosity and went with Marcoline to the theatre, without knowing what had passed.

On the way Marcoline sang the praises of Madame Audibert, but did not say a word of the proposal she must have made to her. About the middle of the piece, however, I thought I saw the explanation of the riddle, for the young man was in the pit, and did not come to our box though there were two empty places.

We returned home without a word about the merchant or Madame Audibert, but as I knew in my own mind what had happened, I felt disposed to be grateful, and I saw that Marcoline was overjoyed to find me more affectionate than ever. At last, amidst our amorous assaults, Marcoline, feeling how dearly I loved her, told me what had passed between her and Madame Audibert.

"She spoke to me so kindly and so sensibly," said she, "but I contented myself with saying that I would never marry till you told me to do so. All the same I thank you with all my heart for the ten thousand crowns you are willing to give me. You have tossed the ball to me and I have sent it back. I will go back to Venice whenever you please if you will not take me to England with you, but I will never marry. I expect we shall see no more of the young gentleman, though if I had never met you I might have loved him."

It was evidently all over, and I liked her for the part she had taken, for a man who knows his own worth is not likely to sigh long at the feet of an obdurate lady.

The wedding-day of my late niece came round. Marcoline was there, without diamonds, but clad in a rich dress which set off her beauty and satisfied my vanity.

CHAPTER IV

I Leave Marseilles—Henriette at Aix—Irene at Avignon
—Treachery of Possano—Madame d'Urfé Leaves Lyons

THE wedding only interested me because of the bride. The plentiful rather than choice repast, the numerous and noisy company, the empty compliments, the silly conversation, the roars of laughter at very poor jokes—all this would have driven me to despair if it had not been for Madame Audibert, whom I did not leave for a moment. Marcoline followed the young bride about like a shadow, and the latter, who was going to Genoa in a week, wanted Marcoline to come in her train, promising to have her taken to Venice by a person of trust, but my sweetheart would listen to no proposal for separating her from me.

"I won't go to Venice," she said, "till you send me there."

The splendours of her friend's marriage did not make her experience the least regret at having refused the young wine merchant. The bride beamed with happiness, and on my congratulating her she confessed her joy to be great, adding that it was increased by the fact that she owed it all to me. She was also very glad to be going to Genoa, where she was sure of finding a true friend in Rosalie, who would sympathize with her, their fortunes having been very similar.

The day after the wedding I began to make preparations for my departure. The first thing I disposed of

was the box containing the planetary offerings. I kept
the diamonds and precious stones, and took all the gold
and silver to Rousse de Cosse, who still held the sum
which Greppi had placed to my credit. I took a bill of
exchange on Tourton and Bauer, for I should not be
wanting any money at Lyons as Madame d'Urfé was
there, and consequently the three hundred louis I had
about me would be ample. I acted differently where
Marcoline was concerned. I added a sufficient sum to
her six hundred louis to give her a capital in round numbers of fifteen thousand francs. I got a bill drawn on
Lyons for that amount, for I intended at the first opportunity to send her back to Venice, and with that idea
had her trunks packed separately with all the linen and
dresses which I had given her in abundance.

On the eve of our departure we took leave of the
newly-married couple and the whole family at supper,
and we parted with tears, promising each other a life-
long friendship.

The next day we set out intending to travel all night
and not to stop till we got to Avignon, but about five
o'clock the chain of the carriage broke, and we could go
no further until a wheelwright had repaired the damage.
We settled ourselves down to wait patiently, and Clairmont went to get information at a fine house on our
right, which was approached by an alley of trees. As I
had only one postillion, I did not allow him to leave his
horses for a moment. Before long we saw Clairmont
reappear with two servants, one of whom invited me, on
behalf of his master, to await the arrival of the wheelwright at his house. It would have been churlish to
refuse this invitation which was in the true spirit of
French politeness, so leaving Clairmont in charge Mar-

coline and I began to wend our way towards the hospitable abode.

Three ladies and two gentleman came to meet us, and one of the gentlemen said they congratulated themselves on my small mishap, since it enabled madam to offer me her house and hospitality. I turned towards the lady whom the gentleman had indicated, and thanked her, saying, that I hoped not to trouble her long, but that I was deeply grateful for her kindness. She made me a graceful curtsy, but I could not make out her features, for a stormy wind was blowing, and she and her two friends had drawn their hoods almost entirely over their faces. Marcoline's beautiful head was uncovered and her hair streaming in the breeze. She only replied by graceful bows and smiles to the compliments which were addressed to her on all sides. The gentleman who had first accosted me asked me, as he gave her his arm, if she were my daughter. Marcoline smiled and I answered that she was my cousin, and that we were both Venetians.

A Frenchman is so bent on flattering a pretty woman that he will always do so, even if it be at the expense of a third party. Nobody could really think that Marcoline was my daughter, for though I was twenty years older than she was, I looked ten years younger than my real age, and so Marcoline smiled suggestively.

We were just going into the house when a large mastiff ran towards us, chasing a pretty spaniel, and the lady, being afraid of getting bitten, began to run, made a false step, and fell to the ground. We ran to help her, but she said she had sprained her ankle, and limped into the house on the arm of one of the gentlemen. Refreshments were brought in, and I saw that Marcoline looked uneasy in the company of a lady who was talking to her. I hastened to excuse her, saying that she did not speak French. As a matter of fact, Marcoline had begun to talk a sort of French, but the most charming language in the world will not bear being spoken badly, and I had begged her not to speak at all till she had learned to express herself properly. It is better to remain silent than to make strangers laugh by odd expressions and absurd equivocations.

The less pretty, or rather the uglier, of the two ladies said that it was astonishing that the education of young ladies was neglected in such a shocking manner at Venice. "Fancy not teaching them French!"

"It is certainly very wrong, but in my country young ladies are neither taught foreign languages nor round games. These important branches of education are attended to afterwards."

"Then you are a Venetian, too?"

"Yes, madam."

"Really, I should not have thought so."

I made a bow in return for this compliment, which in reality was only an insult; for if flattering to me it was insulting to the rest of my fellow-countrymen, and Marcoline thought as much for she made a little grimace accompanied by a knowing smile.

"I see that the young lady understands French," said our flattering friend, "she laughs exactly in the right place."

"Yes, she understands it, and as for her laughter it was due to the fact that she knows me to be like all other Venetians."

"Possibly, but it is easy to see that you have lived a long time in France."

"Yes, madam," said Marcoline; and these words in her pretty Venetian accent were a pleasure to hear.

The gentleman who had taken the lady to her room said that she found her foot to be rather swollen, and had gone to bed hoping we would all come upstairs.

We found her lying in a splendid bed, placed in an alcove which the thick curtains of red satin made still darker. I could not see whether she was young or old, pretty or ugly. I said that I was very sorry to be the indirect cause of her mishap, and she replied in good Italian that it was a matter of no consequence, and that she did not think she could pay too dear for the privilege of entertaining such pleasant guests.

"Your ladyship must have lived in Venice to speak the language with so much correctness."

"No, I have never been there, but I have associated a good deal with Venetians."

A servant came and told me that the wheelwright had arrived, and that he would take four hours to mend my carriage, so I went downstairs. The man lived at a quarter of a league's distance, and by tying the carriage pole with ropes, I could drive to his place, and wait there for the carriage to be mended. I was about to do so, when the gentleman who did the honours of the house came and asked me, on behalf of the lady, to sup and pass the night at her house, as to go to the wheelwright's would be out of my way; the man would have to work by night, I should be uncomfortable, and the work would be ill done. I assented to the countess's proposal, and having agreed with the man to come early the next day and bring his tools with him, I told Clairmont to take my belongings into the room which was assigned to me.

When I returned to the countess's room I found everyone laughing at Marcoline's sallies, which the countess translated. I was not astonished at seeing the way in which my fair Venetian caressed the countess, but I was enraged at not being able to see her, for I knew Marcoline would not treat any woman in that manner unless she were pretty.

The table was spread in the bedroom of the countess, whom I hoped to see at supper-time, but I was disappointed; for she declared that she could not take anything, and all supper-time she talked to Marcoline and myself, shewing intelligence, education, and a great knowledge of Italian. She let fall the expression, "my late husband," so I knew her for a widow, but as I did not dare to ask any questions, my knowledge ended at that point. When Clairmont was undressing me he told me her married name, but as I knew nothing of the family that was no addition to my information.

When we had finished supper, Marcoline took up her old position by the countess's bed, and they talked so volubly to one another that nobody else could get in a word.

When politeness bade me retire, my pretended cousin said she was going to sleep with the countess. As the latter laughingly assented, I refrained from telling my madcap that she was too forward, and I could see by their mutual embraces that they were agreed in the matter. I satisfied myself with saying that I could not guarantee the sex of the countess's bed-fellow, but she answered,——

"Never mind; if there be a mistake I shall be the gainer."

This struck me as rather free, but I was not the man to be scandalized. I was amused at the tastes of my fair Venetian, and at the manner in which she contrived to gratify them as she had done at Genoa with my last niece. As a rule the Provençal women are inclined this way, and far from reproaching them I like them all the better for it.

The next day I rose at day-break to hurry on the wheelwright, and when the work was done I asked if the countess were visible. Directly after Marcoline came out with one of the gentlemen, who begged me to excuse the countess, as she could not receive me in her present extremely scanty attire; "but she hopes that whenever you are in these parts you will honour her and her house by your company, whether you are alone or with friends."

This refusal, gilded as it was, was a bitter pill for me to swallow, but I concealed my disgust, as I could only put it down to Marcoline's doings; she seemed in high spirits, and I did not like to mortify her. I thanked the gentleman with effusion, and placing a louis in the hands of all the servants who were present I took my leave.

I kissed Marcoline affectionately, so that she should not notice my ill humour, and asked how she and the countess spent the night."

"Capitally," said she. "The countess is charming, and we amused ourselves all night with the tricks of two amorous women."

"Is she pretty or old?"

"She is only thirty-three, and, I assure you, she is as pretty as my friend Mdlle. Crosin. I can speak with authority for we saw each other in a state of nature."

"You are a singular creature; you were unfaithful to me for a woman, and left me to pass the night by myself."

"You must forgive me, and I had to sleep with her as she was the first to declare her love."

"Really? How was that?"

"When I gave her the first of my kisses she returned it in the Florentine manner, and our tongues met. After

supper, I confess, I was the first to begin the sugges-
tive caresses, but she met me half-way. I could only
make her happy by spending the night with her. Look,
this will shew you how pleased she was."

With these words Marcoline drew a superb ring, set
with brilliants, from her finger. I was astonished.

"Truly," I said, "this woman is fond of pleasure and
deserves to have it."

I gave my Lesbian (who might have vied with Sappho)
a hundred kisses, and forgave her her infidelity.

"But," I remarked, "I can't think why she did not
want me to see her; I think she has treated me rather
cavalierly."

"No, I think the reason was that she was ashamed
to be seen by my lover after having made me unfaithful
to him; I had to confess that we were lovers."

"Maybe. At all events you have been well paid; that
ring is worth two hundred louis."

"But I may as well tell you that I was well enough
paid for the pleasure I gave by the pleasure I received."

"That's right; I am delighted to see you happy."

"If you want to make me really happy, take me to
England with you. My uncle will be there, and I could
go back to Venice with him."

"What! you have an uncle in England? Do you really
mean it? It sounds like a fairy-tale. You never told me
of it before."

"I have never said anything about it up to now, because I have always imagined that this might prevent
your accomplishing your desire."

"Is your uncle a Venetian? What is he doing in England? Are you sure that he will welcome you?"

"Yes."

"What is his name? And how are we to find him in a town of more than a million inhabitants?"

"He is ready found. His name is Mattio Boisi, and he is *valet de chambre* to M. Querini, the Venetian ambassador sent to England to congratulate the new king; he is accompanied by the Procurator Morosini. My uncle is my mother's brother; he is very fond of me, and will forgive my fault, especially when he finds I am rich. When he went to England he said he would be back in Venice in July, and we shall just catch him on the point of departure."

As far as the embassy went I knew it was all true, from the letters I had received from M. de Bragadin, and as for the rest Marcoline seemed to me to be speaking the truth. I was flattered by her proposal and agreed to take her to England so that I should possess her for five or six weeks longer without committing myself to anything.

We reached Avignon at the close of the day, and found ourselves very hungry. I knew that the "St. Omer" was an excellent inn, and when I got there I ordered a choice meal and horses for five o'clock the next morning. Marcoline, who did not like night travelling, was in high glee, and threw her arms around my neck, saying,——

"Are we at Avignon now?"

"Yes, dearest."

"Then I can conscientiously discharge the trust which the countess placed in me when she embraced me for the last time this morning. She made me swear not to say a word about it till we got to Avignon."

"All this puzzles me, dearest; explain yourself."

"She gave me a letter for you."

"A letter?"

"Will you forgive me for not placing it in your hands sooner?"

"Certainly, if you passed your word to the countess; but where is this letter?"

"Wait a minute."

She drew a large bundle of papers from her pocket, saying,——

"This is my certificate of baptism."

"I see you were born in 1746."

"This is a certificate of good conduct."

"Keep it, it may be useful to you."

"This is my certificate of virginity."

"That's no use. Did you get it from a midwife?"

"No, from the Patriarch of Venice."

"Did he test the matter for himself?"

"No, he was too old; he trusted in me."

"Well, well, let me see the letter."

"I hope I haven't lost it."

"I hope not, to God."

"Here is your brother's promise of marriage; he wanted to be a Protestant."

"You may throw that into the fire."

"What is a Protestant?"

"I will tell you another time. Give me the letter."

"Praised be God, here it is!"

"That's lucky; but it has no address."

My heart beat fast, as I opened it, and found, instead of an address, these words in Italian:

"To the most honest man of my acquaintance."

Could this be meant for me? I turned down the leaf, and read one word—*Henriette!* Nothing else; the rest of the paper was blank.

At the sight of that word I was for a moment annihilated.

"Io non mori, e non rimasi vivo."

Henriette! It was her style, eloquent in its brevity. I recollected her last letter from Pontarlier, which I had received at Geneva, and which contained only one word —*Farewell!*

Henriette, whom I had loved so well, whom I seemed at that moment to love as well as ever. "Cruel Henriette," said I to myself, "you saw me and would not let me see you. No doubt you thought your charms would not have their old power, and feared lest I should discover that after all you were but mortal. And yet I love you with all the ardour of my early passion. Why did you not let me learn from your own mouth that you were happy? That is the only question I should have asked you, cruel fair one. I should not have enquired whether you loved me still, for I feel my unworthiness— I, who have loved other women after loving the most perfect of her sex. Adorable Henriette, I will fly to you to-morrow, since you told me that I should be always welcome."

I turned these thoughts over in my own mind, and fortified myself in this resolve; but at last I said,——

"No, your behaviour proves that you do not wish to see me now, and your wishes shall be respected; but I must see you once before I die."

Marcoline scarcely dared breathe to see me thus motionless and lost in thought, and I do not know when I should have come to myself if the landlord had not come in saying that he remembered my tastes, and had got me a delicious supper. This brought me to my senses, and I made my fair Venetian happy again by embracing her in a sort of ecstacy.

"Do you know," she said, "you quite frightened me? You were as pale and still as a dead man, and remained for a quarter of an hour in a kind of swoon, the like of which I have never seen. What is the reason? I knew that the countess was acquainted with you, but I should never have thought that her name by itself could have such an astonishing effect."

"Well, it is strange; but how did you find out that the countess knew me?"

"She told me as much twenty times over in the night, but she made me promise to say nothing about it till I had given you the letter."

"What did she say to you about me?"

"She only repeated in different ways what she has written for an address."

"What a letter it is! Her name, and nothing more."

"It is very strange."

"Yes, but the name tells all."

"She told me that if I wanted to be happy I should always remain with you. I said I knew that well; but that you wanted to send me back to Venice, though you were very fond of me. I can guess now that you were lovers. How long ago was it?"

"Sixteen or seventeen years."

"She must have been very young, but she cannot have been prettier than she is now."

"Be quiet, Marcoline."

"Did your union with her last long?"

"We lived together four months in perfect happiness."

"I shall not be happy for so long as that."

"Yes you will, and longer, too; but with another man, and one more suitable to you in age. I am going to England to try to get my daughter from her mother."

"Your daughter? The countess asked me if you were married, and I said no."

"You were right; she is my illegitimate daughter. She

must be ten now, and when you see her you will confess
that she must belong to me."

Just as we were sitting down to table we heard someone going downstairs to the table d'hôte in the room
where I had made Madame Stuard's acquaintance. Our
door was open, and we could see the people on the stairs;
and one of them seeing us gave a cry of joy, and came
running in, exclaiming, "My dear papa!" I turned to
the light and saw Irene, the same whom I had treated so
rudely at Genoa after my discussion with her father
about biribi. I embraced her effusively, and the sly
little puss, pretending to be surprised to see Marcoline,
made her a profound bow, which was returned with much
grace. Marcoline listened attentively to our conversation.

"What are you doing here, fair Irene?"

"We have been here for the last fortnight. Good
heavens! how lucky I am to find you again. I am quite
weak. Will you allow me to sit down, madam?"

"Yes, yes, my dear," said I, "sit down;" and I gave
her a glass of wine which restored her.

A waiter came up, and said they were waiting for her
at supper, but she said, "I won't take any supper;" and
Marcoline, always desirous of pleasing me, ordered a
third place to be laid. I made her happy by giving an
approving nod.

We sat down to table, and ate our meal with
great appetite. "When we have done," I said to Irene,
"you must tell us what chance has brought you to
Avignon."

Marcoline, who had not spoken a word hitherto, noticing how hungry Irene was, said pleasantly that it would
have been a mistake if she had not taken any supper.
Irene was delighted to hear Venetian spoken, and

thanked her for her kindness, and in three or four minutes they had kissed and become friends.

It amused me to see the way in which Marcoline always fell in love with pretty women, just as if she had been a man.

In the course of conversation I found that Irene's father and mother were at the table d'hôte below, and from sundry exclamations, such as "you have been brought to Avignon out of God's goodness," I learned that they were in distress. In spite of that Irene's mirthful countenance matched Marcoline's sallies, and the latter was delighted to hear that Irene had only called me papa because her mother had styled her my daughter at Milan.

We had only got half-way through our supper when Rinaldi and his wife came in. I asked them to sit down, but if it had not been for Irene I should have given the old rascal a very warm reception. He began to chide his daughter for troubling me with her presence when I had such fair company already, but Marcoline hastened to say that Irene could only have given me pleasure, for in my capacity of her uncle I was always glad when she was able to enjoy the society of a sweet young girl.

"I hope," she added, "that if she doesn't mind she will sleep with me."

"Yes, yes," resounded on all sides, and though I should have preferred to sleep with Marcoline by herself, I laughed and agreed; I have always been able to accommodate myself to circumstances.

Irene shared Marcoline's desires, for when it was settled that they should sleep together they seemed wild with joy, and I added fuel to the fire by plying them with punch and champagne.

Rinaldi and his wife did not leave us till they were quite drunk. When we had got rid of them, Irene told us how a Frenchman had fallen in love with her at Genoa, and had persuaded her father to go to Nice where high play was going on, but meeting with no luck there she had been obliged to sell what she had to pay the inn-keeper. Her lover had assured her that he would make it up to her at Aix, where there was some money owing to him, and she persuaded her father to go there; but the persons who owed the money having gone to Avignon, there had to be another sale of goods.

"When we got here the luck was no better, and the poor young man, whom my father reproached bitterly, would have killed himself if I had not given him the mantle you gave me that he might pawn it and go on his quest. He got four louis for it, and sent me the ticket with a very tender letter, in which he assured me that he would find some money at Lyons, and that he would then return and take us to Bordeaux, where we are to find treasures. In the meanwhile we are penniless, and as we have nothing more to sell the landlord threatens to turn us out naked."

"And what does your father mean to do?"

"I don't know. He says Providence will take care of us."

"What does your mother say?"

"Oh! she was as quiet as usual."

"How about yourself?"

"Alas! I have to bear a thousand mortifications every day. They are continually reproaching me with having fallen in love with this Frenchman, and bringing them to this dreadful pass."

"Were you really in love with him?"

"Yes, really."

"Then you must be very unhappy."

"Yes, very; but not on account of my love, for I shall get over that in time, but because of that which will happen to-morrow."

"Can't you make any conquests at the table-d'hôte?"

"Some of the men say pretty things to me, but as they all know how poor we are they are afraid to come to our room."

"And yet in spite of all you keep cheerful; you don't look sad like most of the unhappy. I congratulate you on your good spirits."

Irene's tale was like the fair Stuard's story over again, and Marcoline, though she had taken rather too much champagne, was deeply moved at this picture of misery. She kissed the girl, telling her that I would not forsake her, and that in the meanwhile they would spend a pleasant night.

"Come! let us to bed!" said she; and after taking off her clothes she helped Irene to undress. I had no wish to fight against two, and said that I wanted to rest. The fair Venetian burst out laughing and said,——

"Go to bed and leave us alone."

"I did so, and amused myself by watching the two Bacchantes; but Irene, who had evidently never engaged in such a combat before, was not nearly so adroit as Marcoline.

Before long Marcoline brought Irene in her arms to my bedside, and told me to kiss her.

"Leave me alone, dearest," said I, "the punch has got into your head, and you don't know what you are doing."

This stung her; and urging Irene to follow her example, she took up a position in my bed by force; and as there was not enough room for three, Marcoline got on top of Irene, calling her her wife.

I was virtuous enough to remain a wholly passive spectator of the scene, which was always new to me, though I had seen it so often; but at last they flung themselves on me with such violence that I was obliged to give way, and for the most part of the night I performed my share of the work, till they saw that I was completely exhausted. We fell asleep, and I did not wake up till noon, and then I saw my two beauties still asleep, with their limbs interlaced like the branches of a tree. I thought with a sigh of the pleasures of such a sleep, and got out of bed gently for fear of rousing them. I ordered a good dinner to be prepared, and countermanded the horses which had been waiting several hours.

The landlord remembering what I had done for Madame Stuard guessed I was going to do the same for the Rinaldis, and left them in peace.

When I came back I found my two Lesbians awake, and they gave me such an amorous welcome that I felt inclined to complete the work of the night with a lover's good morning; but I began to feel the need of husbanding my forces, so I did nothing, and bore their sarcasms in silence till one o'clock, when I told them to get up, as we ought to have gone at five o'clock, and here was two o'clock and breakfast not done.

"We have enjoyed ourselves," said Marcoline, "and time that is given to enjoyment is never lost."

When they were dressed, I had coffee brought in, and I gave Irene sixteen louis, four of which were to redeem her cloak. Her father and mother who had just dined came in to bid us good-day, and Irene proudly gave her father twelve louis, telling him to scold her a little less in future. He laughed, wept, and went out, and then came back and said he found a good way of getting to Antibes at a small cost, but they would have to go directly, as the driver wanted to get to St. Andiol by nightfall.

"I am quite ready."

"No, dear Irene," said I, "you shall not go; you shall dine with your friend, and your driver can wait. Make him do so, Count Rinaldi; my niece will pay, will you not, Marcoline?"

"Certainly. I should like to dine here, and still better to put off our departure till the next day."

Her wishes were my orders. We had a delicious supper at five o'clock, and at eight we went to bed and spent the night in wantonness, but at five in the morning all were ready to start. Irene, who wore her handsome cloak, shed hot tears at parting from Marcoline, who also wept with all her heart. Old Rinaldi, who proved himself no prophet, told me that I should make a great fortune in England, and his daughter sighed to be in Marcoline's place. We shall hear of Rinaldi later on.

We drove on for fifteen posts without stopping, and passed the night at Valence. The food was bad, but Marcoline forgot her discomfort in talking of Irene.

"Do you know," said she, "that if it had been in my power I should have taken her from her parents. I believe she is your daughter, though she is not like you."

"How can she be my daughter when I have never known her mother?"

"She told me that certainly."

"Didn't she tell you anything else?"

"Yes, she told me that you lived with her for three days and bought her maidenhead for a thousand sequins."

"Quite so, but did she tell you that I paid the money to her father?"

"Yes, the little fool doesn't keep anything for herself. I don't think I should ever be jealous of your mistresses, if you let me sleep with them. Is not that a mark of a good disposition? Tell me."

"You have, no doubt, a good disposition, but you could be quite as good without your dominant passion."

"It is not a passion. I only have desires for those I love."

"Who gave you this taste?"

"Nature. I began at seven, and in the last ten years I have certainly had four hundred sweethearts."

"You begin early. But when did you begin to have male sweethearts?"

"At eleven."

"Tell me all about it."

"Father Molini, a monk, was my confessor, and he expressed a desire to know the girl who was then my sweetheart. It was in the carnival time, and he gave us a moral discourse, telling us that he would take us to the play if we would promise to abstain for a week. We promised to do so, and at the end of the week we went to tell him that we had kept our word faithfully. The next day Father Molini called on my sweetheart's aunt in a mask, and as she knew him, and as he was a monk and a confessor, we were allowed to go with him. Besides, we were mere children; my sweetheart was only a year older than I.

"After the play the father took us to an inn, and gave us some supper; and when the meal was over he spoke to us of our sin, and wanted to see our privates. 'It's a great sin between two girls,' said he, 'but between a man and a woman it is a venial matter. Do you know how men are made?' We both knew, but we said no with one consent. 'Then would you like to know?' said he. We said we should like to know very much, and he added, 'If you will promise to keep it a secret, I may be able to satisfy your curiosity.' We gave our promises, and the good father proceeded to gratify us with a sight of the riches which nature had lavished on him, and in the course of an hour he had turned us into women. I must confess that he understood so well how to work on our curiosity that the request came from us. Three years later, when I was fourteen, I became the mistress of a young jeweller. Then came your brother; but he got nothing from me, because he began by saying that he could not ask me to give him any favours till we were married."

"You must have been amused at that."

"Yes, it did make me laugh, because I did not know that a priest could get married; and he excited my curiosity by telling me that they managed it at Geneva. Curiosity and wantonness made me escape with him; you know the rest."

Thus did Marcoline amuse me during the evening, and then we went to bed and slept quietly till the morning. We started from Valence at five, and in the evening we were set down at the "Hotel du Parc" at Lyons.

As soon as I was settled in the pleasant apartments allotted to me I went to Madame d'Urfé, who was staying in the Place Bellecour, and said, as usual, that she was sure I was coming on that day. She wanted to know if she had performed the ceremonies correctly, and Paralis, of course, informed her that she had, whereat she was much flattered. The young Aranda was with her, and after I had kissed him affectionately I told the marchioness that I would be with her at ten o'clock the next morning, and so I left her.

I kept the appointment and we spent the whole of the day in close conference, asking of the oracle concerning her being brought to bed, how she was to make her will, and how she should contrive to escape poverty in her regenerated shape. The oracle told her that she must go to Paris for her lying-in, and leave all her possessions to her son, who would not be a bastard, as Paralis promised that as soon as I got to London an English gentleman should be sent over to marry her. Finally, the oracle ordered her to prepare to start in three days, and to take Aranda with her. I had to take the latter to London and return him to his mother, for his real position in life was no longer a mystery, the little rascal having confessed all; however, I had found a remedy for his indiscretion as for the treachery of the Corticelli and Possano.

I longed to return him to the keeping of his mother, who constantly wrote me impertinent letters. I also wished to take my daughter, who, according to her mother, had become a prodigy of grace and beauty.

After the oracular business had been settled, I returned to the "Hotel du Parc" to dine with Marcoline. It was very late, and as I could not take my sweetheart to the play I called on M. Bono to enquire whether he had sent my brother to Paris. He told me that he had gone the day before, and that my great enemy, Possano, was still in Lyons, and that I would do well to be on my guard as far as he was concerned.

"I have seen him," said Bono; "he looks pale and undone, and seems scarcely able to stand. 'I shall die before long,' said he, 'for that scoundrel Casanova has had me poisoned; but I will make him pay dearly

for his crime, and in this very town of Lyons, where I
know he will come, sooner or later.'

"In fact, in the course of half an hour, he made some
terrible accusations against you, speaking as if he were
in a fury. He wants all the world to know that you
are the greatest villain unhung, that you are ruining
Madame d'Urfé with your impious lies; that you are
a sorcerer, a forger, an utter of false moneys, a poisoner—in short, the worst of men. He does not intend
to publish a libellous pamphlet upon you, but to accuse
you before the courts, alleging that he wants reparation
for the wrongs you have done his person, his honour,
and his life, for he says you are killing him by a slow
poison. He adds that for every article he possesses the
strongest proof.

"I will say nothing about the vague abuse he adds
to these formal accusations, but I have felt it my duty
to warn you of his treacherous designs that you may be
able to defeat them. It's no good saying he is a miserable wretch, and that you despise him; you know how
strong a thing calumny is."

"Where does the fellow live?"

"I don't know in the least."

"How can I find out?"

"I can't say, for if he is hiding himself on purpose
it would be hard to get at him."

"Nevertheless, Lyons is not so vast a place."

"Lyons is a perfect maze, and there is no better
hiding-place, especially to a man with money, and Possano has money."

"But what can he do to me?"

"He can institute proceedings against you in the criminal court, which would cause you immense anxiety and

bring down your good name to the dust, even though you be the most innocent, the most just of men."

"It seems to me, then, that the best thing I can do will be to be first in the field."

"So I think, but even then you cannot avoid publicity."

"Tell me frankly if you feel disposed to bear witness to what the rascal has said in a court of justice."

"I will tell all I know with perfect truth."

"Be kind enough to tell me of a good advocate."

"I will give you the address of one of the best; but reflect before you do anything. The affair will make a noise."

"As I don't know where he lives, I have really no choice in the matter."

If I had known where he lived I could have had Possano expelled from Lyons through the influence of Madame d'Urfé, whose relative, M. de la Rochebaron, was the governor; but as it was, I had no other course than the one I took.

Although Possano was a liar and an ungrateful, treacherous hound, yet I could not help being uneasy. I went to my hotel, and proceeded to ask for police protection against a man in hiding in Lyons, who had designs against my life and honour.

The next day M. Bono came to dissuade me from the course I had taken.

"For," said he, "the police will begin to search for him, and as soon as he hears of it he will take proceedings against you in the criminal courts, and then your positions will be changed. It seems to me that if you have no important business at Lyons you had better hasten your departure."

"Do you think I would do such a thing for a miserable fellow like Possano? No! I would despise myself if I did. I would die rather than hasten my departure on account of a rascal whom I loaded with kindnesses, despite his unworthiness! I would give a hundred louis to know where he is now."

"I am delighted to say that I do not know anything about it, for if I did I would tell you, and then God knows what would happen! You won't go any sooner; well, then, begin proceedings, and I will give my evidence by word of mouth or writing whenever you please."

I went to the advocate whom M. Bono had recommended to me, and told him my business. When he heard what I wanted he said,——

"I can do nothing for you, sir, as I have undertaken the case of your opponent. You need not be alarmed, however, at having spoken to me, for I assure you that I will make no use whatever of the information. Possano's plea or accusation will not be drawn up till the day after to-morrow, but I will not tell him to make haste for fear of your anticipating him, as I have only been informed of your intentions by hazard. However, you will find plenty of advocates at Lyons as honest as I am, and more skilled."

"Could you give me the name of one?"

"That would not be etiquette, but M. Bono, who seems to have kindly spoken of me with some esteem, will be able to serve you."

"Can you tell me where your client lives?"

"Since his chief aim is to remain hidden, and with good cause, you will see that I could not think of doing such a thing."

In bidding him farewell I put a louis on the table,

and though I did it with the utmost delicacy he ran after me and made me take it back.

"For once in a way," I said to myself, "here's an honest advocate." As I walked along I thought of putting a spy on Possano and finding out his abode, for I felt a strong desire to have him beaten to death; but where was I to find a spy in a town of which I knew nothing? M. Bono gave me the name of another advocate, and advised me to make haste.

" 'Tis a criminal matter," said he, "and in such cases the first comer always has the advantage."

I asked him to find me a trusty fellow to track out the rascally Possano, but the worthy man would not hear of it. He shewed me that it would be dishonourable to set a spy on the actions of Possano's advocate. I knew it myself; but what man is there who has not yielded to the voice of vengeance, the most violent and least reasonable of all the passions.

I went to the second advocate, whom I found to be a man venerable not only in years but in wisdom. I told him all the circumstances of the affair, which he agreed to take up, saying he would present my plea in the course of the day.

"That's just what I want you to do," said I, "for his own advocate told me that his pleas would be presented the day after to-morrow."

"That, sir," said he, "would not induce me to act with any greater promptness, as I could not consent to your abusing the confidence of my colleague."

"But there is nothing dishonourable in making use of information which one has acquired by chance."

"That may be a tenable position in some cases, but in the present instance the nature of the affair justifies prompt action. *Prior in tempore, potior in jure.* Prudence bids us attack our enemy. Be so kind, if you please, to call here at three o'clock in the afternoon."

"I will not fail to do so, and in the meanwhile here are six louis."

"I will keep account of my expenditure on your behalf."

"I want you not to spare money."

"Sir, I shall spend only what is absolutely necessary."

I almost believed that probity had chosen a home for herself amongst the Lyons advocates, and here I may say, to the honour of the French bar, that I have never known a more honest body of men than the advocates of France.

At three o'clock, having seen that the plan was properly drawn up, I went to Madame d'Urfé's, and for four hours I worked the oracle in a manner that filled her with delight, and in spite of my vexation I could not help laughing at her insane fancies on the subject of her pregnancy. She was certain of it; she felt all the symptoms. Then she said how sorry she felt that she would not be alive to laugh at all the hypotheses of the Paris doctors as to her being delivered of a child, which would be thought very extraordinary in a woman of her age.

When I got back to the inn I found Marcoline very melancholy. She said she had been waiting for me to take her to the play, according to my promise, and that I should not have made her wait in vain.

"You are right, dearest, but an affair of importance has kept me with the marchioness. Don't be put out."

I had need of some such advice myself, for the legal affair worried me, and I slept very ill. Early the next morning I saw my counsel, who told me that my plea had been laid before the criminal lieutenant.

"For the present," said he, "there is nothing more to be done, for as we don't know where he is we can't cite him to appear."

"Could I not set the police on his track?"

"You might, but I don't advise you to do so. Let us consider what the result would be. The accuser finding himself accused would have to defend himself and prove the accusation he has made against you. But in the present state of things, if he does not put in an appearance we will get judgment against him for contempt of court and also for libel. Even his counsel will leave him in the lurch if he persistently refuses to shew himself."

This quieted my fears a little, and I spent the rest of the day with Madame d'Urfé, who was going to Paris on the morrow. I promised to be with her as soon as I had dealt with certain matters which concerned the honour of the Fraternity R. C.

Her great maxim was always to respect my secrets, and never to trouble me with her curiosity. Marcoline, who had been pining by herself all day, breathed again when I told her that henceforth I should be all for her.

In the morning M. Bono came to me and begged me to go with him to Possano's counsel, who wanted to speak to me. The advocate said that his client was a sort of madman who was ready to do anything, as he believed himself to be dying from the effects of a slow poison.

"He says that even if you are first in the field he will have you condemned to death. He says he doesn't care if he is sent to prison, as he is certain of coming out in triumph as he has the proof of all his accusations.

He shews twenty-five louis which you gave him, all of which are clipped, and he exhibits documents dated from Genoa stating that you clipped a number of gold pieces, which were melted by M. Grimaldi in order that the police might not find them in your possession. He has even a letter from your brother, the abbé, deposing against you. He is a madman, a victim to syphilis, who wishes to send you to the other world before himself, if he can. Now my advice to you is to give him some money and get rid of him. He tells me that he is the father of a family, and that if M. Bono would give him a thousand louis he would sacrifice vengeance to necessity. He told me to speak to M. Bono about it; and now, sir what do you say?"

"That which my just indignation inspires me to say regarding a rascal whom I rescued from poverty, and who nevertheless pursues me with atrocious calumnies; he shall not have one single farthing of mine."

I then told the Genoa story, putting things in their true light, and adding that I could call M. Grimaldi as a witness if necessary.

"I have delayed presenting the plea," said the counsel, "to see if the scandal could be hushed up in any way, but I warn you that I shall now present it."

"Do so; I shall be greatly obliged to you."

I immediately called on my advocate, and told him of the rascal's proposal; and he said I was quite right to refuse to have any dealings with such a fellow. He added that as I had M. Bono as a witness I ought to make Possano's advocate present his plea, and I authorized him to take proceedings in my name.

A clerk was immediately sent to the criminal lieutenant, praying him to command the advocate to bring before him, in three days, the plea of one Anami, *alias*

Pogomas, *alias* Possano, the said plea being against Jacques Casanova, commonly called the Chevalier de Seingalt. This document, to which I affixed my signature, was laid before the criminal lieutenant.

I did not care for the three days' delay, but my counsel told me it was always given, and that I must make up my mind to submit to all the vexation I should be obliged to undergo, even if we were wholly successful.

As Madame d'Urfé had taken her departure in conformity with the orders of Paralis, I dined with Marcoline at the inn, and tried to raise my spirits by all the means in my power. I took my mistress to the best milliners and dressmakers in the town, and bought her everything she took a fancy to; and then we went to the theatre, where she must have been pleased to see all eyes fixed on her. Madame Pernon, who was in the next box to ours, made me introduce Marcoline to her; and from the way they embraced each other when the play was over I saw they were likely to become intimate, the only obstacle to their friendship being that Madame Pernon did not know a word of Italian, and that Marcoline did not dare to speak a word of French for fear of making herself ridiculous. When we got back to the inn, Marcoline told me that her new friend had given her the Florentine kiss: this is the shibboleth of the sect.

The pretty nick-nacks I had given her had made her happy; her ardour was redoubled, and the night passed joyously.

I spent the next day in going from shop to shop, making fresh purchases for Marcoline, and we supped merrily at Madame Pernon's.

The day after, M. Bono came to see me at an early hour with a smile of content on his face.

"Let us go and breakfast at a coffee-house," said he; "we will have some discussion together."

When we were breakfasting he shewed me a letter written by Possano, in which the rascal said that he was ready to abandon proceedings provided that M. de Seingalt gave him a hundred louis, on receipt of which he promised to leave Lyons immediately.

"I should be a great fool," said I, "if I gave the knave more money to escape from the hands of justice. Let him go if he likes, I won't prevent him; but he had better not expect me to give him anything. He will have a writ out against him to-morrow. I should like to see him branded by the hangman. He has slandered me, his benefactor, too grievously; let him prove what he says, or be dishonoured before all men."

"His abandoning the proceedings," said M. Bono, "would in my opinion amount to the same thing as his failing to prove his charges, and you would do well to prefer it to a trial which would do your reputation no good, even if you were completely successful. And the hundred louis is nothing in comparison with the costs of such a trial."

"M. Bono, I value your advice very highly, and still more highly the kindly feelings which prompt you, but you must allow me to follow my own opinion in this case."

I went to my counsel and told him of the fresh proposal that Possano had made, and of my refusal to listen to it, begging him to take measures for the arrest of the villain who had vowed my death.

The same evening I had Madame Pernon and M. Bono, who was her lover, to sup with me; and as the latter had a good knowledge of Italian Marcoline was able to take part in the merriment of the company.

The next day Bono wrote to tell me that Possano had left Lyons never to return, and that he had signed a full and satisfactory retraction. I was not surprised to hear of his flight, but the other circumstance I could not understand. I therefore hastened to call on Bono, who shewed me the document, which was certainly plain enough.

"Will that do?" said he.

"So well that I forgive him, but I wonder he did not insist on the hundred louis."

"My dear sir, I gave him the money with pleasure, to prevent a scandalous affair which would have done us all harm in becoming public. If I had told you nothing, you couldn't have taken any steps in the matter, and I felt myself obliged to repair the mischief I had done in this way. You would have known nothing about it, if you had said that you were not satisfied. I am only too glad to have been enabled to shew my friendship by this trifling service. We will say no more about it."

"Very good," said I, embracing him, "we will say no more, but please to receive the assurance of my gratitude."

I confess I felt much relieved at being freed from this troublesome business.

CHAPTER V

*I Meet the Venetian Ambassadors at Lyons, and also
Marcoline's Uncle—I Part from Marcoline and Set
Out for Paris—An Amorous Journey*

THUS freed from the cares which the dreadful slan-
ders of Possano had caused me, I gave myself up
to the enjoyment of my fair Venetian, doing all in my
power to increase her happiness, as if I had had a pre-
monition that we should soon be separated from one
another.

The day after the supper I gave to Madame Pernon
and M. Bono, we went to the theatre together, and in
the box opposite to us I saw M. Querini, the procurator,
Morosini, M. Memmo, and Count Stratico, a Professor
of the University of Padua. I knew all these gentlemen;
they had been in London, and were passing through
Lyons on their return to Venice.

"Farewell, fair Marcoline!" I said to myself, feeling
quite broken-hearted, but I remained calm, and said
nothing to her. She did not notice them as she was
absorbed in her conversation with M. Bono, and besides,
she did not know them by sight. I saw that M. Memmo
had seen me and was telling the procurator of my presence, and as I knew the latter very well I felt bound to
pay them my respects then and there.

Querini received me very politely for a devotee, as
also did Morosini, while Memmo seemed moved; but no
doubt he remembered that it was chiefly due to his

mother that I had been imprisoned eight years ago. I congratulated the gentlemen on their embassy to England, on their return to their native land, and for form's sake commended myself to their good offices to enable me to return also. M. Morosini, noticing the richness of my dress and my general appearance of prosperity, said that while I had to stay away he had to return, and that he considered me the luckier man.

"Your excellency is well aware," said I, "that nothing is sweeter than forbidden fruit."

He smiled, and asked me whither I went and whence I came.

"I come from Rome," I answered, "where I had some converse with the Holy Father, whom I knew before, and I am going through Paris on my way to London."

"Call on me here, if you have time, I have a little commission to give you."

"I shall always have time to serve your excellency in. Are you stopping here for long?"

"Three or four days."

When I got back to my box Marcoline asked me who were the gentlemen to whom I had been speaking. I answered coolly and indifferently, but watching her as I spoke, that they were the Venetian ambassadors on their way from London. The flush of her cheek died away and was replaced by pallor; she raised her eyes to heaven, lowered them, and said not a word. My heart was broken. A few minutes afterwards she asked me which was M. Querini, and after I had pointed him out to her she watched him furtively for the rest of the evening.

The curtain fell, we left our box, and at the door of the theatre we found the ambassadors waiting for

their carriage. Mine was in the same line as theirs. The
ambassador Querini said,——

"You have a very pretty young lady with you."

Marcoline stepped forward, seized his hand, and kissed
it before I could answer.

Querini, who was greatly astonished, thanked her and
said,——

"What have I done to deserve this honour?"

"Because," said Marcoline, speaking in the Venetian
dialect, "I have the honour of knowing his excellency
M. Querini."

"What are you doing with M. Casanova?"

"He is my uncle."

My carriage came up. I made a profound bow to the
ambassadors, and called out to the coachman, "To the
'Hotel du Parc.'" It was the best hotel in Lyons, and
I was not sorry for the Venetians to hear where I was
staying.

Marcoline was in despair, for she saw that the time
for parting was near at hand.

"We have three or four days before us," said I, "in
which we can contrive how to communicate with your
uncle Mattio. I must commend you highly for kissing
M. Querini's hand. That was a master-stroke indeed.
All will go off well; but I hope you will be merry, for
sadness I abhor."

We were still at table when I heard the voice of M.
Memmo in the ante-chamber; he was a young man, intelligent and good-natured. I warned Marcoline not to
say a word about our private affairs, but to display a
moderate gaiety. The servant announced the young
nobleman, and we rose to welcome him; but he made us
sit down again, and sat beside us, and drank a glass of
wine with the utmost cordiality. He told me how he had

been supping with the old devotee Querini, who had had his hand kissed by a young and fair Venetian. The ambassadors were much amused at the circumstance, and Querini himself, in spite of his scrupulous conscience, was greatly flattered.

"May I ask you, mademoiselle," he added, "how you came to know M. Querini?"

"It's a mystery, sir."

"A mystery, is it? What fun we shall have to-morrow! I have come," he said, addressing himself to me, "to ask you to dine with us to-morrow, and you must bring your charming niece."

"Would you like to go, Marcoline?"

"*Con grandissimo piacere!* We shall speak Venetian, shall we not?"

"Certainly."

"*E viva!* I cannot learn French."

"M. Querini is in the same position," said M. Memmo.

After half an hour's agreeable conversation he left us, and Marcoline embraced me with delight at having made such a good impression on these gentlemen.

"Put on your best dress to-morrow," said I, "and do not forget your jewels. Be agreeable to everybody, but pretend not to see your Uncle Mattio, who will be sure to wait at table."

"You may be sure I shall follow your advice to the letter."

"And I mean to make the recognition a scene worthy of the drama. I intend that you shall be taken back to Venice by M. Querini himself, while your uncle will take care of you by his special orders."

"I shall be delighted with this arrangement, provided it succeeds."

"You may trust to me for that."

At nine o'clock the next day I called on Morosini concerning the commissions he had for me. He gave me a little box and a letter for Lady Harrington, and another letter with the words,——

"The Procurator Morosini is very sorry not to have been able to take a last leave of Mdlle. Charpillon."

"Where shall I find her?"

"I really don't know. If you find her, give her the letter; if not, it doesn't matter. That's a dazzling beauty you have with you, Casanova."

"Well, she has dazzled me."

"But how did she know Querini?"

"She has seen him at Venice, but she has never spoken to him."

"I thought so; we have been laughing over it, but Querini is hugely pleased. But how did you get hold of her? She must be very young, as Memmo says she cannot speak French."

"It would be a long story to tell, and after all we met through a mere chance."

"She is not your niece."

"Nay, she is more—she is my queen."

"You will have to teach her French, as when you get to London . . ."

"I am not going to take her there; she wants to return to Venice."

"I pity you if you are in love with her! I hope she will dine with us?"

"Oh, yes! she is delighted with the honour."

"And we are delighted to have our poor repast animated by such a charming person."

"You will find her worthy of your company; she is full of wit."

When I got back to the inn I told Marcoline that if

anything was said at dinner about her return to Venice, she was to reply that no one could make her return except M. Querini, but that if she could have his protection she would gladly go back with him.

"I will draw you out of the difficulty," said I; and she promised to carry out my instructions.

Marcoline followed my advice with regard to her toilette, and looked brilliant in all respects; and I, wishing to shine in the eyes of the proud Venetian nobles, had dressed myself with the utmost richness. I wore a suit of grey velvet, trimmed with gold and silver lace; my point lace shirt was worth at least fifty louis; and my diamonds, my watches, my chains, my sword of the finest English steel, my snuff-box set with brilliants, my cross set with diamonds, my buckles set with the same stones, were altogether worth more than fifty thousand crowns. This ostentation, though puerile in itself, yet had a purpose, for I wished M. de Bragadin to know that I did not cut a bad figure in the world; and I wished the proud magistrates who had made me quit my native land to learn that I had lost nothing, and could laugh at their severity.

In this gorgeous style we drove to the ambassador's dinner at half-past one.

All present were Venetians, and they welcomed Marcoline enthusiastically. She who was born with the instinct of good manners behaved with the grace of a nymph and the dignity of a French princess; and as soon as she was seated between two grave and reverend signors, she began by saying that she was delighted to find herself the only representative of her sex in this distinguished company, and also that there were no Frenchmen present.

"Then you don't like the French," said M. Memmo.

"I like them well enough so far as I know them, but I am only acquainted with their exterior, as I don't speak or understand the language."

After this everybody knew how to take her, and the gaiety became general.

She answered all questions to the point, and entertained the company with her remarks on French manners, so different to Venetian customs.

In the course of dinner M. Querini asked how she had known him, and she replied that she had often seen him at Divine service, whereat the devotee seemed greatly flattered. M. Morosini, pretending not to know that she was to return to Venice, told her that unless she made haste to acquire French, the universal language, she would find London very tedious, as the Italian language was very little known there.

"I hope," she replied, "that M. de Seingalt will not bring me into the society of people with whom I cannot exchange ideas. I know I shall never be able to learn French."

When we had left the table the ambassadors begged me to tell the story of my escape from The Leads, and I was glad to oblige them. My story lasted for two whole hours; and as it was noticed that Marcoline's eyes became wet with tears when I came to speak of my great danger. She was rallied upon the circumstance, and told that nieces were not usually so emotional.

"That may be, gentlemen," she replied, "though I do not see why a niece should not love her uncle. But I have never loved anyone else but the hero of the tale, and I cannot see what difference there can be between one kind of love and another."

"There are five kinds of love known to man," said M.

Querini. "The love of one's neighbour, the love of God, which is beyond compare, the highest of all, love matrimonial, the love of house and home, and the love of self, which ought to come last of all, though many place it in the first rank."

The nobleman commented briefly on these diverse kinds of love, but when he came to the love of God he began to soar, and I was greatly astonished to see Marcoline shedding tears, which she wiped away hastily as if to hide them from the sight of the worthy old man whom wine had made more theological than usual. Feigning to be enthusiastic, Marcoline took his hand and kissed it, while he in his vain exaltation drew her towards him and kissed her on the brow, saying, *"Poveretta,* you are an angel!"

At this incident, in which there was more love of our neighbour than love of God, we all bit our lips to prevent ourselves bursting out laughing, and the sly little puss pretended to be extremely moved.

I never knew Marcoline's capacities till then, for she confessed that her emotion was wholly fictitious, and designed to win the old man's good graces; and that if she had followed her own inclinations she would have laughed heartily. She was designed to act a part either upon the stage or on a throne. Chance had ordained that she should be born of the people, and her education had been neglected; but if she had been properly tutored she would have been fit for anything.

Before returning home we were warmly invited to dinner the next day.

As we wanted to be together, we did not go to the theatre that day and when we got home I did not wait for Marcoline to undress to cover her with kisses.

"Dear heart," said I, "you have not shewn me all your perfections till now, when we are about to part; you make me regret you are going back to Venice. To-day you won all hearts."

"Keep me then, with you, and I will ever be as I have been to-day. By the way, did you see my uncle?"

"I think so. Was it not he who was in continual attendance?"

"Yes. I recognized him by his ring. Did he look at me?"

"All the time, and with an air of the greatest astonishment. I avoided catching his eye, which roved from you to me continually."

"I should like to know what the good man thinks! You will see him again to-morrow. I am sure he will have told M. Querini that I am his niece, and consequently not yours."

"I expect so, too."

"And if M. Querini says as much to me to-morrow, I expect I shall have to admit the fact. What do you think?"

"You must undoubtedly tell him the truth, but frankly and openly, and so as not to let him think that you have need of him to return to Venice. He is not your father, and has no right over your liberty."

"Certainly not."

"Very good. You must also agree that I am not your uncle, and that the bond between us is of the most tender description. Will there be any difficulty in that?"

"How can you ask me such a question? The link between us makes me feel proud, and will ever do so."

"Well, well, I say no more. I trust entirely in your tact. Remember that Querini and no other must take you back to Venice; he must treat you as if you were

his daughter. If he will not consent, you shall not return at all."

"Would to God it were so!"

Early the next morning I got a note from M. Querini
requesting me to call on him, as he wanted to speak to
me on a matter of importance.

"We are getting on," said Marcoline. "I am very
glad that things have taken this turn, for when you come
back you can tell me the whole story, and I can regulate
my conduct accordingly."

I found Querini and Morosini together. They gave
me their hands when I came in, and Querini asked me
to sit down, saying that there would be nothing in our
discussion which M. Morosini might not hear.

"I have a confidence to make to you, M. Casanova,"
he began; "but first I want you to do me the same
favour."

"I can have no secrets from your excellency."

"I am obliged to you, and will try to deserve your
good opinion. I beg that you will tell me sincerely
whether you know the young person who is with you,
for no one believes that she is your niece."

"It is true that she is not my niece, but not being
acquainted with her relations or family I cannot be said
to know her in the sense which your excellency gives to
the word. Nevertheless, I am proud to confess that I
love her with an affection which will not end save with
my life."

"I am delighted to hear you say so. How long have
you had her?"

"Nearly two months."

"Very good! How did she fall into your hands?"

"That is a point which only concerns her, and you
will allow me not to answer that question."

"Good! we will go on. Though you are in love with her, it is very possible that you have never made any enquiries respecting her family."

"She has told me that she has a father and a mother, poor but honest, but I confess I have never been curious enough to enquire her name. I only know her baptismal name, which is possibly not her true one, but it does quite well for me."

"She has given you her true name."

"Your excellency surprises me! You know her, then?"

"Yes; I did not know her yesterday, but I do now. Two months . . . Marcoline . . . yes, it must be she. I am now certain that my man is not mad."

"Your man?"

"Yes, she is his niece. When we were at London he heard that she had left the paternal roof about the middle of Lent. Marcoline's mother, who is his sister, wrote to him. He was afraid to speak to her yesterday, because she looked so grand. He even thought he must be mistaken, and he would have been afraid of offending me by speaking to a grand lady at my table. She must have seen him, too."

"I don't think so, she has said nothing about it to me."

"It is true that he was standing behind her all the time. But let us come to the point. Is Marcoline your wife, or have you any intention of marrying her?"

"I love her as tenderly as any man can love a woman, but I cannot make her a wife; the reasons are known only to herself and me."

"I respect your secret; but tell me if you would object to my begging her to return to Venice with her uncle?"

"I think Marcoline is happy, but if she has succeeded in gaining the favour of your excellency, she is happier still; and I feel sure that if she were to go back to Venice under the exalted patronage of your excellency, she would efface all stains on her reputation. As to permitting her to go, I can put no stumbling-block in the way, for I am not her master. As her lover I would defend her to the last drop of my blood, but if she wants to leave me I can only assent, though with sorrow."

"You speak with much sense, and I hope you will not be displeased at my undertaking this good work. Of course I shall do nothing without your consent."

"I respect the decrees of fate when they are promulgated by such a man as you. If your excellency can induce Marcoline to leave me, I will make no objection; but I warn you that she must be won mildly. She is intelligent, she loves me, and she knows that she is independent; besides she reckons on me, and she has cause to do so. Speak to her to-day by herself; my presence would only be in your way. Wait till dinner is over; the interview might last some time."

"My dear Casanova, you are an honest man. I am delighted to have made your acquaintance."

"You do me too much honour. I may say that Marcoline will hear nothing of all this."

When I got back to the inn, I gave Marcoline an exact account of the whole conversation, warning her that she would be supposed to know nothing about it.

"You must execute a masterly stroke, dearest," said I, "to persuade M. Querini that I did not lie in saying that you had not seen your uncle. As soon as you see him, you must give a shout of surprise, exclaim, 'My dear uncle!' and rush to his arms. This would be a splendid and dramatic situation, which would do you honour in the eyes of all the company."

"You may be sure that I shall play the part very well, although my heart be sad."

At the time appointed we waited on the ambassadors, and found that all the other guests had assembled. Marcoline, as blithe and smiling as before, first accosted M. Querini, and then did the polite to all the company. A few minutes before dinner Mattio brought in his master's spectacles on a silver tray. Marcoline, who was sitting next to M. Querini, stopped short in something she was saying, and staring at the man, exclaimed in a questioning voice,——

"My uncle?"

"Yes, my dear niece."

Marcoline flung herself into his arms, and there was a moving scene, which excited the admiration of all.

"I knew you had left Venice, dear uncle, but I did not know you were in his excellency's service. I am so glad to see you again! You will tell my father and mother about me? You see I am happy. Where were you yesterday?"

"Here."

"And you didn't see me?"

"Yes; but your uncle there . . ."

"Well," said I, laughing, "let us know each other, cousin, and be good friends. Marcoline, I congratulate you on having such an honest man for an uncle."

"That is really very fine," said M. Querini; and everybody exclaimed, "Very affecting, very affecting indeed!"

The newly-found uncle departed, and we sat down to dinner, but in spirits which differed from those of yesterday. Marcoline bore traces of those mingled emotions of happiness and regret which move loyal hearts when they call to mind ther native land. M. Querini looked at her admiringly, and seemed to have all the confidence of success which a good action gives to the mind. M. Morosini sat a pleased spectator. The others were attentive and curious as to what would come next. They listened to what was said, and hung on Marcoline's lips. After the first course there was greater unison in the company, and M. Morosini told Marcoline that if she would return to Venice she would be sure of finding a husband worthy of her.

"I must be the judge of that," said she.

"Yes, but it is a good thing to have recourse to the advice of discreet persons who are interested in the happiness of both parties."

"Excuse me, but I do not think so. If I ever marry, my husband will have to please me first."

"Who has taught you this maxim?" said Querini.

"My uncle, Casanova, who has, I verily believe, taught me everything that can be learnt in the two months I have been happy enough to live with him."

"I congratulate the master and the pupil, but you are both too young to have learnt all the range of science. Moral science cannot be learnt in two months."

"What his excellency has just said," said I, turning to Marcoline, "is perfectly correct. In affairs of marriage both parties should rely to a great extent on the advice of friends, for mere marriages of inclination are often unhappy."

"That is a really philosophical remark, my dear Marcoline," said Querini; "but tell me the qualities which in your opinion are desirable in a husband."

"I should be puzzled to name them, but they would all become manifest in the man that pleased me."

"And supposing he were a worthless fellow?"

"He would certainly not please me, and that's the reason why I have made up my mind never to marry a man whom I have not studied."

"Supposing you made a mistake?"

"Then I would weep in secret."

"How if you were poor?"

"She need never fear poverty, my lord," said I. "She has an income of fifty crowns a month for the remainder of her life."

"Oh, that's a different matter. If that is so, sweetheart, you are privileged. You will be able to live at Venice in perfect independence."

"I think that to live honourably there I only need the protection of a lord like your excellency."

"As to that, Marcoline, I give you my word that I will do all in my power for you if you come to Venice. But let me ask you one question, how are you sure of your income of fifty crowns a month? You are laughing."

"I laugh because I am such a silly little thing. I don't have any heed for my own business. My friend there will tell you all about it."

"You have not been joking, have you?" said the worthy old man to me.

"Marcoline," said I, "has not only capital which will produce a larger sum than that which I have named, but she has also valuable possessions. Your excellency will note her wisdom in saying that she would need your lordship's protection at Venice, for she will require someone to look after the investment of her capital. The whole amount is in my hands, and if she likes Marcoline can have it all in less than two hours."

"Very good; then you must start for Venice the day after to-morrow. Mattio is quite ready to receive you."

"I have the greatest respect and love for my uncle, but it is not to his care that your excellency must commend me if I resolve to go."

"Then to whom?"

"To your own care, my lord. Your excellency has called me dear daughter two or three times, lead me, then, to Venice, like a good father, and I will come willingly; otherwise I protest I will not leave the man to whom I owe all I have. I will start for London with him the day after to-morrow."

At these words which delighted me silence fell on all. They waited for M. Querini to speak, and the general opinion seemed to be that he had gone too far to be able to draw back. Nevertheless, the old man kept silence; perhaps in his character of devotee he was afraid of being led into temptation, or of giving occasion to scandal, and the other guests were silent like him, and ate to keep each other in countenance. Mattio's hand trembled as he waited; Marcoline alone was calm and collected. Dessert was served, and still no one dared to say a word. All at once this wonderful girl said, in an inspired voice, as if speaking to herself,——

"We must adore the decrees of Divine Providence, but after the issue, since mortals are not able to discern the future, whether it be good or whether it be evil."

"What does that reflection relate to, my dear daughter?" said M. Querini, "and why do you kiss my hand now?"

"I kiss your hand because you have called me your dear daughter for the fourth time."

This judicious remark elicited a smile of approval from all, and restored the general gaiety; but M. Querini asked Marcoline to explain her observation on Providence.

"It was an inspiration, and the result of self-examination. I am well; I have learned something of life; I am only seventeen, and in the course of two months I have become rich by honest means. I am all happy, and yet I owe my happiness to the greatest error a maiden can commit. Thus I humble myself before the decrees of Providence and adore its wisdom."

"You are right, but none the less you ought to repent of what you have done."

"That's where I am puzzled; for before I can repent I must think of it, and when I think of it I find nothing for which to repent. I suppose I shall have to consult some great theologian on the point."

"That will not be necessary; you are intelligent, and your heart is good, and I will give you the necessary instruction on the way. When one repents there is no need to think of the pleasure which our sins have given us."

In his character of apostle the good M. Querini was becoming piously amorous of his fair proselyte. He left the table for a few moments, and when he returned he told Marcoline that if he had a young lady to take to Venice he should be obliged to leave her in the care of his housekeeper, Dame Veneranda, in whom he had every confidence.

"I have just been speaking to her; and if you would like to come, all is arranged. You shall sleep with her and dine with us till we get to Venice, and then I will deliver you into your mother's keeping in the presence of your uncle. What do you say?"

"I will come with pleasure."

"Come and see Dame Veneranda."

"Willingly."

"Come with us, Casanova."

Dame Veneranda looked a perfect canoness, and I did not think that Marcoline would fall in love with her, but she seemed sensible and trustworthy. M. Querini told her in our presence what he had just told Marcoline, and the duenna assured him that she would take the utmost care of the young lady. Marcoline kissed her and called her mother, thus gaining the old lady's good graces. We rejoined the company, who expressed to Marcoline their intense pleasure at having her for a companion on their journey.

"I shall have to put my steward in another carriage," said M. Querini, "as the calash only holds two."

"That will not be necessary," I remarked, "for Marcoline has her carriage, and Mistress Veneranda will find it a very comfortable one. It will hold her luggage as well."

"You want to give me your carriage," said Marcoline. "You are too good to me."

I could make no reply, my emotion was so great. I turned aside and wiped away my tears. Returning to the company, I found that Marcoline had vanished and M. Morosini, who was also much affected, told me she had gone to speak to Mistress Veneranda. Everybody was melancholy, and seeing that I was the cause I began to talk about England, where I hoped to make my fortune with a project of mine, the success of which only depended on Lord Egremont. M. de Morosini said he would give me a letter for Lord Egremont and another for M. Zuccata, the Venetian ambassador.

"Are you not afraid," said M. Querini, "of getting into trouble with the State Inquisitors for recommending M. Casanova?"

Morosini replied coldly that as the Inquisitors had not told him for what crime I was condemned, he did not feel himself bound to share their judgment. Old Querini, who was extremely particular, shook his head and said nothing.

Just then Marcoline came back to the room, and everybody could see that she had been weeping. I confess that this mark of her affection was as pleasing to my vanity as to my love; but such is man, and such, doubtless, is the reader who may be censuring my conduct.

This charming girl, who still, after all these years, dwells in my old heart, asked me to take her back to the inn, as she wanted to pack up her trunks. We left directly, after having promised to come to dinner on the following day.

I wept bitterly when I got to my room. I told Clairmont to see that the carriage was in good order, and then, hastily undressing, I flung myself on the bed in my dressing-gown, and wept as if some blessing was being taken from me against my will. Marcoline, who was much more sensible, did what she could to console me, but I liked to torment myself, and her words did but increase my despair.

"Reflect," said she, "that it is not I who am leaving you, but you who are sending me away; that I long to spend the rest of my days with you, and that you have only got to say a word to keep me."

I knew that she was right; but still a fatal fear which has always swayed me, the fear of being bound to anyone, and the hypocrisy of a libertine ever longing for change, both these feelings made me persist in my resolution and my sadness.

About six o'clock MM. Morosini and Querini came into the courtyard and looked at the carriage, which was being inspected by the wheelwright. They spoke to Clairmont, and then came to see us.

"Good heavens!" said M. Querini, seeing the numerous boxes which she was going to place on her carriage; and when he had heard that her carriage was the one he had just looked at, he seemed surprised; it was indeed a very good vehicle.

M. Morosini told Marcoline that if she liked to sell it when she got to Venice he would give her a thousand Venetian ducats, or three thousand francs for it.

"You might give her double that amount," said I, "for it is worth three thousand ducats."

"We will arrange all that," said he; and Querini added,——

"It will be a considerable addition to the capital she proposes to invest."

After some agreeable conversation I told M. Querini that I would give him a bill of exchange for five thousand ducats, which, with the three or four thousand ducats the sale of her jewellery would realize, and the thousand for the carriage, would give her a capital of nine or ten thousand ducats, the interest of which would bring her in a handsome income.

Next morning I got M. Bono to give me a bill of exchange on M. Querini's order, and at dinner-time Marcoline handed it over to her new protector, who wrote her a formal receipt. M. Morosini gave me the letters he had promised, and their departure was fixed for eleven o'clock the next day. The reader may imagine that our dinner-party was not over gay. Marcoline was depressed, I as gloomy as a splenetic Englishman, and between us we made the feast more like a funeral than a meeting of friends.

I will not attempt to describe the night I passed with my charmer. She asked me again and again how I could be my own executioner; but I could not answer, for I did not know. But how often have I done things which caused me pain, but to which I was impelled by some occult force it was my whim not to resist.

In the morning, when I had put on my boots and spurs, and told Clairmont not to be uneasy if I did not return that night, Marcoline and I drove to the ambassadors' residence. We breakfasted together, silently enough, for Marcoline had tears in her eyes, and everyone knowing my noble conduct towards her respected her natural grief. After breakfast we set out, I sitting in the forepart of the carriage, facing Marcoline and Dame Veneranda, who would have made me laugh under any other circumstances, her astonishment at finding herself in a more gorgeous carriage than the ambassador's was so great. She expatiated on the elegance and comfort of the equipage, and amused us by saying that her master was quite right in saying that the people would take her for the ambassadress. But in spite of this piece of comedy, Marcoline and I were sad all the way. M. Querini, who did not like night travelling, made us stop at Pont-Boivoisin, at nine o'clock, and after a bad supper everyone went to bed to be ready to start at daybreak. Marcoline was to sleep with Veneranda, so I accompanied her, and the worthy old woman went to bed without any ceremony, lying so close to the wall that there was room for two more; but after Marcoline had got into bed I sat down on a chair, and placing my head beside hers on the pillow we mingled our sobs and tears all night.

When Veneranda, who had slept soundly, awoke, she was much astonished to see me still in the same position. She was a great devotee, but women's piety easily gives place to pity, and she had moved to the furthest extremity of the bed with the intention of giving me another night of love. But my melancholy prevented my profiting by her kindness.

I had ordered a saddle horse to be ready for me in the morning. We took a hasty cup of coffee and bade each other mutual farewells. I placed Marcoline in the carriage, gave her a last embrace, and waited for the crack of the postillion's whip to gallop back to Lyons. I tore along like a madman, for I felt as if I should like to send the horse to the ground and kill myself. But death never comes to him that desires it, save in the fable of the worthy Lafontaine. In six hours I had accomplished the eighteen leagues between Pont-Boivoisin and Lyons, only stopping to change horses. I tore off my clothes and threw myself on the bed, where thirty hours before I had enjoyed all the delights of love. I hoped that the bliss I had lost would return to me in my dreams. However, I slept profoundly, and did not wake till eight o'clock. I had been asleep about nineteen hours.

I rang for Clairmont, and told him to bring up my breakfast, which I devoured eagerly. When my stomach was restored in this manner I fell asleep again, and did not get up till the next morning, feeling quite well, and as if I could support life a little longer.

Three days after Marcoline's departure I bought a comfortable two-wheeled carriage with patent springs, and sent my trunks to Paris by the diligence. I kept a portmanteau containing the merest necessaries, for I meant to travel in a dressing-gown and night-cap, and keep to myself all the way to Paris. I intended this as a sort of homage to Marcoline, but I reckoned without my host.

I was putting my jewellery together in a casket when Clairmont announced a tradesman and his daughter, a pretty girl whom I had remarked at dinner, for since the departure of my fair Venetian I had dined at the table-d'hôte by way of distraction.

I shut up my jewels and asked them to come in, and the father addressed me politely, saying,——

"Sir, I have come to ask you to do me a favour which will cost you but little, while it will be of immense service to my daughter and myself."

"What can I do for you? I am leaving Lyons at day-break to-morrow."

"I know it, for you said so at dinner; but we shall be ready at any hour. Be kind enough to give my daughter a seat in your carriage. I will, of course, pay for a third horse, and will ride post."

"You cannot have seen the carriage."

"Excuse me, I have done so. It is, I know, only meant for one, but she could easily squeeze into it. I know I am troubling you, but if you were aware of the convenience it would be to me I am sure you would not refuse. All the places in the diligence are taken up to next week, and if I don't get to Paris in six days I might as well stay away altogether. If I were a rich man I would post, but that would cost four hundred francs, and I cannot afford to spend so much. The only course open to me is to leave by the diligence to-morrow, and to have myself and my daughter bound to the roof. You see, sir, the idea makes her weep, and I don't like it much better myself."

I looked attentively at the girl, and found her too pretty for me to keep within bounds if I travelled alone with her. I was sad, and the torment I had endured in parting from Marcoline had made me resolve to avoid all occasions which might have similar results. I thought this resolve necessary for my peace of mind.

"This girl," I said to myself, "may be so charming

that I should fall in love with her if I yield to the father's request, and I do not wish for any such result."

I turned to the father and said,——

"I sympathize with you sincerely; but I really don't see what I can do for you without causing myself the greatest inconvenience."

"Perhaps you think that I shall not be able to ride so many posts in succession, but you needn't be afraid on that score."

"The horse might give in; you might have a fall, and I know that I should feel obliged to stop, and I am in a hurry. If that reason does not strike you as a cogent one, I am sorry, for to me it appears unanswerable."

"Let us run the risk, sir, at all events."

"There is a still greater risk of which I can tell you nothing. In brief, sir, you ask what is impossible."

"In Heaven's name, sir," said the girl, with a voice and a look that would have pierced a heart of stone, "rescue me from that dreadful journey on the roof of the diligence! The very idea makes me shudder; I should be afraid of falling off all the way; besides, there is something mean in travelling that way. Do but grant me this favour, and I will sit at your feet so as not to discomfort you."

"This is too much! You do not know me, mademoiselle. I am neither cruel nor impolite, especially where your sex is concerned, though my refusal must make you feel otherwise. If I give way you may regret it afterwards, and I do not wish that to happen." Then, turning to the father, I said,——

"A post-chaise costs six louis. Here they are; take them. I will put off my departure for a few hours, if necessary, to answer for the chaise, supposing you are not known here, and an extra horse will cost four louis;

take them. As to the rest, you would have spent as much in taking two places in the diligence."

"You are very kind, sir, but I cannot accept your gift. I am not worthy of it, and I should be still less worthy if I accepted the money. Adèle, let us go. Forgive us, sir, if we have wasted half an hour of your time. Come, my poor child."

"Wait a moment, father."

Adèle begged him to wait, as her sobs almost choked her. I was furious with everything, but having received one look from her beautiful eyes I could not withstand her sorrow any longer, and said,——

"Calm yourself, mademoiselle. It shall never be said that I remained unmoved while beauty wept. I yield to your request, for if I did not I should not be able to sleep all night. But I accede on one condition," I added, turning to her father, "and that is that you sit at the back of the carriage."

"Certainly; but what is to become of your servant?"

"He will ride on in front. Everything is settled. Go to bed now, and be ready to start at six o'clock."

"Certainly, but you will allow me to pay for the extra horse?"

"You shall pay nothing at all; it would be a shame if I received any money from you. You have told me you are poor, and poverty is no dishonour; well, I may tell you that I am rich, and riches are no honour save when they are used in doing good. Therefore, as I said, I will pay for all."

"Very good, but I will pay for the extra horse in the carriage."

"Certainly not, and let us have no bargaining, please; it is time to go to bed. I will put you down at Paris without the journey costing you a farthing, and then if you like you may thank me: these are the only conditions on which I will take you. Look! Mdlle. Adèle is laughing, that's reward enough for me."

"I am laughing for joy at having escaped that dreadful diligence roof."

"I see, but I hope you will not weep in my carriage, for all sadness is an abomination to me."

I went to bed, resolved to struggle against my fate no longer. I saw that I could not withstand the tempting charms of this new beauty, and I determined that everything should be over in a couple of days. Adèle had beautiful blue eyes, a complexion wherein were mingled the lily and the rose, a small mouth, excellent teeth, a figure still slender but full of promise; here, surely, were enough motives for a fresh fall. I fell asleep, thanking my good genius for thus providing me with amusement on the journey.

Just before we started the father came and asked if it was all the same to me whether we went by Burgundy or the Bourbonnais.

"Certainly. Do you prefer any particular route?"

"If I went through Nevers I might be able to collect a small account."

"Then we will go by the Bourbonnais."

Directly after Adèle, simply but neatly dressed, came down and wished me good day, telling me that her father was going to put a small trunk containing their belongings at the back of the carriage. Seeing me busy, she asked if she could help me in any way.

"No," I replied, "you had better take a seat."

She did so, but in a timid manner, which annoyed me, because it seemed to express that she was a dependent of mine. I told her so gently, and made her take some coffee with me, and her shyness soon wore off.

We were just stepping into the carriage when a man came and told me that the lamps were out of repair and would come off if something were not done to them. He offered to put them into good repair in the course of an hour. I was in a terrible rage, and called Clairmont and began to scold him, but he said that the lamps were all right a short while ago, and that the man must have put them out of order that he might have the task of repairing them.

He had hit it off exactly. I had heard of the trick before, and I called out to the man; and on his answering me rather impudently, I began to kick him, with my pistol in my hand. He ran off swearing, and the noise brought up the landlord and five or six of his people. Everybody said I was in the right, but all the same I had to waste two hours as it would not have been prudent to travel without lamps.

Another lamp-maker was summoned; he looked at the damage, and laughed at the rascally trick his fellow-tradesman had played me.

"Can I imprison the rascal?" I said to the landlord. "I should like to have the satisfaction of doing so, were it to cost me two louis."

"Two louis! Your honour shall be attended to in a moment."

I was in a dreadful rage, and did not notice Adèle, who was quite afraid of me. A police official came up to take my information, and examine witnesses, and to draw up the case.

"How much is your time worth, sir?" he asked me.

"Five louis."

With these words I slid two louis into his hand, and he immediately wrote down a fine of twenty louis against the lamp-maker, and then went his way, saying,——

"Your man will be in prison in the next ten minutes."

I breathed again at the prospect of vengeance. I then begged Mdlle. Adèle's pardon, who asked mine in her turn, not knowing how I had offended her. This might have led to some affectionate passages, but her father came in saying that the rascal was in prison, and that everyone said I was right.

"I am perfectly ready to swear that he did the damage," said he.

"You saw him, did you?"

"No, but that's of no consequence, as everybody is sure he did it."

This piece of simplicity restored my good temper completely, and I began to ask Moreau, as he called himself, several questions. He told me he was a widower, that Adèle was his only child, that he was going to set up in business at Louviers, and so on.

In the course of an hour the farce turned into a tragedy, in the following manner. Two women, one of them with a baby at her breast, and followed by four brats, all of whom might have been put under a bushel measure, came before me, and falling on their knees made me guess the reason of this pitiful sight. They were the wife, the mother, and the children of the delinquent.

My heart was soon moved with pity for them, for my vengeance had been complete, and I did not harbour resentment; but the wife almost put me in a fury again by saying that her husband was an innocent man, and that they who had accused him were rascals.

The mother, seeing the storm ready to burst, attacked me more adroitly, admitting that her son might be guilty, but that he must have been driven to it by misery, as he had got no bread wherewith to feed his children. She added,——

"My good sir, take pity on us, for he is our only support. Do a good deed and set him free, for he would stay in prison all his days unless we sold our beds to pay you."

"My worthy woman, I forgive him completely. Hand this document to the police magistrate and all will be well."

At the same time I gave her a louis and told her to go, not wishing to be troubled with her thanks. A few moments after, the official came to get my signature for the man's release, and I had to pay him the legal costs. My lamps cost twelve francs to mend, and at nine o'clock I started, having spent four or five louis for nothing.

Adèle was obliged to sit between my legs, but she was ill at ease. I told her to sit further back, but as she would have had to lean on me, I did not urge her; it would have been rather a dangerous situation to begin with. Moreau sat at the back of the carriage, Clairmont went on in front, and we were thus neck and neck, or rather neck and back, the whole way.

We got down to change horses, and as we were getting into the carriage again Adèle had to lift her leg, and shewed me a pair of black breeches. I have always had a horror of women with breeches, but above all of black breeches.

"Sir," said I to her father, "your daughter has shewn me her black breeches."

"It's uncommonly lucky for her that she didn't shew you something else."

I liked the reply, but the cursed breeches had so offended me that I became quite sulky. It seemed to me that such clothes were a kind of rampart or outwork, very natural, no doubt, but I thought a young girl should know nothing of the danger, or, at all events, pretend ignorance if she did not possess it. As I could neither scold her nor overcome my bad temper, I contented myself with being polite, but I did not speak again till we got to St. Simphorien, unless it was to ask her to sit more comfortably.

When we got to St. Simphorien I told Clairmont to go on in front and order us a good supper at Roanne, and to sleep there. When we were about half-way Adèle told me that she must be a trouble to me, as I was not so gay as I had been. I assured her that it was not so, and that I only kept silence that she might be able to rest.

"You are very kind," she answered, "but it is quite a mistake for you to think that you would disturb me by talking. Allow me to tell you that you are concealing the real cause of your silence."

"Do you know the real cause?"

"Yes, I think I do."

"Well, what is it?"

"You have changed since you saw my breeches."

"You are right, this black attire has clothed my soul with gloom."

"I am very sorry, but you must allow that in the first place I was not to suppose that you were going to see my breeches, and in the second place that I could not be aware that the colour would be distasteful to you."

"True again, but as I chanced to see the articles you must forgive my disgust. This black has filled my soul with funereal images, just as white would have cheered me. Do you always wear those dreadful breeches?"

"I am wearing them for the first time to-day."

"Then you must allow that you have committed an unbecoming action."

"Unbecoming?"

"Yes, what would you have said if I had come down in petticoats this morning? You would have pronounced them unbecoming. You are laughing."

"Forgive me, but I never heard anything so amusing. But your comparison will not stand; everyone would have seen your petticoats, whereas no one has any business to see my breeches."

I assented to her logic, delighted to find her capable of tearing my sophism to pieces, but I still preserved silence.

At Roanne we had a good enough supper, and Moreau, who knew very well that if it had not been for his daughter there would have been no free journey and free supper for him, was delighted when I told him that she kept me good company. I told him about our discussion on breeches, and he pronounced his daughter to be in the wrong, laughing pleasantly. After supper I told him that he and his daughter were to sleep in the room in which we were sitting, while I would pass the night in a neighbouring closet.

Just as we were starting the next morning, Clairmont told me that he would go on in front, to see that our beds were ready, adding that as we had lost one night it would not do much harm if we were to lose another.

This speech let me know that my faithful Clairmont began to feel the need of rest, and his health was dear to me. I told him to stop at St. Pierre le Mortier, and to take care that a good supper was ready for us. When we were in the carriage again, Adèle thanked me.

"Then you don't like night travelling?" I said.

"I shouldn't mind it if I were not afraid of going to sleep and falling on you."

"Why, I should like it. A pretty girl like you is an agreeable burden."

She made no reply, but I saw that she understood; my declaration was made, but something more was wanted before I could rely on her docility. I relapsed into silence again till we got to Varennes, and then I said,——

"If I thought you could eat a roast fowl with as good an appetite as mine, I would dine here."

"Try me, I will endeavour to match you."

We ate well and drank better, and by the time we started again we were a little drunk. Adèle, who was only accustomed to drink wine two or three times a year, laughed at not being able to stand upright, but seemed to be afraid that something would happen. I comforted her by saying that the fumes of champagne soon evaporated; but though she strove with all her might to keep awake, nature conquered, and letting her pretty head fall on my breast she fell asleep, and did not rouse herself for two hours. I treated her with the greatest respect, though I could not resist ascertaining that the article of clothing which had displeased me so much had entirely disappeared.

While she slept I enjoyed the pleasure of gazing on the swelling curves of her budding breast, but I restrained my ardour, as the disappearance of the black breeches assured me that I should find her perfectly submissive whenever I chose to make the assault. I wished, however, that she should give herself up to me of her own free will, or at any rate come half-way to meet me, and I knew that I had only to smooth the path to make her do so.

When she awoke and found that she had been sleeping in my arms, her astonishment was extreme. She apologized and begged me to forgive her, while I thought the best way to put her at ease would be to give her an affectionate kiss. The result was satisfactory; who does not know the effect of a kiss given at the proper time?

As her dress was in some disorder she tried to re-adjust it, but we were rather pushed for space, and by an awkward movement she uncovered her knee. I burst out laughing and she joined me, and had the presence of mind to say,——

"I hope the black colour has given you no funereal thoughts this time."

"The hue of the rose, dear Adèle, can only inspire me with delicious fancies."

I saw that she lowered her eyes, but in a manner that shewed she was pleased.

With this talk—and, so to speak, casting oil on the flames—we reached Moulin, and got down for a few moments. A crowd of women assailed us with knives and edged tools of all sorts, and I bought the father and daughter whatever they fancied. We went on our way, leaving the women quarrelling and fighting because some had sold their wares and others had not.

In the evening we reached St. Pierre; but during the four hours that had elapsed since we left Moulin we had made way, and Adèle had become quite familiar with me.

Thanks to Clairmont, who had arrived two hours before, an excellent supper awaited us. We supped in a large room, where two great white beds stood ready to receive us.

I told Moreau that he and his daughter should sleep in one bed, and I in the other; but he replied that I and Adèle could each have a bed to ourselves, as he wanted to start for Nevers directly after supper, so as to be able to catch his debtor at daybreak, and to rejoin us when we got there the following day.

"If you had told me before, we would have gone on to Nevers and slept there."

"You are too kind. I mean to ride the three and a half stages. The riding will do me good, and I like it. I leave my daughter in your care. She will not be so near you as in the carriage."

"Oh, we will be very discreet, you may be sure!"

After his departure I told Adèle to go to bed in her clothes, if she were afraid of me.

"I shan't be offended," I added.

"It would be very wrong of me," she answered, "to give you such a proof of my want of confidence."

She rose, went out a moment, and when she came back she locked the door, and as soon as she was ready to slip off her last article of clothing came and kissed me. I happened to be writing at the time, and as she had come up on tiptoe I was surprised, though in a very agreeable manner. She fled to her bed, saying saucily,——

"You are frightened of me, I think?"

"You are wrong, but you surprised me. Come back, I want to see you fall asleep in my arms."

"Come and see me sleep."

"Will you sleep all the time?"

"Of course I shall."

"We will see about that."

I flung the pen down, and in a moment I held her in my arms, smiling, ardent, submissive to my desires, and only entreating me to spare her. I did my best, and though she helped me to the best of her ability, the first assault was a labour of Hercules. The others were pleasanter, for it is only the first step that is painful, and when the field had been stained with the blood of three successive battles, we abandoned ourselves to repose. At five o'clock in the morning Clairmont knocked, and I told him to get us some coffee. I was obliged to get up without giving fair Adèle good day, but I promised that she should have it on the way.

When she was dressed she looked at the altar where she had offered her first sacrifice to love, and viewed the signs of her defeat with a sigh. She was pensive for some time, but when we were in the carriage again her gaiety returned, and in our mutual transports we forgot to grieve over our approaching parting.

We found Moreau at Nevers; he was in a great state because he could not get his money before noon. He dared not ask me to wait for him, but I said that we would have a good dinner and start when the money was paid.

While dinner was being prepared we shut ourselves up in a room to avoid the crowd of women who pestered us to buy a thousand trifles, and at two o'clock we started, Moreau having got his money. We got to Cosne at twilight, and though Clairmont was waiting for us at Briane, I decided on stopping where I was, and this night proved superior to the first. The next day we made a breakfast of the meal which had been prepared for our supper, and we slept at Fontainebleau, where I enjoyed Adèle for the last time. In the morning I promised to come and see her at Louviers, when I returned from England, but I could not keep my word.

We took four hours to get from Fontainebleau to Paris, but how quickly the time passed. I stopped the carriage near the Pont St. Michel, opposite to a clockmaker's shop, and after looking at several watches I gave one to Adèle, and then dropped her and her father at the corner of the Rue aux Ours. I got down at the "Hotel de Montmorenci," not wanting to stop with Madame d'Urfé, but after dressing I went to dine with her.

CHAPTER VI

*I Drive My Brother The Abbé From Paris—Madame
du Rumain Recovers Her Voice Through My Cabala
—A Bad Joke—The Corticelli—I Take d'Aranda to
London—My Arrival At Calais*

AS USUAL, Madame d'Urfé received me with open
arms, but I was surprised at hearing her tell Aranda
to fetch the sealed letter she had given him in the
morning. I opened it, found it was dated the same day,
and contained the following:

"My genius told me at day-break that Galtinardus
was starting from Fontainebleau, and that he will come
and dine with me to-day."

She chanced to be right, but I have had many similar
experiences in the course of my life—experiences which
would have turned any other man's head. I confess
they have surprised me, but they have never made me
lose my reasoning powers. Men make a guess which
turns out to be correct, and they immediately claim
prophetic power; but they forgot all about the many
cases in which they have been mistaken. Six months
ago I was silly enough to bet that a bitch would have a
litter of five bitch pups on a certain day, and I won.
Everyone thought it a marvel except myself, for if I had
chanced to lose I should have been the first to laugh.

I naturally expressed my admiration for Madame
d'Urfé's genius, and shared her joy in finding herself so
well during her pregnancy. The worthy lunatic had

given orders that she was not at home to her usual callers, in expectation of my arrival, and so we spent the rest of the day together, consulting how we could make Aranda go to London of his own free will; and as I did not in the least know how it was to be done, the replies of the oracle were very obscure. Madame d'Urfé had such a strong dislike to bidding him go, that I could not presume on her obedience to that extent, and I had to rack my brains to find out some way of making the little man ask to be taken to London as a favour.

I went to the Comédie Italienne, where I found Madame du Rumain, who seemed glad to see me back in Paris again.

"I want to consult the oracle on a matter of the greatest importance," said she, "and I hope you will come and see me to-morrow."

I, of course, promised to do so.

I did not care for the performance, and should have left the theatre if I had not wanted to see the ballet, though I could not guess the peculiar interest it would have for me. What was my surprise to see the Corticelli amongst the dancers. I thought I would like to speak to her, not for any amorous reasons, but because I felt curious to hear her adventures. As I came out I met the worthy Baletti, who told me he had left the stage and was living on an annuity. I asked him about the Corticelli, and he gave me her address, telling me that she was in a poor way.

I went to sup with my brother and his wife, who were delighted to see me, and told me that I had come just in time to use a little gentle persuasion on our friend the abbé, of whom they had got tired.

"Where is he?"

"You will see him before long, for it is near supper-time; and as eating and drinking are the chief concerns of his life, he will not fail to put in an appearance."

"What has he done?"

"Everything that a good-for-nothing can do; but I hear him coming, and I will tell you all about it in his presence."

The abbé was astonished to see me, and began a polite speech, although I did not favour him with so much as a look. Then he asked me what I had against him.

"All that an honest man can have against a monster. I have read the letter you wrote to Possano, in which I am styled a cheat, a spy, a coiner, and a poisoner. What does the abbé think of that?"

He sat down to table without a word, and my brother began as follows:

"When this fine gentleman first came here, my wife and I gave him a most cordial welcome. I allowed him a nice room, and told him to look upon my house as his own. Possibly with the idea of interesting us in his favour, he began by saying that you were the greatest rascal in the world. To prove it he told us how he had carried off a girl from Venice with the idea of marrying her, and went to you at Genoa as he was in great necessity. He confesses that you rescued him from his misery, but he says that you traitorously took possession of the girl, associating her with two other mistresses you had at that time. In fine, he says that you lay with her before his eyes, and that you drove him from Marseilles that you might be able to enjoy her with greater freedom.

"He finished his story by saying that as he could not go back to Venice, he needed our help till he could find some means of living on his talents or through his profession as a priest. I asked him what his talents were, and he said he could teach Italian; but as he speaks it vilely, and doesn't know a word of French, we laughed at him. We were therefore reduced to seeing what we could do for him in his character of priest, and the very next day my wife spoke to M. de Sauci, the ecclesiastical commissioner, begging him to give my brother an introduction to the Archbishop of Paris, who might give him something that might lead to his obtaining a good benefice. He would have to go to our parish church, and I spoke to the rector of St. Sauveur, who promised to let him say mass, for which he would receive the usual sum of twelve sols. This was a very good beginning, and might have led to something worth having; but when we told the worthy abbé of our success, he got into a rage, saying that he was not the man to say mass for twelve sols, nor to toady the archbishop in the hope of being taken into his service. No, he was not going to be in anyone's service. We concealed our indignation, but for the three weeks he has been here he has turned everything upside down. My wife's maid left us yesterday, to our great annoyance, because of him; and the cook says she will go if he remains, as he is always bothering her in the kitchen. We are therefore resolved that he shall go, for his society is intolerable to us. I am delighted to have you here, as I think we ought to be able to drive him away between us, and the sooner the better."

"Nothing easier," said I; "if he likes to stay in Paris, let him do so. You can send off his rags to some furnished apartments, and serve him with a police order not to put foot in your house again. On the other hand if he wants to go away, let him say where, and I will pay his journey-money this evening."

"Nothing could be more generous. What do you say, abbé?"

"I say that this is the way in which he drove me from Marseilles. What intolerable violence!"

"Give God thanks, monster, that instead of thrashing you within an inch of your life as you deserve, I am going to give you some money! You thought you would get me hanged at Lyons, did you?"

"Where is Marcoline?"

"What is that to you? Make haste and choose between Rome and Paris, and remember that if you choose Paris you will have nothing to live on."

"Then I will go to Rome."

"Good! The journey only costs twenty louis, but I will give you twenty-five."

"Hand them over."

"Patience. Give me pens, ink and paper."

"What are you going to write?"

"Bills of exchange on Lyons, Turin, Genoa, Florence, and Rome. Your place will be paid as far as Lyons, and there you will be able to get five louis, and the same sum in the other towns, but as long as you stay in Paris not one single farthing will I give you. I am staying at the 'Hotel Montmorenci;' that's all you need know about me."

I then bade farewell to my brother and his wife, telling them that we should meet again. Checco, as we called my brother, told me he would send on the abbé's trunk the day following, and I bade him do so by all means.

The next day trunk and abbé came together. I did not even look at him, but after I had seen that a room had been assigned to him, I called out to the landlord that I would be answerable for the abbé's board and lodging for three days, and not a moment more. The abbé tried to speak to me, but I sternly declined to have anything to say to him, strictly forbidding Clairmont to admit him to my apartments.

When I went to Madame du Rumain's, the porter said,——

"Sir, everybody is still asleep, but who are you? I have instructions."

"I am the Chevalier de Seingalt."

"Kindly come into my lodge, and amuse yourself with my niece. I will soon be with you."

I went in, and found a neatly-dressed and charming girl.

"Mademoiselle," said I, "your uncle has told me to come and amuse myself with you."

"He is a rascal, for he consulted neither of us."

"Yes, but he knew well enough that there could be no doubt about my opinion after I had seen you."

"You are very flattering, sir, but I know the value of compliments."

"Yes, I suppose that you often get them, and you well deserve them all."

The conversation, as well as the pretty eyes of the niece, began to interest me, but fortunately the uncle put an end to it by begging me to follow him. He took me to the maid's room, and I found her putting on a petticoat, and grumbling the while.

"What is the matter, my pretty maid? You don't seem to be in a good humour."

"You would have done better to come at noon; it is not nine o'clock yet, and madame did not come home till three o'clock this morning. I am just going to wake her, and I am sorry for her."

I was taken into the room directly, and though her

eyes were half closed she thanked me for awaking her, while I apologized for having disturbed her sleep.

"Raton," said she, "give us the writing materials, and go away. Don't come till I call you, and if anyone asks for me, I am asleep."

"Very good, madam, and I will go to sleep also."

"My dear M. Casanova, how is it that the oracle has deceived us? M. du Rumain is still alive, and he ought to have died six months ago. It is true that he is not well, but we will not go into all that again. The really important question is this: You know that music is my favourite pursuit, and that my voice is famous for its strength and compass; well, I have completely lost it. I have not sung a note for three months. The doctors have stuffed me with remedies which have had no effect. It makes me very unhappy, for singing was the one thing that made me cling to life. I entreat you to ask the oracle how I can recover my voice. How delighted I should be if I could sing by to-morrow. I have a great many people coming here, and I should enjoy the general astonishment. If the oracle wills it I am sure that it might be so, for I have a very strong chest. That is my question; it is a long one, but so much the better; the answer will be long too, and I like long answers."

I was of the same opinion, for when the question was a long one, I had time to think over the answer as I made the pyramid. Madame Rumain's complaint was evidently something trifling, but I was no physician, and knew nothing about medicine. Besides, for the honour of the cabala, the oracle must have nothing to do with mere empiric remedies. I soon made up my mind that a little care in her way of living would soon restore the throat to its normal condition, and any doctor with brains in his head could have told her as much. In the position I was in, I had to make use of the language of a charlatan, so I resolved on prescribing a ceremonial worship to the sun, at an hour which would insure some regularity in her mode of life.

The oracle declared that she would recover her voice in twenty-one days, reckoning from the new moon, if she worshipped the rising sun every morning, in a room which had at least one window looking to the east.

A second reply bade her sleep seven hours in succession before she sacrificed to the sun, each hour symbolizing one of the seven planets; and before she went to sleep she was to take a bath in honour of the moon, placing her legs in lukewarm water up to the knees. I then pointed out the psalms which she was to recite to the moon, and those which she was to say in the face of the rising sun, at a closed window.

This last direction filled her with admiration, "for," said she, "the oracle knew that I should catch cold if the window were open. I will do everything the oracle bids me," added the credulous lady, "but I hope you will get me everything necessary for the ceremonies."

"I will not only take care that you have all the requisites, but as a proof of my zeal for you, I will come and do the suffumigations myself that you may learn how it is done."

She seemed deeply moved by this offer, but I expected as much. I knew how the most trifling services are assessed at the highest rates; and herein lies the great secret of success in the world, above all, where ladies of fashion are concerned.

As we had to begin the next day, being the new moon, I called on her at nine o'clock. As she had to sleep for seven successive hours before performing the ceremonies to the rising sun, she would have to go to bed before ten; and the observance of all these trifles was of importance, as anyone can understand.

I was sure that if anything could restore this lady's voice a careful regimen would do it. I proved to be right, and at London I received a grateful letter announcing the success of my method.

Madame du Rumain, whose daughter married the Prince de Polignac, was a lover of pleasure, and haunted grand supper-parties. She could not expect to enjoy perfect health, and she had lost her voice by the way in which she had abused it. When she had recovered her voice, as she thought, by the influence of the genii, she laughed at anyone who told her that there was no such thing as magic.

I found a letter from Thérèse at Madame d'Urfé's, in which she informed me that she would come to Paris and take her son back by force if I did not bring him to London, adding that she wanted a positive reply. I did not ask for anything more, but I thought Thérèse very insolent.

I told Aranda that his mother would be waiting for us at Abbeville in a week's time, and that she wanted to see him.

"We will both give her the pleasure of seeing us."

"Certainly," said he; "but as you are going on to London, how shall I come back?"

"By yourself," said Madame d'Urfé, "dressed as a postillion."

"What! shall I ride post? How delightful!"

"You must only cover eight or ten posts a day, for you have no need to risk your life by riding all night."

"Yes, yes; but I am to dress like a postillion, am I not?"

"Yes; I will have a handsome jacket and a pair of

leather breeches made for you, and you shall have a flag with the arms of France on it."

"They will take me for a courier going to London."

With the idea that to throw difficulties in the way would confirm him in his desire to go, I said roughly that I could not hear of it, as the horse might fall and break his neck. I had to be begged and entreated for three days before I would give in, and I did so on the condition that he should only ride on his way back.

As he was certain of returning to Paris, he only took linen sufficient for a very short absence; but as I knew that once at Abbeville he could not escape me, I sent his trunk on to Calais, where we found it on our arrival. However, the worthy Madame d'Urfé got him a magnificent postillion's suit, not forgetting the top-boots.

This business which offered a good many difficulties was happily arranged by the action of pure chance; and I am glad to confess that often in my life has chance turned the scale in my favour.

I called on a banker and got him to give me heavy credits on several of the most important houses in London, where I wished to make numerous acquaintances.

While I was crossing the Place des Victoires, I passed by the house where the Corticelli lived, and my curiosity made me enter. She was astonished to see me, and after a long silence she burst into tears, and said,——

"I should never have been unhappy if I had never known you."

"Yes, you would, only in some other way; your misfortunes are the result of your bad conduct. But tell me what are your misfortunes."

"As I could not stay in Turin after you had dishonoured me . . . ."

"You came to dishonour yourself here, I suppose. Drop that tone, or else I will leave you."

She began her wretched tale, which struck me with consternation, for I could not help feeling that I was the first and final cause of this long list of woes. Hence I felt it was my duty to succour her, however ill she had treated me in the past.

"Then," said I, "you are at present the victim of a fearful disease, heavily in debt, likely to be turned out of doors and imprisoned by your creditors. What do you propose to do?"

"Do. Why, throw myself in the Seine, to be sure; that's all that is left for me to do. I have not a farthing left."

"And what would you do if you had some money?"

"I would put myself under the doctor's hands, in the first place, and then if any money was left I would go to Bologna and try to get a living somehow. Perhaps I should have learnt a little wisdom by experience."

"Poor girl, I pity you! and in spite of your bad treatment of me, which has brought you to this pass, I will not abandon you. Here are four louis for your present wants, and to-morrow I will tell you where you are to go for your cure. When you have got well again, I will give you enough money for the journey. Dry your tears, repent, amend your ways, and may God have mercy on you!"

The poor girl threw herself on the ground before me, and covered one of my hands with kisses, begging me to forgive her for the ill she had done me. I comforted her and went my way, feeling very sad. I took a coach and drove to the Rue de Seine, where I called on an old surgeon I knew, told him the story, and what I wanted him to do. He told me he could cure her in six weeks without anybody hearing about it, but that he must be paid in advance.

"Certainly; but the girl is poor, and I am doing it out of charity."

The worthy man took a piece of paper and gave me a note addressed to a house in the Faubourg St. Antoine, which ran as follows:

"You will take in the person who brings you this note and three hundred francs, and in six weeks you will send her back cured, if it please God. The person has reasons for not wishing to be known."

I was delighted to have managed the matter so speedily and at such a cheap rate, and I went to bed in a calmer state of mind, deferring my interview with my brother till the next day.

He came at eight o'clock, and, constant to his folly, told me he had a plan to which he was sure I could have no objection.

"I don't want to hear anything about it; make your choice, Paris or Rome."

"Give me the journey-money, I will remain at Paris; but I will give a written engagement not to trouble you or your brother again. That should be sufficient."

"It is not for you to judge of that. Begone! I have neither the time nor the wish to listen to you. Remember, Paris without a farthing, or Rome with twenty-five louis."

Thereupon I called Clairmont, and told him to put the abbé out.

I was in a hurry to have done with the Corticelli affair, and went to the house in the Faubourg St. Antoine, where I found a kindly and intelligent-looking man and woman, and all the arrangements of the house satisfactory and appropriate to the performance of secret cures. I saw the room and the bath destined for the new boarder, everything was clean and neat, and I gave them a hundred crowns, for which they handed me a receipt. I told them that the lady would either come in the course of the day, or on the day following.

I went to dine with Madame d'Urfé and the young Count d'Aranda. After dinner the worthy marchioness talked to me for a long time of her pregnancy, dwelling on her symptoms, and on the happiness that would be hers when the babe stirred within her. I had put to a strong restrain upon myself to avoid bursting out laughing. When I had finished with her I went to the Corticelli, who called me her saviour and her guardian angel. I gave her two louis to get some linen out of pawn, and promised to come and see her before I left Paris, to give her a hundred crowns, which would take her back to Bologna. Then I waited on Madame du Rumain who had said farewell to society for three weeks.

This lady had an excellent heart, and was pretty as well, but she had so curious a society-manner that she often made me laugh most heartily. She talked of the sun and moon as if they were two Exalted Personages, to whom she was about to be presented. She was once discussing with me the state of the elect in heaven, and said that their greatest happiness was, no doubt, to love God *to distraction,* for she had no idea of calm and peaceful bliss.

I gave her the incense for the fumigation, and told her what psalms to recite, and then we had a delicious supper. She told her chamber-maid to escort me at ten o'clock to a room on the second floor which she had furnished for me with the utmost luxury, adding,——

"Take care that the Chevalier de Seingalt is able to come into my room at five o'clock to-morrow."

At nine o'clock I placed her legs in a bath of lukewarm water, and taught her how to suffumigate. Her legs were moulded by the hand of the Graces and I wiped them amorously, laughing within myself at her expression of gratitude, and I then laid her in bed, contenting myself with a solemn kiss on her pretty forehead. When it was over I went up to my room where I was waited on by the pretty maid, who performed her duties with that grace peculiar to the French *soubrette,* and told me that as I had become her mistress's chambermaid it was only right that she should be my valet. Her mirth was infectious, and I tried to make her sit down on my knee; but she fled away like a deer, telling me that I ought to take care of myself if I wanted to cut a good figure at five o'clock the next day. She was wrong, but appearances were certainly against us, and it is well known that servants do not give their masters and mistresses the benefit of the doubt.

At five o'clock in the morning I found Madame du Rumain nearly dressed when I went into her room, and we immediately went into another, from which the rising sun might have been see if the "Hotel de Bouillon" had not been in the way, but that, of course, was a matter of no consequence. Madame du Rumain performed the ceremonies with all the dignity of an ancient priestess of Baal. She then sat down to her piano, telling me that to find some occupation for the long morning of nine hours would prove the hardest of all the rules, for she did not dine till two, which was then the fashionable hour. We had a meat breakfast without coffee, which

I had proscribed, and I left her, promising to call again before I left Paris.

When I got back to my inn, I found my brother there looking very uneasy at my absence at such an early hour. When I saw him I cried,——

"Rome or Paris, which is it to be?"

"Rome," he replied, cringingly.

"Wait in the ante-chamber. I will do your business for you."

When I had finished I called him in, and found my other brother and his wife, who said they had come to ask me to give them a dinner.

"Welcome!" said I. "You are come just in time to see me deal with the abbé, who has resolved at last to go to Rome and to follow my directions."

I sent Clairmont to the diligence office, and told him to book a place for Lyons; and then I wrote out five bills of exchange, of five louis each, on Lyons, Turin, Genoa, Florence, and Rome.

"Who is to assure me that these bills will be honoured?"

"I assure you, blockhead. If you don't like them you can leave them."

Clairmont brought the ticket for the diligence and I gave it to the abbé, telling him roughly to be gone.

"But I may dine with you, surely?" said he.

"No, I have done with you. Go and dine with Possano, as you are his accomplice in the horrible attempt he made to murder me. Clairmont, shew this man out, and never let him set foot here again."

No doubt more than one of my readers will pronounce my treatment of the abbé to have been barbarous; but putting aside the fact that I owe no man an account of my thoughts, deeds, and words, nature had implanted in me a strong dislike to this brother of mine, and his conduct as a man and a priest, and, above all, his connivance with Possano, had made him so hateful to me that I should have watched him being hanged with the utmost indifference, not to say with the greatest pleasure. Let everyone have his own principles and his own passions, and my favourite passion has always been vengeance.

"What did you do with the girl he eloped with?" said my sister-in-law.

"I sent her back to Venice with the ambassadors the better by thirty thousand francs, some fine jewels, and a perfect outfit of clothes. She travelled in a carriage I gave her which was worth more than two hundred louis."

"That's all very fine, but you must make some allowance for the abbé's grief and rage at seeing you sleep with her."

"Fools, my dear sister, are made to suffer such grief, and many others besides. Did he tell you that she would not let him have anything to do with her, and that she used to box his ears?"

"On the the contrary, he was always talking of her love for him."

"He made himself a fine fellow, I have no doubt, but the truth is, it was a very ugly business."

After several hours of pleasant conversation my brother left, and I took my sister-in-law to the opera. As soon as we were alone this poor sister of mine began to make the most bitter complaints of my brother.

"I am no more his wife now," said she, "than I was the night before our marriage."

"What! Still a maid?"

"As much a maid as at the moment I was born. They

tell me I could easily obtain a dissolution of the marriage, but besides the scandal that would arise, I unhappily love him, and I should not like to do anything that would give him pain."

"You are a wonderful woman, but why do you not provide a substitute for him?"

"I know I might do so, without having to endure much remorse, but I prefer to bear it."

"You are very praiseworthy, but in the other ways you are happy?"

"He is overwhelmed with debt, and if I liked to call upon him to give me back my dowry he would not have a shirt to his back. Why did he marry me? He must have known his impotence. It was a dreadful thing to do."

"Yes, but you must forgive him for it."

She had cause for complaint, for marriage without enjoyment is a thorn without roses. She was passionate, but her principles were stronger than her passions, or else she would have sought for what she wanted elsewhere. My impotent brother excused himself by saying that he loved her so well that he thought cohabitation with her would restore the missing faculty; he deceived himself and her at the same time. In time she died, and he married another woman with the same idea, but this time passion was stronger than virtue, and his new wife drove him away from Paris. I shall say more of him in twenty years time.

At six o'clock the next morning the abbé went off in the diligence, and I did not see him for six years. I spent the day with Madame d'Urfé, and I agreed, outwardly, that young d'Aranda should return to Paris as a postillion. I fixed our departure for the day after next.

The following day, after dining with Madame d'Urfé who continued to revel in the joys of her regeneration, I paid a visit to the Corticelli in her asylum. I found her sad and suffering, but content, and well pleased with the gentleness of the surgeon and his wife, who told me they would effect a radical cure. I gave her twelve louis, promising to send her twelve more as soon as I had received a letter from her written at Bologna. She promised she would write to me, but the poor unfortunate was never able to keep her word, for she succumbed to the treatment, as the old surgeon wrote to me, when I was at London. He asked what he should do with the twelve louis which she had left to one Madame Laura, who was perhaps known to me. I sent him her address, and the honest surgeon hastened to fulfil the last wishes of the deceased.

All the persons who helped me in my magical operations with Madame d'Urfé betrayed me, Marcoline excepted, and all save the fair Venetian died miserably. Later on the reader will hear more of Possano and Costa.

The day before I left for London I supped with Madame du Rumain, who told me that her voice was already beginning to return. She added a sage reflection which pleased me highly.

"I should think," she observed, "that the careful living prescribed by the cabala must have a good effect on my health."

"Most certainly," said I, "and if you continue to observe the rules you will keep both your health and your voice."

I knew that it is often necessary to deceive before one can instruct; the shadows must come before the dawn.

I took leave of my worthy Madame d'Urfê with an

emotion which I had never experienced before; it must have been a warning that I should never see her again. I assured her that I would faithfully observe all my promises, and she replied that her happiness was complete, and that she knew she owed it all to me. In fine, I took d'Aranda and his top-boots, which he was continually admiring, to my inn, whence we started in the evening, as he had begged me to travel by night. He was ashamed to be seen in a carriage dressed as a courier.

When we reached Abbeville he asked me where his mother was.

"We will see about it after dinner."

"But you can find out in a moment whether she is here or not?"

"Yes, but there is no hurry."

"And what will you do if she is not here?"

"We will go on till we meet her on the way. In the meanwhile let us go and see the famous manufactory of M. Varobes before dinner."

"Go by yourself. I am tired, and I will sleep till you come back."

"Very good."

I spent two hours in going over the magnificent establishment, the owner himself shewing it me, and then I went back to dinner and called for my young gentleman.

"He started for Paris riding post," replied the innkeeper, who was also the post-master, "five minutes after you left. He said he was going after some dispatches you had left at Paris."

"If you don't get him back I will ruin you with law-suits; you had no business to let him have a horse without my orders."

"I will capture the little rascal, sir, before he has got to Amiens."

He called a smart-looking postillion, who laughed when he heard what was wanted.

"I would catch him up," said he, "even if he had four hours start. You shall have him here at six o'clock."

"I will give you two louis."

"I would catch him for *that*, though he were a very lark."

He was in the saddle in five minutes, and by the rate at which he started I did not doubt his success. Nevertheless I could not enjoy my dinner. I felt so ashamed to have been taken in by a lad without any knowledge of the world. I lay down on a bed and slept till the postillion aroused me by coming in with the runaway, who looked half dead. I said nothing to him, but gave orders that he should be locked up in a good room, with a good bed to sleep on, and a good supper; and I told the landlord that I should hold him answerable for the lad as long as I was in his inn. The postillion had caught him up at the fifth post, just before Amiens, and as he was already quite tired out the little man surrendered like a lamb.

At day-break I summoned him before me, and asked him if he would come to London of his own free will or bound hand and foot.

"I will come with you, I give you my word of honour; but you must let me ride on before you. Otherwise, with this dress of mine, I should be ashamed to go. I don't want it to be thought that you had to give chase to me, as if I had robbed you."

"I accept your word of honour, but be careful to keep

it. Embrace me, and order another saddle-horse."

He mounted his horse in high spirits, and rode in front of the carriage with Clairmont. He was quite astonished to find his trunk at Calais, which he reached two hours before me.

CHAPTER VII

My Arrival in London; Madame Cornelis—I Am Presented at Court—I Rent a Furnished House—I Make a Large Circle of Acquaintance—Manners of the English

WHEN I got to Calais I consigned my post-chaise to the care of the landlord of the inn, and hired a packet. There was only one available for a private party, there being another for public use at six francs apiece. I paid six guineas in advance, taking care to get a proper receipt, for I knew that at Calais a man finds himself in an awkward position if he is unable to support his claim by documents.

Before the tide was out Clairmont got all my belongings on board, and I ordered my supper. The landlord told me that louis were not current in England, and offered to give me guineas in exchange for mine; but I was surprised when I found he gave me the same number of guineas as I had given him of louis. I wanted him to take the difference—four per cent.—but he refused, saying that he did not allow anything when the English gave him guineas for louis. I do not know whether he found his system a profitable one on the whole, but it was certainly so for me.

The young Count d'Aranda, to whom I had restored his humble name of Trenti, was quite resigned, but proud of having given me a specimen of his knowingness by riding post. We were just going to sit down at table, well pleased with one another, when I heard a loud conversation in English going on near my door, and mine host came in to tell me what it was about.

"It's the courier of the Duke of Bedford, the English ambassador," said he; "he announces the approach of his master, and is disputing with the captain of the packet. He says he hired the boat by letter, and that the captain had no right to let it to you. The master maintains that he has received no such letter, and no one can prove that he is telling a lie."

I congratulated myself on having taken the packet and paid the earnest-money, and went to bed. At day-break the landlord said that the ambassador had arrived at midnight, and that his man wanted to see me.

He came in and told me that the nobleman, his master, was in a great hurry to get to London, and that I should oblige him very much by yielding the boat to him.

I did not answer a word, but wrote a note which ran as follows:

"My lord duke may dispose of the whole of the packet, with the exception of the space necessary for my own accommodation, that of two other persons, and my luggage. I am delighted to have the opportunity of obliging the English ambassador."

The valet took the note, and returned to thank me on behalf of his master, who stipulated, however, that he should be allowed to pay for the packet.

"Tell him that it is out of the question, as the boat is paid for already."

"He will give you the six guineas."

"Tell your master that I cannot allow him to pay. I do not buy to sell again."

The duke called on me in the course of half an hour, and said that we were both of us in the right.

"However," he added, "there is a middle course, let us adopt it, and I shall be just as much indebted to you."

"What is that, my lord?"

"We will each pay half."

"My desire to oblige you, my lord, will not allow me to refuse, but it is I who will be indebted to you for the honour your lordship does me. We will start as soon as you like, and I can make my arrangements accordingly."

He shook my hand and left the room, and when he had gone I found three guineas on the table. He had placed them there without my noticing them. An hour afterwards I returned his call, and then told the master to take the duke and his carriages on board.

We took two hours and a half in crossing the Channel; the wind was strong, but we made a good passage.

The stranger who sets his foot on English soil has need of a good deal of patience. The custom-house officials made a minute, vexatious and even an impertinent perquisition; but as the duke and ambassador had to submit, I thought it best to follow his example; besides, resistance would be useless. The Englishman, who prides himself on his strict adherence to the law of the land, is curt and rude in his manner, and the English officials cannot be compared to the French, who know how to combine politeness with the exercise of their rights.

English is different in every respect from the rest of Europe; even the country has a different aspect, and the water of the Thames has a taste peculiar to itself. Everything has its own characteristics, and the fish, cattle, horses, men, and women are of a type not found in any other land. Their manner of living is wholly different from that of other countries, especially their cookery. The most striking feature in their character

is their national pride; they exalt themselves above all
other nations.

My attention was attracted by the universal cleanliness, the beauty of the country, the goodness of the
roads, the reasonable charges for posting, the quickness
of the horses, although they never go beyond a trot;
and lastly, the construction of the towns on the Dover
road; Canterbury and Rochester for instance, though
large and populous, are like long passages; they are all
length and no breadth.

We got to London in the evening and stopped at the
house of Madame Cornelis, as Thérèse called herself.
She was originally married to an actor named Imer, then
to the dancer Pompeati, who committed suicide at
Venice by ripping up his stomach with a razor.

In Holland she had been known as Madame Trenti,
but at London she had taken the name of her lover
Cornelius Rigerboos, whom she had contrived to ruin.

She lived in Soho Square, almost facing the house of
the Venetian ambassador. When I arrived I followed
the instructions I had received in her last letter. I left
her son in the carriage, and sent up my name, expecting
she would fly to meet me; but the porter told me to
wait, and in a few minutes a servant in grand livery
brought me a note in which Madame Cornelis asked me
to get down at the house to which her servant would conduct me. I thought this rather strange behaviour, but
still she might have her reasons for acting in this manner, so I did not let my indignation appear. When we
got to the house, a fat woman named Rancour, and two
servants, welcomed us, or rather welcomed my young
friend; for the lady embraced him, told him how glad
she was to see him, and did not appear to be aware
of my existence.

Our trunks were taken in, and Madame Rancour having ascertained which belonged to Cornelis, had them placed in a fine suite of three rooms, and said, pointing out to him the apartment and the two servants,——

"This apartment and the two servants are for you, and I, too, am your most humble servant."

Clairmont told me that he had put my things in a room which communicated with Cornelis's. I went to inspect it, and saw directly that I was being treated as if I were a person of no consequence. The storm of anger was gathering, but wonderful to relate, I subdued myself, and did not say a word.

"Where is your room?" I said to Clairmont.

"Near the roof, and I am to share it with one of those two louts you saw."

The worthy Clairmont, who knew my disposition, was surprised at the calm with which I said,——

"Take your trunk there."

"Shall I open yours?"

"No. We will see what can be done to-morrow."

I still kept on my mask, and returned to the room of the young gentleman who seemed to be considered as my master. I found him listening with a foolish stare to Madame Rancour, who was telling him of the splendid position his mother occupied, her great enterprise, her immense credit, the splendid house she had built, her thirty-three servants, her two secretaries, her six horses, her country house, etc., etc.

"How is my sister Sophie?" said the young gentleman.

"Her name is Sophie, is it? She is only known as Miss Cornelis. She is a beauty, a perfect prodigy, she plays at sight on several instruments, dances like Terpsichore, speaks English, French, and Italian equally

well—in a word, she is really wonderful. She has a
governess and a maid. Unfortunately, she is rather
short for her age; she is eight."

She was ten, but as Madame Rancour was not speaking to me I refrained from interrupting her.

My lord Cornelis, who felt very tired, asked at what
hour they were to sup.

"At ten o'clock and not before," said the duenna, "for
Madame Cornelis is always engaged till then. She is
always with her lawyer, on account of an important
law-suit she has against Sir Frederick Fermer."

I could see that I should learn nothing worth learning by listening to the woman's gossip, so I took my hat
and cane and went for a walk in the immense city, taking
care not to lose my way.

It was seven o'clock when I went out, and a quarter
of an hour after, seeing a number of people in a coffee-
house, I entered it. It was the most notorious place in
London, the resort of all the rascally Italians in town. I
had heard of it at Lyons, and had taken a firm resolve
never to set foot in it, but almighty chance made me
go there unknown to myself. But it was my only
visit.

I sat down by myself and called for a glass of lemon-
ade, and before long a man came and sat by me to
profit by the light. He had a printed paper in his hand,
and I could see that the words were Italian. He had a
pencil with which he scratched out some words and
letters, writing the corrections in the margin. Idle
curiosity made me follow him in his work, and I noticed
him correcting the word *ancora*, putting in an *h* in the
margin. I was irritated by this barbarous spelling, and
told him that for four centuries *ancora* had been spelt
without an *h*.

"Quite so," said he, "but I am quoting from Boccaccio, and one should be exact in quotations."

"I apologize, sir; I see you are a man of letters."

"Well, in a small way. My name is Martinelli."

"Then you are in a great way indeed. I know you by repute, and if I am not mistaken you are a relation of Calsabigi, who has spoken of you to me. I have read some of your satires."

"May I ask to whom I have the honour of speaking?"

"My name is Seingalt. Have you finished your edition of the *Decameron?*"

"I am still at work on it, and trying to increase the number of my subscribers."

"If you will be so kind I should be glad to be of the number."

"You do me honour."

He gave me a ticket, and seeing that it was only for a guinea I took four, and telling him I hoped to see him again at the same coffee-house, the name of which I asked him, he told it me, evidently astonished at my ignorance; but his surprise vanished when I informed him that I had only been in London for an hour, and that it was my first visit to the great city.

"You will experience some trouble in finding your way back," said he, "allow me to accompany you."

When we had got out he gave me to understand that chance had led me to the "Orange Coffee House," the most disreputable house in London.

"But you go there."

"Yes, but I can say with Juvenal:

" *'Cantabit vacuus coram latrone viator.'*

"The rogues can't hurt me; I know them and they know me; we never trouble each other."

"You have been a long time in London, I suppose."

"Five years."

"I presume you know a good many people."

"Yes, but I seldom wait on anyone but Lord Spencer. I am occupied with literary work and live all by myself. I don't make much, but enough to live on. I live in furnished apartments, and have twelve shirts and the clothes you see on my back, and that is enough for my happiness.

" 'Nec ultra deos lacesso.' "

I was pleased with this honest man, who spoke Italian with the most exquisite correctness.

On the way back I asked him what I had better do to get a comfortable lodging. When he heard the style in which I wished to live and the time I proposed to spend in London, he advised me to take a house completely furnished.

"You will be given an inventory of the goods," said he, "and as soon as you get a surety your house will be your castle."

"I like the idea," I answered, "but how shall I find such a house?"

"That is easily done."

"He went into a shop, begged the mistress to lend him the *Advertiser*, noted down several advertisements, and said,——

"That's all we have to do."

The nearest house was in Pall Mall and we went to see it. An old woman opened the door to us, and shewed us the ground floor and the three floors above. Each floor contained two rooms and a closet. Everything shone with cleanliness; linen, furniture, carpets, mirrors, and china, and even the bells and the bolts on the doors. The necessary linen was kept in a large press, and in another was the silver plate and several sets of china. The arrangements in the kitchen were excellent, and in a word, nothing was lacking in the way of comfort. The rent was twenty guineas a week, and, not stopping to bargain, which is never of any use in London, I told Martinelli that I would take it on the spot.

Martinelli translated what I said to the old woman, who told me that if I liked to keep her on as housekeeper I need not have a surety, and that it would only be necessary for me to pay for each week in advance. I answered that I would do so, but that she must get me a servant who could speak French or Italian as well as English. She promised to get one in a day's time, and I paid her for four weeks' rent on the spot, for which she gave me a receipt under the name of the Chevalier de Seingalt. This was the name by which I was known during the whole of my stay in London.

Thus in less than two hours I was comfortably settled in a town which is sometimes described as a chaos, especially for a stranger. But in London everything is easy to him who has money and is not afraid of spending it. I was delighted to be able to escape so soon from a house where I was welcomed so ill, though I had a right to the best reception; but I was still more pleased at the chance which had made me acquainted with Martinelli, whom I had known by repute for six years.

When I got back Madame Cornelis had not yet arrived, though ten o'clock had struck. Young Cornelis was asleep on the sofa. I was enraged at the way the woman treated me, but I resolved to put a good face on it.

Before long three loud knocks announced the arrival

of Madame Cornelis in a sedan-chair, and I heard her ascending the stairs. She came in and seemed glad to see me, but did not come and give me those caresses which I had a right to expect. She ran to her son and took him on her knee, but the sleepy boy did not respond to her kisses with any great warmth.

"He is very tired, like myself," said I, "and considering that we are travellers in need of rest you have kept us waiting a long time."

I do not know whether she would have answered at all, or, if so, what her answer would have been, for just at that moment a servant came in and said that supper was ready. She rose and did me the honour to take my arm, and we went into another room which I had not seen. The table was laid for four, and I was curious enough to enquire who was the fourth person.

"It was to have been my daughter, but I left her behind, as when I told her that you and her brother had arrived she asked me if you were well."

"And you have punished her for doing so?"

"Certainly, for in my opinion she ought to have asked for her brother first and then for you. Don't you think I was right?"

"Poor Sophie! I am sorry for her. Gratitude has evidently more influence over her than blood relationship."

"It is not a question of sentiment, but of teaching young persons to think with propriety."

"Propriety is often far from proper."

The woman told her son that she was working hard to leave him a fortune when she died, and that she had been obliged to summon him to England as he was old enough to help her in her business.

"And how am I to help you, my dear mother?"

"I give twelve balls and twelve suppers to the nobility, and the same number to the middle classes in the year. I have often as many as six hundred guests at two guineas a head. The expenses are enormous, and alone as I am I must be robbed, for I can't be in two places at once. Now that you are here you can keep everything under lock and key, keep the books, pay and receive accounts, and see that everyone is properly attended to at the assemblies; in fine, you will perform the duties of the master."

"And do you think that I can do all that?"

"You will easily learn it."

"I think it will be very difficult."

"One of my secretaries will come and live with you, and instruct you in everything. During the first year you will only have to acquire the English language, and to be present at my assemblies, that I may introduce you to the most distinguished people in London. You will get quite English before long."

"I would rather remain French."

"That's mere prejudice, my dear, you will like the sound of *Mister* Cornelis by-and-bye."

"Cornelis?"

"Yes; that is your name."

"It's a very funny one."

"I will write it down, so that you may not forget it."

Thinking that her dear son was joking. Madame Cornelis looked at me in some astonishment, and told him to go to bed, which he did instantly. When we were alone she said he struck her as badly educated, and too small for his age.

"I am very much afraid," said she, "that we shall have to begin his education all over again. What has he learnt in the last six years?"

"He might have learnt a great deal, for he went to the best boarding school in Paris; but he only learnt what he liked, and what he liked was not much. He can play the flute, ride, fence, dance a minuet, change his shirt every day, answer politely, make a graceful bow, talk elegant trifles, and dress well. As he never had any application, he doesn't know anything about literature; he can scarcely write, his spelling is abominable, his arithmetic limited, and I doubt whether he knows in what continent England is situated."

"He has used the six years well, certainly."

"Say, rather, he has wasted them; but he will waste many more."

"My daughter will laugh at him; but then it is I who have had the care of her education. He will be ashamed when he finds her so well instructed though she is only eight."

"He will never see her at eight, if I know anything of reckoning; she is fully ten."

"I think I ought to know the age of my own daughter. She knows geography, history, languages, and music; she argues correctly, and behaves in a manner which is surprising in so young a child. All the ladies are in love with her. I keep her at a school of design all day; she shews a great taste for drawing. She dines with me on Sundays, and if you would care to come to dinner next Sunday you will confess that I have not exaggerated her capacities."

It was Monday. I said nothing, but I thought it strange that she did not seem to consider that I was impatient to see my daughter. She should have asked me to meet her at supper the following evening.

"You are just in time," said she, "to witness the last assembly of the year; for in a few weeks all the nobility will leave town in order to pass the summer in the country. I can't give you a ticket, as they are only issued to the nobility, but you can come as my friend and keep close to me. You will see everything. If I am asked who you are, I will say that you have superintended the education of my son in Paris, and have brought him back to me."

"You do me too much honour."

We continued talking till two o'clock in the morning, and she told me all about the suit she had with Sir Frederick Fermer. He maintained that the house she had built at a cost of ten thousand guineas belonged to him as he had furnished the money. In equity he was right, but according to English law wrong, for it was she who had paid the workmen, the contractors, and the architect; it was she that had given and received receipts, and signed all documents. The house, therefore, belonged to her, and Fermer admitted as much; but he claimed the sum he had furnished, and here was the kernel of the whole case, for she had defied him to produce a single acknowledgment of money received.

"I confess," said this honest woman, "that you have often given me a thousand pounds at a time, but that was a friendly gift, and nothing to be wondered at in a rich Englishman, considering that we were lovers and lived together."

She had won her suit four times over in two years, but Fermer took advantage of the intricacies of English law to appeal again and again, and now he had gone to the House of Lords, the appeal to which might last fifteen years.

"This suit," said the honest lady, "dishonours Fermer."

"I should think it did, but you surely don't think it honours you."

"Certainly I do."

"I don't quite understand how you make that out."

"I will explain it all to you."

"We will talk it over again."

In the three hours for which we talked together this woman did not once ask me how I was, whether I was comfortable, how long I intended to stay in London, or whether I had made much money. In short she made no enquiries what ever about me, only saying with a smile, but not heedlessly,——

"I never have a penny to spare."

Her receipts amounted to more than twenty-four-thousand pounds per annum, but her expenses were enormous and she had debts.

I avenged myself on her indifference by not saying a word about myself. I was dresssed simply but neatly, and had not any jewellry or diamonds about my person.

I went to bed annoyed with her, but glad to have discovered the badness of her heart. In spite of my longing to see my daughter I determined not to take any steps to meet her till the ensuing Sunday, when I was invited to dinner.

Early next morning I told Clairmont to pull all my goods and chattels in a carriage, and when all was ready I went to take leave of young Cornelis, telling him I was going to live in Pall Mall, and leaving him my address.

"You are not going to stay with me, then?" said he.

"No, your mother doesn't know how to welcome or to treat me."

"I think you are right. I shall go back to Paris."

"Don't do anything so silly. Remember that here you are at home, and that in Paris you might not find a roof to shelter you. Farewell; I shall see you on Sunday."

I was soon settled in my new house, and I went out to call on M. Zuccato, the Venetian ambassador. I gave him M. Morosini's letter, and he said, coldly, that he was glad to make my acquaintance. When I asked him to present me at Court the insolent fool only replied with a smile, which might fairly be described as contemptuous. It was the aristocratic pride coming out, so I returned his smile with a cold bow, and never set foot in his house again.

On leaving Zuccato I called on Lord Egremont, and finding him ill left my letter with the porter. He died a few days after, so M. Morosini's letters were both useless through no fault of his. We shall learn presently what was the result of the little note.

I then went to the Comte de Guerchi, the French ambassador, with a letter from the Marquis Chauvelin, and I received a warm welcome. This nobleman asked me to dine with him the following day, and told me that if I liked he would present me at Court after chapel on Sunday. It was at that ambassador's table that I made the acquaintance of the Chevalier d'Eon, the secretary of the embassy, who afterwards became famous. This Chevalier d'Eon was a handsome woman who had been an advocate and a captain of dragoons before entering the diplomatic service; she served Louis XV. as a valiant soldier and a diplomatist of consummate skill. In spite of her manly ways I soon recognized her as a woman; her voice was not that of a *castrato,* and her shape was too rounded to be a man's. I say nothing of the absence of hair on her face, as that might be an accident.

In the first days of my stay in London I made the

acquaintance of my bankers; who held at least three hundred thousand francs of my money. They all honoured my drafts and offered their services to me, but I did not make use of their good offices.

I visited the theatres of Covent Garden and Drury Lane, but I could not extract much enjoyment out of the perfomances as I did not know a word of English. I dined at all the taverns, high and low, to get some insight into the peculiar manners of the English. In the morning I went on 'Change, where I made some friends. It was there that a merchant to whom I spoke got me a Negro servant who spoke English, French, and Italian with equal facility; and the same individual procured me a cook who spoke French. I also visited the bagnios where a rich man can sup, bathe, and sleep with a fashionable courtezan, of which species there are many in London. It makes a magnificent debauch and only costs six guineas. The expense may be reduced to a hundred francs, but economy in pleasure is not to my taste.

On Sunday I made an elegant toilette and went to Court about eleven, and met the Comte de Guerchi as we had arranged. He introduced me to George III., who spoke to me, but in such a low voice that I could not understand him and had to reply by a bow. The queen made up for the king, however, and I was delighted to observe that the proud ambassador from my beloved Venice was also present. When M. de Guerchi introduced me under the name of the Chevalier de Seingalt, Zuccato looked astonished, for Mr. Morosini had called me Casanova in his letter. The queen asked me from what part of France I came, and understanding from my answer that I was from Venice, she looked at the Venetian ambassador, who bowed as if to say that he had no objection to make. Her Majesty then asked me if I knew the ambassadors extraordinary, who had been sent to congratulate the king, and I replied that I had the pleasure of knowing them intimately, and that I had spent three days in their society at Lyons, where M. Morosini gave me letters for my Lord d'Egremont and M. Zuccato.

"M. Querini amused me extremely," said the queen; "he called me a little devil."

"He meant to say that your highness is as witty as an angel."

I longed for the queen to ask me why I had not been presented by M. Zuccatto, for I had a reply on the tip of my tongue that would have deprived the ambassador of his sleep for a week, while I should have slept soundly, for vengeance is a divine pleasure, especially when it is taken on the proud and foolish; but the whole conversation was a compound of nothings, as is usual in courts.

After my interview was over I got into my sedan-chair and went to Soho Square. A man in court dress cannot walk the streets of London without being pelted with mud by the mob, while the gentleman look on and laugh. All customs must be respected; they are all at once worthy and absurd.

When I got to the house of Madame Cornelis, I and my Negro Jarbe were shewn upstairs, and conducted through a suite of gorgeous apartments to a room where the lady of the house was sitting with two English ladies and two English gentlemen. She received me with familiar politeness, made me sit down in an armchair beside her, and then continued the conversation in English without introducing me. When her steward told her that dinner was ready, she gave orders for the children to be brought down.

I had long desired this meeting, and when I saw Sophie I ran to meet her; but she, who had profited by her mother's instructions, drew back with profound courtesy and a compliment learnt by heart. I did not say anything for fear I should embarrass her, but I felt grieved to the heart.

Madame Cornelis then brought forward her son, telling the company that I had brought him to England after superintending his education for six years. She spoke in French, so I was glad to see that her friends understood that language.

We sat down to table; Madame Cornelis between her two children, and I between the two Englishwomen, one of whom delighted me by her pleasant wit. I attached myself to her as soon as I noticed that the mistress of the house only spoke to me by chance, and that Sophie did not look at me. She was so like me that no mistake was possible. I could see that she had been carefully tutored by her mother to behave in this manner, and I felt this treatment to be both absurd and impertinent.

I did not want to let anyone see that I was angry, so I began to discourse in a pleasant strain on the peculiarities of English manners, taking care, however, not to say anything which might wound the insular pride of the English guests. My idea was to make them laugh and to make myself agreeable, and I succeeded, but not a word did I speak to Madame Cornelis; I did not so much as look at her.

The lady next to me, after admiring the beauty of my lace, asked me what was the news at Court.

"It was all news to me," said I, "for I went there to-day for the first time."

"Have you seen the king?" said Sir Joseph Cornelis.

"My dear, you should not ask such questions," said his mother.

"Why not?"

"Because the gentleman may not wish to answer them."

"On the contrary, madam, I like being questioned. I have been teaching your son for the last six years to be always asking something, for that is the way to acquire knowledge. He who asks nothing knows nothing."

I had touched her to the quick, and she fell into a sulky silence.

"You have not told me yet," said the lad, "whether you saw the king."

"Yes, my man, I saw the king and the queen, and both their majesties did me the honour to speak to me."

"Who introduced you?"

"The French ambassador."

"I think you will agree with me," said the mother, "that last question was a little too much."

"Certainly it would be if it were addressed to a stranger, but not to me who am his friend. You will notice that the reply he extracted from me did me honour. If I had not wished it to be known that I had been at Court, I should not have come here in this dress."

"Very good; but as you like to be questioned, may I ask you why you were not presented by your own ambassador?"

"Because the Venetian ambassador would not present

me, knowing that his Government have a bone to pick with me."

By this time we had come to the dessert, and poor Sophie had not uttered a syllable.

"Say something to M. de Seingalt," said her mother.

"I don't know what to say," she answered. "Tell M. de Seingalt to ask me some questions, and I will answer to the best of my ability."

"Well, Sophie, tell me in what studies you are engaged at the present time."

"I am learning drawing; if you like I will shew you some of my work."

"I will look at it with pleasure; but tell me how you think you have offended me; you have a guilty air."

"I, sir? I do not think I have done anything amiss."

"Nor do I, my dear; but as you do not look at me when you speak I thought you must be ashamed of something. Are you ashamed of your fine eyes? You blush. What have you done?"

"You are embarrassing her," said the mother. "Tell him, my dear, that you have done nothing, but that a feeling of modesty and respect prevents you from gazing at the persons you address."

"Yes," said I; "but if modesty bids young ladies lower their eyes, politeness should make them raise them now and again."

No one replied to this objection, which was a sharp cut for the absurd woman; but after an interval of silence we rose from the table, and Sophie went to fetch her drawings.

"I won't look at anything, Sophie, unless you will look at me."

"Come," said her mother, "look at the gentleman."

She obeyed as quickly as lightning, and I saw the prettiest eyes imaginable.

"Now," said I, "I know you again, and perhaps you may remember having seen me."

"Yes, although it is six years ago since we met, I recognized you directly."

"And yet you did not look me in the face! If you knew how impolite it was to lower your eyes when you are addressing anyone, you would not do it. Who can have given you such a bad lesson?"

The child glanced towards her mother, who was standing by a window, and I saw who was her preceptress.

I felt that I had taken sufficient vengeance, and began to examine her drawings, to praise them in detail, and to congratulate her on her talents. I told her that she ought to be thankful to have a mother who had given her so good an education. This indirect compliment pleased Madame Cornelis, and Sophie, now free from all restraint, gazed at me with an expression of child-like affection which ravished me. Her features bore the imprint of a noble soul within, and I pitied her for having to grow up under the authority of a foolish mother. Sophie went to the piano, played with feeling, and then sang some Italian airs, to the accompaniment of the guitar, too well for her age. She was too precocious, and wanted much more discretion in her education than Madame Cornelis was able to give her.

When her singing had been applauded by the company, her mother told her to dance a minuet with her brother, who had learnt in Paris, but danced badly for want of a good carriage. His sister told him so with a kiss, and then asked me to dance with her, which I did very readily. Her mother, who thought she had danced exquisitely, as was indeed the case, told her that she must give me a kiss. She came up to me, and drawing her on my knee I covered her face with kisses, which she returned with the greatest affection. Her mother laughed with all her heart, and then Sophie, beginning to be doubtful again, went up to her and asked if she were angry. Her mother comforted her with a kiss.

After we had taken coffee, which was served in the French fashion, Madame Cornelis shewed me a magnificent hall which she had built, in which she could give supper to four hundred persons seated at one table. She told me, and I could easily believe her, that there was not such another in all London.

The last assembly was given before the prorogation of Parliament; it was to take place in four or five days. She had a score of pretty girls in her service, and a dozen footmen all in full livery.

"They all rob me," said she, "but I have to put up with it. What I want is a sharp man to help me and watch over my interests; if I had such an one I should make an immense fortune in a comparatively short time; for when it is a question of pleasure, the English do not care what they spend."

I told her I hoped she would find such man and make the fortune, and then I left her, admiring her enterprise.

When I left Soho Square I went to St. James's Park to see Lady Harrington for whom I bore a letter, as I have mentioned. This lady lived in the precincts of the Court, and received company every Sunday. It was allowable to play in her house, as the park is under the jurisdiction of the Crown. In any other place there is no playing cards or singing on Sundays. The town abounds in spies, and if they have reason to suppose that there is any gaming or music going on, they watch for their opportunity, slip into the house, and arrest all the bad Christians, who are diverting themselves in a manner which is thought innocent enough in any other country. But to make up for this severity the Englishman may go in perfect liberty to the tavern or the brothel, and sanctify the Sabbath as he pleases.

I called on Lady Harrington, and having sent up my letter she summoned me into her presence. I found her in the midst of about thirty persons, but the hostess was easily distinguished by the air of welcome she had for me.

After I had made my bow she told me she had seen me at Court in the morning, and that without knowing who I was she had been desirous of making my acquaintance. Our conversation lasted three-quarters of an hour, and was composed of those frivolous observations and idle questions which are commonly addressed to a traveller.

The lady was forty, but she was still handsome. She was well known for her gallantries and her influence at Court. She introduced me to her husband and her four daughters, charming girls of a marriageable age. She asked me why I had come to London when everybody was on the point of going out of town. I told her that as I always obeyed the impulse of the moment, I should find it difficult to answer her question; besides, I intended staying for a year, so that the pleasure would be deferred but not lost.

My reply seemed to please her by its character of English independence, and she offered with exquisite grace to do all in her power for me.

"In the meanwhile," said she, "we will begin by letting you see all the nobility at Madame Cornelis's on Thursday next. I can give you a ticket to admit to ball and supper. It is two guineas."

I gave her the money, and she took the ticket again, writing on it, "Paid.—Harrington."

"Is this formality necessary, my lady?"

"Yes; or else they would ask you for the money at the doors."

I did not think it necessary to say anything about my connection with the lady of Soho Square.

While Lady Harrington was making up a rubber at whist, she asked me if I had any other letters for ladies.

"Yes," said I, "I have one which I intend to present to-morrow. It is a singular letter, being merely a portrait."

"Have you got it about you?"

"Yes, my lady."

"May I see it?"

"Certainly. Here it is."

"It is the Duchess of Northumberland. We will go and give it her."

"With pleasure."

"Just wait till they have marked the game."

Lord Percy had given me this portrait as a letter of introduction to his mother.

"My dear duchess," said Lady Harrington, "here is a letter of introduction which this gentleman begs to present to you."

"I know, it is M. de Seingalt. My son has written to me about him. I am delighted to see you, Chevalier, and I hope you will come and see me. I receive thrice a week."

"Will your ladyship allow me to present my valuable letter in person?"

"Certainly. You are right."

I played a rubber of whist for very small stakes, and lost fifteen guineas, which I paid on the spot. Directly afterwards Lady Harrington took me apart, and gave me a lesson which I deem worthy of record.

"You paid in gold," said she; "I suppose you had no bank notes about you?"

"Yes, my lady, I have notes for fifty and a hundred pounds."

"Then you must change one of them or wait till another time to pay, for in England to pay in gold is a solecism only pardonable in a stranger. Perhaps you noticed that the lady smiled?"

"Yes; who is she?"

"Lady Coventry, sister of the Duchess of Hamilton."

"Ought I to apologize?"

"Not at all, the offence is not one of those which require an apology. She must have been more surprised than offended, for she made fifteen shillings by your paying her in gold."

I was vexed by this small mischance, for Lady Coventry was an exquisitely beautiful brunette. I comforted myself, however, without much trouble.

The same day I made the acquaintance of Lord Hervey, the nobleman who conquered Havana, a pleasant an intelligent person. He had married Miss Chudleigh, but the marriage was annulled. This celebrated Miss Chudleigh was maid of honour to the Princess Dowager of Wales, and afterwards became Duchess of Kingston. As her history is well known I shall say something more of her in due course. I went home well enough pleased with my day's work.

The next day I began dining at home, and found my cook very satisfactory; for, besides the usual English dishes, he was acquainted with the French system of cooking, and did fricandeaus, cutlets, ragouts, and above all, the excellent French soup, which is one of the principal glories of France.

My table and my house were not enough for my happiness. I was alone, and the reader will understand by this that Nature had not meant me for a hermit. I had neither a mistress nor a friend, and at London one may invite a man to dinner at a tavern where he pays for himself, but not to one's own table. One day I was invited by a younger son of the Duke of Bedford to eat oysters and drink a bottle of champagne. I accepted the invitation, and he ordered the oysters and the champagne, but we drank two bottles, and he made me pay half the price of the second bottle. Such are manners on the other side of the Channel. People laughed in my face when I said that I did not care to dine at a tavern as I could not get any soup.

"Are you ill?" they said, "soup is only fit for invalids."

The Englishman is entirely carnivorous. He eats very little bread, and calls himself economical because he spares himself the expense of soup and dessert, which circumstance made me remark that an English dinner is like eternity: it has no beginning and no end. Soup is considered very extravagant, as the very servants refuse to eat the meat from which it has been made. They say it is only fit to give to dogs. The salt beef which they use is certainly excellent. I cannot say the same for their beer, which was so bitter that I could not drink it. However, I could not be expected to like beer after the excellent French wines with which the wine merchant supplied me, certainly at a very heavy cost.

I had been a week in my new home without seeing

Martinelli. He came on a Monday morning, and I asked him to dine with me. He told me that he had to go to the Museum, and my curiosity to see the famous collection which is such an honour to England made me accompany him. It was there that I made the acquaintance of Dr. Mati, of whom I shall speak in due course.

At dinner Martinelli made himself extremely pleasant. He had a profound knowledge of the English manners and customs which it behoved me to know if I wished to get on. I happened to speak of the impoliteness of which I had been guilty in paying a gaming debt in gold instead of paper, and on this text he preached me a sermon on the national prosperity, demonstrating that the preference given to paper shews the confidence which is felt in the Bank, which may or may not be misplaced, but which is certainly a source of wealth. This confidence might be destroyed by a too large issue of paper money, and if that ever took place by reason of a protracted or unfortunate war, bankruptcy would be inevitable, and no one could calculate the final results.

After a long discussion on politics, national manners, literature, in which subjects Martinelli shone, we went to Drury Lane Theatre, where I had a specimen of the rough insular manners. By some accident or other the company could not give the piece that had been announced, and the audience were in a tumult. Garrick, the celebrated actor who was buried twenty years later in Westminster Abbey, came forward and tried in vain to restore order. He was obliged to retire behind the curtain. Then the king, the queen, and all the fashionables left the theatre, and in less than an hour the theatre was gutted, till nothing but the bare walls were left.

After this destruction, which went on without any authority interposing, the mad populace rushed to the taverns to consume gin and beer. In a fortnight the theatre was refitted and the piece announced again, and when Garrick appeared before the curtain to implore the indulgence of the house, a voice from the pit shouted, "On your knees." A thousand voices took up the cry "On your knees," and the English Roscius was obliged to kneel down and beg forgiveness. Then came a thunder of applause, and everything was over. Such are the English, and above all, the Londoners. They hoot the king and the royal family when they appear in public, and the consequence is, that they are never seen, save on great occasions, when order is kept by hundreds of constables.

One day, as I was walking by myself, I saw Sir Augustus Hervey, whose acquaintance I had made, speaking to a gentleman, whom he left to come to me. I asked him whom he had been speaking to.

"That's the brother of Earl Ferrers," said he, "who was hanged a couple of months ago for murdering one of his people."

"And you speak to his brother?"

"Why shouldn't I?"

"Is he not dishonoured by the execution of his relative?"

"Dishonoured! Certainly not; even his brother was not dishonoured. He broke the law, but he paid for it with his life, and owed society nothing more. He's a man of honour, who played high and lost; that's all. I don't know that there is any penalty in the statute book which dishonours the culprit; that would be tyrannical, and we would not bear it. I may break any law I like, so long as I am willing to pay the penalty. It is only a dishonour when the criminal tries to escape punishment by base or cowardly actions."

"How do you mean?"

"To ask for the royal mercy, to beg forgiveness of the people, and the like."

"How about escaping from justice?"

"That is no dishonour, for to fly is an act of courage; it continues the defiance of the law, and if the law cannot exact obedience, so much the worse for it. It is an honour for you to have escaped from the tyranny of your magistrates; your flight from The Leads was a virtuous action. In such cases man fights with death and flees from it. *Vir fugiens denuo pugnabit.*"

"What do you think of highway robbers, then?"

"I detest them as wretches dangerous to society, but I pity them when I reflect that they are always riding towards the gallows. You go out in a coach to pay a visit to a friend three or four miles out of London. A determined and agile-looking fellow springs upon you with his pistol in his hand, and says, 'Your money or your life.' What would you do in such a case?"

"If I had a pistol handy I would blow out his brains, and if not I would give him my purse and call him a scoundrelly assassin."

"You would be wrong in both cases. If you killed him, you would be hanged, for you have no right to take the law into your own hands; and if you called him an assassin, he would tell you that he was no assassin as he attacked you openly and gave you a free choice. Nay, he is generous, for he might kill you and take your money as well. You might, indeed, tell him he has an evil trade, and he would tell you that you were right, and that he would try to avoid the gallows as long as possible. He would then thank you and advise you never to drive out of London without being accompanied by a mounted servant, as then no robber would dare to attack you. We English always carry two purses on our journeys; a small one for the robbers and a large one for ourselves."

What answer could I make to such arguments, based as they were on the national manners? England is a rich sea, but strewn with reefs, and those who voyage there would do well to take precautions. Sir Augustus Hervey's discourse gave me great pleasure.

Going from one topic to another, as is always the way with a desultory conversation, Sir Augustus deplored the fate of an unhappy Englishman who had absconded to France with seventy thousand pounds, and had been brought back to London, and was to be hanged.

"How could that be?" I asked.

"The Crown asked the Duc de Nivernois to extradite him, and Louis XV. granted the request to make England assent to some articles of the peace. It was an act unworthy of a king, for it violates the right of nations. It is true that the man is a wretch, but that has nothing to do with the principle of the thing."

"Of course they have got back the seventy thousand pounds?"

"Not a shilling of it."

"How was that?"

"Because no money was found on him. He has most likely left his little fortune to his wife, who can marry again as she is still young and pretty."

"I wonder the police have not been after her."

"Such a thing is never thought of. What could they do? It's not likely that she would confess that her husband left her the stolen money. The law says robbers shall be hanged, but it says nothing about what they have stolen, as they are supposed to have made away with it. Then if we had to take into account the thieves

who had kept their theft and thieves who had spent it,
we should have to make two sets of laws, and make all
manner of allowances; the end of it would be inextricable confusion. It seems to us Englishmen that it
would not be just to ordain two punishments for theft.
The robber becomes the owner of what he has stolen;
true, he got it by violence, but it is none the less his, for
he can do what he likes with it. That being the case,
everyone should be careful to keep what he has, since
he knows that once stolen he will never see it again. I
have taken Havana from Spain: this was robbery on a
large scale."

He talked at once like a philosopher and a faithful
subject of his king.

Engaged in this discussion we walked towards the
Duchess of Northumberland's, where I made the acquaintance of Lady Rochefort, whose husband had just
been appointed Spanish ambassador. This lady's gallantries were innumerable, and furnished a fresh topic
of conversation every day.

The day before the assembly at Soho Square Martinelli dined with me, and told me that Madame Cornelis was heavily in debt, and dared not go out except on
Sundays, when debtors are privileged.

"The enormous and unnecessary expense which she
puts herself to," said he, "will soon bring her to ruin.
She owes four times the amount of her assets, even counting in the house, which is a doubtful item, as it is the
subject of litigation."

This news only distressed me for her children's sake,
for I thought that she herself well deserved such a fate.

CHAPTER VIII

The Assembly—Adventure at Ranelagh—The English
Courtezans—Pauline

I WENT in due time to the assembly, and the secretary at the door wrote down my name as I handed
in my ticket. When Madame Cornelis saw me she said
she was delighted I had come in by ticket, and that she
had had some doubts as to whether I would come.

"You might have spared yourself the trouble of doubt-
ing," said I, "for after hearing that I had been to Court
you might have guessed that a matter of two guineas
would not have kept me away. I am sorry for our old
friendship's sake that I did not pay the money to you;
for you might have known that I would not condescend
to be present in the modest manner you indicated."

This address, delivered with an ironical accent, embarrassed Madame Cornelis, but Lady Harrington, a
great supporter of hers, came to her rescue.

"I have a number of guineas to hand over to you, my
dear Cornelis, and amongst others two from M. de Seingalt, who, I fancy, is an old friend of yours. Nevertheless, I did not dare to tell him so," she added, with a
sly glance in my direction.

"Why not, my lady? I have known Madame Cornelis for many years."

"I should think you have," she answered, laughing,
"and I congratulate you both. I suppose you know the
delightful Miss Sophie too, Chevalier?"

"Certainly, my lady, whoso knows the mother knows the daughter."

"Quite so, quite so."

Sophie was standing by, and after kissing her fondly Lady Harrington said,——

"If you love yourself, you ought to love her, for she is the image of you."

"Yes, it is a freak of nature."

"I think there is something more than a freak in this instance."

With these words the lady took Sophie's hand, and leaning on my arm she led us through the crowd, and I had to bear in silence the remarks of everyone.

"There is Madame Cornelis's husband."

"That must be M. Cornelis."

"Oh! there can be no doubt about it."

"No, no," said Lady Harrington, "you are all quite wrong."

I got tired of these remarks, which were all founded on the remarkable likeness between myself and Sophie. I wanted Lady Harrington to let the child go, but she was too much amused to do so.

"Stay by me," she said, "if you want to know the names of the guests." She sat down, making me sit on one side and Sophie on the other.

Madame Cornelis then made her appearance, and everyone asked her the same questions, and made the same remarks about me. She said bravely that I was her best and her oldest friend, and that the likeness between me and her daughter might possibly be capable of explanation. Everyone laughed and said it was very natural that it should be so. To change the subject, Madame Cornelis remarked that Sophie had learnt the minuet and danced it admirably.

"Then fetch a violin player," said Lady Harrington, "that we may have the pleasure of witnessing the young artist's performance."

The ball had not yet begun, and as soon as the violinist appeared, I stepped forward and danced with Sophie, to the delight of the select circle of spectators.

The ball lasted all night without ceasing, as the company ate by relays, and at all times and hours; the waste and prodigality were worthy of a prince's palace. I made the acquaintance of all the nobility and the Royal Family, for they were all there, with the exception of the king and queen, and the Prince of Wales. Madame Cornelis must have received more than twelve hundred guineas, but the outlay was enormous, without any control or safeguard against the thefts, which must have been perpetrated on all sides. She tried to introduce her son to everybody, but the poor lad looked like a victim, and did nothing but make profound bows. I pitied him from my heart.

As soon as I got home I went to bed and spent the whole of the next day there. The day after I went to the "Staven Tavern," as I had been told that the prettiest girls in London resorted to it. Lord Pembroke gave me this piece of information; he went there very frequently himself. When I got to the tavern I asked for a private room, and the landlord, perceiving that I did not know English, accosted me in French, and came to keep me company. I was astonished at his grave and reverend manner of speaking, and did not like to tell him that I wanted to dine with a pretty English-woman. At last, however, I summoned up courage to say, with a great deal of circumlocution, that I did not know whether Lord Pembroke had deceived me in informing me that I should find the prettiest girls in London at his house.

"No, sir," said he, "my lord has not deceived you, and you can have as many as you like."

"That's what I came for."

He called out some name, and a tidy-looking lad making his appearance, he told him to get me a wench just as though he were ordering a bottle of champagne. The lad went out, and presently a girl of herculean proportions entered.

"Sir," said I, "I don't like the looks of this girl."

"Give her a shilling and send her away. We don't trouble ourselves about ceremonies in London."

This put me at my ease, so I paid my shilling and called for a prettier wench. The second was worse than the first, and I sent her away, and ten others after her, while I could see that my fastidiousness amused the landlord immensely.

"I'll see no more girls," said I at last, "let me have a good dinner. I think the procurer must have been making game of me for the sake of the shillings."

"It's very likely; indeed it often happens so when a gentleman does not give the name and address of the wench he wants."

In the evening as I was walking in St. James's Park, I remembered it was a Ranelagh evening, and wishing to see the place I took a coach and drove there, intending to amuse myself till midnight, and to find a beauty to my taste.

I was pleased with the rotunda. I had some tea, I danced some minuets, but I made no acquaintances; and although I saw several pretty women, I did not dare to attack any of them. I got tired, and as it was near midnight I went out thinking to find my coach, for which I had not paid, still there, but it was gone, and I did not know what to do. An extremely pretty woman who was waiting for her carriage in the doorway, noticed my distress, and said that if I lived anywhere near Whitehall, she could take me home. I thanked her gratefully, and told her where I lived. Her carriage came up, her man opened the door, and she stepped in on my arm, telling me to sit beside her, and to stop the carriage when it got to my house.

As soon as we were in the carriage, I burst out into expressions of gratitude; and after telling her my name I expressed my regret at not having seen her at Soho Square.

"I was not in London," she replied, "I returned from Bath to-day."

I apostrophised my happiness in having met her. I covered her hands with kisses, and dared to kiss her on the cheek; and finding that she smiled graciously, I fastened my lips on hers, and before long had given her an unequivocal mark of the ardour with which she had inspired me.

She took my attentions so easily that I flattered myself I had not displeased her, and I begged her to tell me where I could call on her and pay my court while I remained in London, but she replied,——

"We shall see each other again; we must be careful."

I swore secrecy, and urged her no more. Directly after the carriage stopped, I kissed her hand and was set down at my door, well pleased with the ride home.

For a fortnight I saw nothing of her, but I met her again in a house where Lady Harrington had told me to present myself, giving her name. It was Lady Betty German's, and I found her out, but was asked to sit down and wait as she would be in soon. I was pleasantly surprised to find my fair friend of Ranelagh in the room, reading a newspaper. I conceived the idea of asking her to introduce me to Lady Betty, so I went up to her and proffered my request, but she replied politely that she could not do so not having the honour to know my name.

"I have told you my name, madam. Do you not remember me?"

"I remember you perfectly, but a piece of folly is not a title of acquaintance."

I was dumbfounded at the extraordinary reply, while the lady calmly returned to her newspaper, and did not speak another word till the arrival of Lady Betty.

The fair philosopher talked for two hours without giving the least sign of knowing who I was, although she answered me with great politeness whenever I ventured to address her. She turned out to be a lady of high birth and of great reputation.

Happening to call on Martinelli, I asked him who was the pretty girl who was kissing her hands to me from the house opposite. I was pleasantly surprised to hear that she was a dancer named Binetti. Four years ago she had done me a great service at Stuttgart, but I did not know she was in London. I took leave of Martinelli to go and see her, and did so all the more eagerly when I heard that she had parted from her husband, though they were obliged to dance together at the Haymarket.

She received me with open arms, telling me that she had recognized me directly.

"I am surprised, my dear elder," said she, "to see you in London."

She called me "elder" because I was the oldest of her friends.

"Nor did I know that you were here. I came to town

after the close of the opera. How is it that you are not living with your husband?"

"Because he games, loses, and despoils me of all I possess. Besides, a woman of my condition, if she be married, cannot hope that a rich lover will come and see her, while if she be alone she can receive visits without any constraint."

"I shouldn't have thought they would be afraid of Binetti; he used to be far from jealous."

"Nor is he jealous now; but you must know that there is an English law which allows the husband to arrest his wife and her lover if he finds them *in flagrante delicto*. He only wants two witnesses, and it is enough that they are sitting together on a bed. The lover is forced to pay to the husband the half of all he possesses. Several rich Englishmen have been caught in this way, and now they are very shy of visiting married women, especially Italians."

"So you have much to be thankful for. You enjoy perfect liberty, can receive any visitors you like, and are in a fair way to make a fortune."

"Alas! my dear friend, you do not know all. When he has information from his spies that I have had a visitor, he comes to me in a sedan-chair at night, and threatens to turn me out into the street if I do not give him all the money I have. He is a terrible rascal!"

I left the poor woman, after giving her my address, and telling her to come and dine with me whenever she liked. She had given me a lesson on the subject of visiting ladies. England has very good laws, but most of them are capable of abuse. The oath which jurymen have to take to execute them to the letter has caused several to be interpreted in a manner absolutely contrary to the intention of the legislators, thus placing the judges in a difficult predicament. Thus new laws have constantly to be made, and new glosses to explain the old ones.

My Lord Pembroke, seeing me at my window, came in, and after examining my house, including the kitchen, where the cook was at work, told me that there was not a nobleman in town who had such a well-furnished and comfortable house. He made a calculation, and told me that if I wanted to entertain my friends I should require three hundred pounds a month. "You can't live here," said he, "without a pretty girl, and those who know that you keep bachelor's hall are of opinion that you are very wise, and will save a great deal of useless expense."

"Do you keep a girl, my lord?"

"No, for I am unfortunate enough to be disgusted with a woman after I have had her for a day."

"Then you require a fresh one every day?"

"Yes, and without being as comfortable as you I spend four times as much. You must know that I live in London like a stranger. I never dine at my own house. I wonder at your dining alone."

"I can't speak English. I like soup and good wine, and that is enough to keep me from your taverns."

"I expect so, with your French tastes."

"You will confess that they are not bad tastes."

"You are right, for, good Englishman as I am, I get on very well in Paris."

He burst out laughing when I told him how I had dispatched a score of wenches at the "Staven Tavern," and that my disappointment was due to him.

"I did not tell you what names to send for, and I was wrong."

"Yes, you ought to have told me."

"But even if I did they wouldn't have come, for they are not at the orders of the procuress. If you will promise to pay them as I do, I will give you some tickets which will make them come."

"Can I have them here?"

"Just as you like."

"That will be most convenient for me. Write out the tickets and let them know French if you can."

"That's the difficulty; the prettiest only speak English."

"Never mind, we shall understand each other well enough for the purpose I dare say."

He wrote several tickets for four and six guineas each; but one was marked twelve guineas.

"She is doubly pretty, is she?" said I.

"Not exactly, but she has cuckolded a duke of Great Britain who keeps her, and only uses her once or twice a month."

"Would you do me the honour of testing the skill of my cook?"

"Certainly, but I can't make an appointment."

"And supposing I am out."

"I'll go to the tavern."

Having nothing better to do I sent Jarbe to one of the four-guinea wenches, telling him to advise her that she would dine with me. She came. She did not attract me sufficiently to make me attempt more than some slight toying. She went away well pleased with her four guineas, which she had done nothing to earn. Another wench, also at four guineas, supped with me the following evening. She had been very pretty, and, indeed, was so still, but she was too melancholy and quiet for my taste, and I could not make up my mind to tell her to undress.

The third day, not feeling inclined to try another ticket, I went to Covent Garden, and on meeting an attractive young person I accosted her in French, and asked her if she would sup with me.

"How much will you give me at dessert?"

"Three guineas."

"Come along."

After the play I ordered a good supper for two, and she displayed an appetite after mine own heart. When we had supped I asked for her name and address, and I was astonished to find that she was one of the girls whom Lord Pembroke had assessed at six guineas. I concluded that it was best to do one's own business, or, at any rate, not to employ noblemen as agents. As to the other tickets, they procured me but little pleasure. The twelve-guinea one, which I had reserved for the last, as a choice morsel, pleased me the least of all, and I did not care to cuckold the noble duke who kept her.

Lord Pembroke was young, handsome, rich, and full of wit. I went to see him one day, and found him just getting out of bed. He said he would walk with me and told his valet to shave him.

"But," said I, "there's not a trace of beard on your face."

"There never is," said he, "I get myself shaved three times a day."

"Three times?"

"Yes, when I change my shirt I wash my hands; when I wash my hands I have to wash my face, and the proper way to wash a man's face is with a razor."

"When do you make these three ablutions?"

"When I get up, when I dress for dinner, and when I go to bed, for I should not like the woman who is sleeping with me to feel my beard."

We had a short walk together, and then I left him as I had some writing to do. As we parted, he asked me if I dined at home. I replied in the affirmative, and foreseeing that he intended dining with me I warned my cook to serve us well, though I did not let him know that I expected a nobleman to dinner. Vanity has more than one string to its bow.

I had scarcely got home when Madame Binetti came in, and said that if she were not in the way, she would be glad to dine with me. I gave her a warm welcome, and she said I was really doing her a great service, as her husband would suffer the torments of hell in trying to find out with whom she had dined.

This woman still pleased me; and though she was thirty-five, nobody would have taken her for more than twenty-five. Her appearance was in every way pleasing. Her lips were of the hue of the rose, disclosing two exquisite rows of teeth. A fine complexion, splendid eyes, and a forehead where Innocence might have been well enthroned, all this made an exquisite picture. If you add to this, that her breast was of the rarest proportions, you will understand that more fastidious tastes than mine would have been satisfied with her.

She had not been in my house for half an hour when Lord Pembroke came in. They both uttered an exclamation, and the nobleman told me that he had been in love with her for the last six months; that he had written ardent letters to her of which she had taken no notice. "I never would have anything to do with him," said she, "because he is the greatest profligate in all England; and it's a pity," she added, "because he is a kind-hearted nobleman."

This explanation was followed by a score of kisses, and I saw that they were agreed.

We had a choice dinner in the French style, and Lord Pembroke swore he had not eaten so good a dinner for the last year.

"I am sorry for you," he said, "when I think of you being alone every day."

Madame Binetti was as much a *gourmet* as the Englishman, and when we rose from table we felt inclined to pass from the worship of Comus to that of Venus; but the lady was too experienced to give the Englishman anything more than a few trifling kisses.

I busied myself in turning over the leaves of some books I had bought the day before, and left them to talk together to their heart's content; but to prevent their asking me to give them another dinner I said that I hoped chance would bring about such another meeting on another occasion.

At six o'clock, after my guests had left me, I dressed and went to Vauxhaull, where I met a French officer named Malingan, to whom I had given some money at Aix-la-Chapelle. He said he would like to speak to me, so I gave him my name and address. I also met a well-known character, the Chevalier Goudar, who talked to me about gaming and women. Malingan introduced me to an individual who he said might be very useful to me in London. He was a man of forty, and styled himself son of the late Theodore, the pretender to the throne of Corsica, who had died miserably in London fourteen years before, after having been imprisoned for debt for seven years. I should have done better if I had never gone to Vauxhall that evening.

The entrance-fee at Vauxhall was half the sum charged at Ranelagh, but in spite of that the amusements were of the most varied kinds. There was good fare, music, walks in solitary alleys, thousands of lamps, and a crowd of London beauties, both high and low.

In the midst of all these pleasures I was dull, because I had no girl to share my abode or my good table, and make it dear to me. I had been in London for six weeks; and in no other place had I been alone for so long.

My house seemed intended for keeping a mistress with all decency, and as I had the virtue of constancy a mistress was all I wanted to make me happy. But how was I to find a woman who should be the equal of those women I had loved before? I had already seen half a hundred of girls, whom the town pronounced to be pretty, and who did not strike me as even passable. I thought the matter over continually, and at last an odd idea struck me.

I called the old housekeeper, and told her by the servant, who acted as my interpreter, that I wanted to let the second or third floor for the sake of company; and although I was at perfect liberty to do what I liked with the house, I would give her half-a-guinea a week extra. Forthwith I ordered her to affix the following bill to the window:

Second or third floor to be let, furnished, to a young lady speaking English and French, who receives no visitors, either by day or night.

The old Englishwoman, who had seen something of the world, began to laugh so violently when the document was translated to her that I thought she would have choked.

"What are you laughing at, my worthy woman?"

"Because this notice is a laughing matter."

"I suppose you think I shall have no applications?"

"Not at all, the doorstep will be crowded from morn to night, but I shall leave it all to Fanny. Only tell me how much to ask."

"I will arrange about the rent in my interview with the young lady. I don't think I shall have so many enquiries, for the young lady is to speak French and English, and also to be respectable. She must not receive any visits, not even from her father and mother, if she has them."

"But there will be a mob in front of the house reading the notice."

"All the better. Nothing is the worse for being a little odd."

It happened just as the old woman had foretold; as soon as the notice was up, everybody stopped to read it, made various comments, and passed on. On the second day after it was up, my Negro told me that my notice was printed in full in the *St. James's Chronicle,* with some amusing remarks. I had the paper brought up to me, and Fanny translated it. It ran as follows:

"The landlord of the second and third floors probably occupies the first floor himself. He must be a man of the world and of good taste, for he wants a young and pretty lodger; and as he forbids her to receive visits, he will have to keep her company himself."

He added,——

"The landlord should take care lest he become his own dupe, for it is very likely that the pretty lodger would only take the room to sleep in, and possibly only to sleep in now and then; and if she chose she would have a perfect right to refuse to receive the proprietor's visits."

These sensible remarks delighted me, for after reading them I felt forewarned.

Such matters as these give their chief interest to the

English newspapers. They are allowed to gossip about everything, and the writers have the knack of making the merest trifles seem amusing. Happy is the nation where anything may be written and anything said!

Lord Pembroke was the first to come and congratulate me on my idea, and he was succeeded by Martinelli; but he expressed some fears as to the possible consequences, "for," said he, "there are plenty of women in London who would come and lodge with you to be your ruin."

"In that case," I answered, "it would be a case of Greek meeting Greek; however, we shall see. If I am taken in, people will have the fullest right to laugh at me, for I have been warned."

I will not trouble my readers with an account of the hundred women who came in the first ten days, when I refused on one pretext or another, though some of them were not wanting in grace and beauty. But one day, when I was at dinner, I received a visit from a girl of from twenty to twenty-four years, simply but elegantly dressed; her features were sweet and gracious, though somewhat grave, her complexion pale, and her hair black. She gave me a bow which I had to rise to return, and as I remained standing she politely begged me not to put myself out, but to continue my dinner. I begged her to be seated and to take dessert, but she refused with an air of modesty which delighted me.

This fair lady said, not in French, but in Italian worthy of a Sinnese, its purity was so perfect, that she hoped I would let her have a room on the third floor, and that she would gladly submit to all my conditions.

"You may only make use of one room if you like, but all the floor will belong to you."

"Although the notice says the rooms will be let

cheaply, I shall not be able to afford more than one room. Two shillings a week is all I can spend."

"That's exactly what I want for the whole suite of rooms; so you see you can use them all. My maid will wait on you, get you whatever food you may require, and wash your linen as well. You can also employ her to do your commissions, so that you need not go out for trifles."

"Then I will dismiss my maid," she said; "she robs me of little, it is true, but still too much for my small means. I will tell your maid what food to buy for me every day, and she shall have six sols a week for her pains."

"That will be ample. I should advise you to apply to my cook's wife, who will get your dinner and supper for you as cheaply as you could buy it."

"I hardly think so, for I am ashamed to tell you how little I spend."

"Even if you only spend two sols a day, she will give you two sols' worth. All the same I advise you to be content with what you get from the kitchen, without troubling about the price, for I usually have provision made for four, though I dine alone, and the rest is the cook's perquisite. I merely advise you to the best of my ability, and I hope you will not be offended at my interest in your welfare."

"Really, sir, you are too generous."

"Wait a moment, and you will see how everything will be settled comfortably."

I told Clairmont to order up the maid and the cook's wife, and I said to the latter:

"For how much could you provide dinner and supper for this young lady who is not rich, and only wants to eat to live?"

"I can do it very cheaply; for you usually eat alone,
and have enough for four."

"Very good; then I hope you will treat her very well
for the sum she gives you."

"I can only afford five sols a day."

"That will do nicely."

I gave orders that the bill should be taken down directly, and that the young lady's room should be made
comfortable. When the maid and the cook's wife had
left the room, the young lady told me that she should
only go out on Sundays to hear mass at the Bavarian
ambassador's chapel, and once a month to a person who
gave her three guineas to support her.

"You can go out when you like," said I, "and without
rendering an account to anybody of your movements."

She begged me not to introduce anyone to her, and to
tell the porter to deny her to anyone who might come to
the door to make enquiries. I promised that her wishes
should be respected, and she went away saying that
she was going for her trunk.

I immediately ordered my household to treat her with
the utmost respect. The old housekeeper told me that
she had paid the first week in advance, taking a receipt,
and had gone, as she had come, in a sedan-chair. Then
the worthy old woman made free to tell me to be on my
guard.

"Against what? If I fall in love with her, so much
the better; that is just what I want. What name did
she give you?"

"Mistress Pauline. She was quite pale when she came,
and she went away covered with blushes."

I was delighted to hear it. I did not want a woman
merely to satisfy my natural desires, for such can be
found easily enough; I wished for some one whom I

could love. I expected beauty, both of the body and the soul; and my love increased with the difficulties and obstacles I saw before me. As to failure, I confess I did not give it a moment's thought, for there is not a woman in the world who can resist constant and loving attentions, especially when her lover is ready to make great sacrifices.

When I got back from the theatre in the evening the maid told me that the lady had chosen a modest closet at the back, which was only suitable for a servant. She had had a moderate supper, only drinking water, and had begged the cook's wife only to send her up soup and one dish, to which the woman had replied that she must take what was served, and what she did not eat would do for the servant.

"When she finished she shut herself up to write, and wished me good evening with much politeness."

"What is she going to take in the morning?"

"I asked her, and she said she would only take a little bread."

"Then you had better tell her that it is the custom of the house for the cook to serve everybody with coffee, chocolate, or tea, according to taste, in the morning, and that I shall be pained if she refuses to fare like the rest of us. But don't tell her I said so. Here's a crown for you, and you shall have one every week if you will wait upon and care for her properly."

Before going to bed I wrote her a polite note, begging her to leave the closet. She did so, but she went into another back room, and consented to take coffee for her breakfast. Wishing to make her dine and sup with me, I was dressing myself, and preparing to proffer my request in such a way as to make a refusal impossible, when young Cornelis was announced. I received him smilingly, and thanked him for the first visit he had paid me in the course of six weeks.

"Mamma hasn't allowed me to come. I have tried to do so a score of times without her leave. Read this letter, and you will find something which will surprise you."

I opened the letter and read as follows:

"Yesterday a bailiff waited for my door to be opened and slipped in and arrested me. I was obliged to go with him, and I am now in the sponging-house, and if I can't get bail by to-day he will take me to Kings Bench Prison. The bail I require is to the amount of two hundred pounds, to pay a bill which has fallen due. Dear friend, come and succour me or else my other creditors will get wind of my imprisonment and I shall be ruined. You surely will not allow that to happen, if not for my sake at least for the sake of my innocent children. You cannot bail me yourself, but you can easily get a householder to do so. If you have the time come and call on me, and I will shew you that I could not help doing the bill, otherwise I could not have given my last ball, as the whole of my plate and china was pledged."

I felt angry with the impudent woman who had hitherto paid me so little attention, and I wrote that I could only pity her, and that I had no time to go and see her, and that I should be ashamed to ask anyone to bail her out.

When young Cornelis had gone away in a melancholy mood, I told Clairmont to ask Pauline if she would allow me to bid her a good day. She sent word that I was at liberty to do so, and on going upstairs to her room I found her sitting at a table on which were several books.

Some linen on a chest of drawers did not give me the idea that she was very poor.

"I am immensely obliged," said she, "for all your goodness to me."

"Say nothing of that, madam; it is I who have need of your goodness."

"What can I do to shew my gratitude?"

"Could you trouble yourself to take your meals with me? When I am alone I eat like an ogre, and my health suffers. If you do not feel inclined to grant me that favour, do not hesitate to refuse, and I assure you you shall fare just as well as if you had acceded to my request."

"I shall be delighted to dine and sup with you, sir, whenever you are alone and you like to send for me. Nevertheless, I am not sure that my society will amuse you."

"Very good, I am grateful to you, and I promise you you shall never repent of your kindness. I will do my best to amuse you, and I hope I shall succeed, for you have inspired me with the liveliest interest. We will dine at one to-day."

I did not sit down or look at her books, or even ask her if she had spent a good night. The only thing I noted was that she had looked pale and careworn when I came in, and when I went out her cheeks were the colour of the rose.

I went for a walk in the park, feeling quite taken with this charming woman, and resolved to make her love me, for I did not want to owe anything to gratitude. I felt curious to know where she came from, and suspected she was an Italian; but I determined to ask her no questions for fear of offending her.

When I got home Pauline came down of her own

free will, and I was delighted with this, which I took for a good omen. As we had half an hour before us, I asked her how she found her health.

"Nature," she replied, "has favoured me with such a good constitution that I have never had the least sickness in my life, except on the sea."

"You have made a voyage, then."

"I must have done so to come to England."

"You might be an Englishwoman."

"Yes, for the English language has been familiar to me from my childhood."

We were seated on a sofa, and on the table in front of us was a chess-board. Pauline toyed with the pawns, and I asked her if she could play chess.

"Yes, and pretty well too from what they tell me."

"Then we will have a game together; my blunders will amuse you."

We began, and in four moves I was checkmated. She laughed, and I admired her play. We began again, and I was checkmated in five moves. My agreeable guest laughed heartily, and while she laughed I became intoxicated with love, watching the play of her features, her exquisite teeth, and her happy expression. We began another game, Pauline played carelessly, and I placed her in a difficult position.

"I think you may conquer me," said she.

"What happiness for me!"

The servant came in to tell us that dinner was ready.

"Interruptions are often extremely inconvenient," said I, as I offered her my arm, feeling quite sure that she had not lost the significance of my last words, for women find a meaning for everything.

We were just sitting down to table when Clairmont announced my daughter and Madame Rancour.

"Tell them that I am at dinner, and that I shall not be disengaged till three o'clock."

Just as my man was leaving the room to carry back my answer, Sophie rushed in and knelt before me, choking with sobs.

This was too much for me, and raising her I took her on my knees, saying I knew what she had come for, and that for love of her I would do it.

Passing from grief to joy the dear child kissed me, calling me her father, and at last made me weep myself.

"Dine with us, dear Sophie," said I, "I shall be the more likely to do what you wish."

She ran from my arms to embrace Pauline, who was weeping out of sympathy, and we all dined happily together. Sophie begged me to give Madame Rancour some dinner.

"It shall be so if you please, but only for your sake, for that woman Rancour deserves that I should leave her standing at the door to punish her for her impertinence to me when I came to London."

The child amused us in an astonishing way all dinner-time, Pauline keeping her ears open and not saying a word, so surprised was she to hear a child of her age talk in a way that would have excited attention in a woman of twenty. Although perfectly respectful she condemned her mother's conduct, and said that she was unfortunate in being obliged to give her a blind obedience.

"I would wager that you don't love her much."

"I respect, but I cannot love her, for I am always afraid. I never see her without fearing her."

"Why do you weep, then, at her fate?"

"I pity her, and her family still more, and the expressions she used in sending me to you were very affecting."

"What were these expressions?"

" 'Go,' said she, 'kneel before him, for you and you alone can soften his heart.' "

"Then you knelt before me because your mother told you to do so."

"Yes, for if I had followed my own inclination I should have rushed to your arms."

"You answer well. But are you sure of persuading me?"

"No, for one can never be sure of anything; but I have good hopes of success, remembering what you told me at the Hague. My mother told me that I was only three then, but I know I was five. She it was who told me not to look at you when I spoke to you, but fortunately you made her remove her prohibition. Everybody says that you are my father, and at the Hague she told me so herself; but here she is always dinning it into my ears that I am the daughter of M. de Monpernis."

"But, Sophie dear, your mother does wrong in making you a bastard when you are the legitimate daughter of the dancer Pompeati, who killed himself at Vienna."

"Then I am not your daughter?"

"Clearly, for you cannot have two fathers, can you?"

"But how is it that I am your image?"

"It's a mere chance."

"You deprive me of a dream which has made me happy."

Pauline said nothing, but covered her with kisses, which Sophie returned effusively. She asked me if the lady was my wife, and on my replying in the affirmative she called Pauline her "dear mamma," which made "dear mamma" laugh merrily.

When the dessert was served I drew four fifty-pound

notes out of my pocket-book, and giving them to Sophie told her that she might hand them over to her mother if she liked, but that the present was for her and not for her mother.

"If you give her the money," I said, "she will be able to sleep to-night in the fine house where she gave me such a poor reception."

"It makes me unhappy to think of it, but you must forgive her."

"Yes, Sophie; but out of love for you."

"Write to her to the effect that it is to me you give the money, not to her; I dare not tell her so myself."

"I could not do that, my dear; it would be insulting her in her affliction. Do you understand that?"

"Yes, quite well."

"You may tell her that whenever she sends you to dine or sup with me, she will please me very much."

"But you can write that down without wounding her, can you not? Do so, I entreat you. Dear mamma," said she, addressing Pauline, "ask papa to do so, and then I will come and dine with you sometimes."

Pauline laughed with all her heart as she addressed me as *husband*, and begged me to write the desired epistle. The effect on the mother could only let her know how much I loved her daughter, and would consequently increase her love for her child. I gave in, saying that I could not refuse anything to the adorable woman who had honoured me with the name of husband. Sophie kissed us, and went away in a happy mood.

"It's a long time since I have laughed so much," said Pauline, "and I don't think I have ever had such an agreeable meal. That child is a perfect treasure. She is unhappy, poor little girl, but she would not be so if I were her mother."

I then told her of the true relationship between Sophie and myself, and the reasons I had for despising her mother.

"I wonder what she will say when Sophie tells her that she found you at table with your wife."

"She won't believe it, as she knows my horror for the sacrament of matrimony."

"How is that?"

"I hate it because it is the grave of love."

"Not always."

As she said this Pauline sighed, and lowering her eyes changed the conversation. She asked me how long I intended to stay in London and when I had replied, "Nine or ten months," I felt myself entitled to ask her the same question.

"I really can't say," she answered, "my return to my country depends on my getting a letter."

"May I ask you what country you come from?"

"I see I shall soon have no secrets from you, but let me have a little time. I have only made your acquaintance to-day, and in a manner which makes me have a very high opinion of you."

"I shall try my best to deserve the good opinions you have conceived of my character."

"You have shewn yourself to me in a thoroughly estimable light."

"Give me your esteem, I desire it earnestly, but don't say anything of respect, for that seems to shut out friendship; I aspire to yours, and I warn you that I shall do my best to gain it."

"I have no doubt you are very clever in that way, but you are generous too, and I hope you will spare me. If the friendship between us became too ardent, a parting would be dreadful, and we may be parted at any moment, indeed I ought to be looking forward to it."

Our dialogue was getting rather sentimental, and with that ease which is only acquired in the best society, Pauline turned it to other topics, and soon asked me to allow her to go upstairs. I would have gladly spent the whole day with her, for I have never met a woman whose manners were so distinguished and at the same time so pleasant.

When she left me I felt a sort of void, and went to see Madame Binetti, who asked me for news of Pembroke. She was in a rage with him.

"He is a detestable fellow," said she; "he would like to have a fresh wife every day! What do you think of such conduct?"

"I envy him his happiness."

"He enjoys it because all women are such fools. He caught me through meeting me at your house; he would never have done so otherwise. What are you laughing at?"

"Because if he has caught you, you have also caught him; you are therefore quits."

"You don't know what you are talking about."

I came home at eight o'clock, and as soon as Fanny had told Pauline that I had returned she came downstairs. I fancied she was trying to captivate me by her attentions, and as the prospect was quite agreeable to me I thought we should come to an understanding before very long.

Supper was brought in and we stayed at table till midnight, talking about trifles, but so pleasantly that the time passed away very quickly. When she left me she wished me good night, and said my conversation had made her forget her sorrows.

Pembroke came next morning to ask me to give him

breakfast, and congratulated me on the disappearance
of the bill from my window.

"I should very much like to see your boarder," said he.

"I daresay, my lord, but I can't gratify your curiosity
just now, for the lady likes to be alone, and only puts
up with my company because she can't help it."

He did not insist, and to turn the conversation I told
him that Madame Binetti was furious with him for his
inconstancy, which was a testimony to his merits. That
made him laugh, and without giving me any answer he
asked me if I dined at home that day.

"No, my lord, not to-day."

"I understand. Well, it's very natural; bring the affair to a happy conclusion."

"I will do my best."

Martinelli had found two or three parodies of my
notice in the *Advertiser,* and came and read them to me.
I was much amused with them; they were mostly in-
decent, for the liberty of the press is much abused in
London. As for Martinelli he was too discreet and
delicate a man to ask me about my new boarder. As
it was Sunday, I begged him to take me to mass at the
Bavarian ambassador's chapel; and here I must confess
that I was not moved by any feelings of devotion, but
by the hope of seeing Pauline. I had my trouble for
nothing, for, as I heard afterwards, she sat in a dark
corner where no one could see her. The chapel was full,
and Martinelli pointed out several lords and ladies who
were Catholics, and did not conceal their religion.

When I got home I received a note from Madame Cornelis, saying that as it was Sunday and she could go out
freely, she hoped I would let her come to dinner. I
shewed the letter to Pauline, not knowing whether she
would object to dining with her, and she said she would

be happy to do so, provided there were no men. I wrote in answer to Madame Cornelis that I should be glad to see her and her charming daughter at dinner. She came, and Sophie did not leave my side for a moment. Madame Cornelis, who was constrained in Pauline's presence, took me aside to express her gratitude and to communicate to me some chimerical schemes of hers which were soon to make her rich.

Sophie was the life and soul of the party, but as I happened to tell her mother that Pauline was a lady who was lodging in my house, she said,——

"Then she is not your wife?"

"No; such happiness is not for me. It was a joke of mine, and the lady amused herself at the expense of your credulity."

"Well, I should like to sleep with her."

"Really? When?"

"Whenever mamma will let me."

"We must first ascertain," said the mother, "what the lady thinks of the arrangement."

"She needn't fear a refusal," said Pauline, giving the child a kiss.

"Then you shall have her with pleasure, madam. I will get her governess to fetch her away to-morrow."

"At three o'clock," said I, "for she must dine with us."

Sophie, taking her mother's silence for consent, went up to her and kissed her, but these attentions were but coldly received. She unfortunately did not know how to inspire love.

After Madame Cornelis had gone, I asked Pauline if she would like to take a walk with Sophie and myself in the suburbs, where nobody would know her.

"In prudence," said she, "I cannot go out unless I am alone."

"Then shall we stay here?"

"We could not do better."

Pauline and Sophie sang Italian, French, and English duets, and the concert of their voices seemed to me ravishing. We supped gaily, and at midnight I escorted them to the third floor, telling Sophie that I would come and breakfast with her in the morning, but that I should expect to find her in bed. I wanted to see if her body was as beautiful as her face. I would gladly have asked Pauline to grant me the same favour, but I did not think things had advanced far enough for that. In the morning I found Pauline up and dressed.

When Sophie saw me she laughed and hid her head under the sheets, but as soon as she felt me near her she soon let me see her pretty little face, which I covered with kisses.

When she had got up we breakfasted together, and the time went by as pleasantly as possible till Madame Rancour came for her little charge, who went away with a sad heart. Thus I was left alone with my Pauline who began to inspire me with such ardent desires that I dreaded an explosion every moment. And yet I had not so much as kissed her hand.

When Sophie had gone I made her sit beside me, and taking her hand I kissed it rapturously, saying,——

"Are you married, Pauline?"

"Yes."

"Do you know what it is to be a mother?"

"No, but I can partly imagine what happiness it must be."

"Are you separated from your husband?"

"Yes, by circumstances and against our will. We were separated before we had cohabited together."

"Is he at London?"

"No, he is far away, but please don't say anything more about it."

"Only tell me whether my loss will be his gain."

"Yes, and I promise not to leave you till I have to leave England—that is, unless you dismiss me—and I shall leave this happy island to be happy with the husband of my choice."

"But I, dear Pauline, will be left unhappy, for I love you with all my heart, and am afraid to give you any proof of my love."

"Be generous and spare me, for I am not my own mistress, and have no right to give myself to you; and perhaps, if you were so ungenerous as to attack me, I should not have the strength to resist."

"I will obey, but I shall still languish. I cannot be unhappy unless I forfeit your favour."

"I have duties to perform, my dear friend, and I cannot neglect them without becoming contemptible in my own eyes and yours too."

"I should deem myself the most miserable of men if I despised a woman for making me happy."

"Well, I like you too well to think you capable of such conduct, but let us be moderate, for we may have to part to-morrow. You must confess that if we yielded to desire, this parting would be all the more bitter. If you are of another opinion, that only shews that your ideas of love and mine are different."

"Then tell me of what sort of love is that with which I am happy enough to have inspired you?"

"It is of such a kind that enjoyment would only increase it, and yet enjoyment seems to me a mere accident."

"Then what is its essence?"

"To live together in perfect unity."

"That's a blessing we can enjoy from morning to eve, but why should we not add the harmless accident which would take so short a time, and give us such peace and tranquillity. You must confess, Pauline, that the essence cannot exist long without the accident."

"Yes, but you in your turn, you will agree that the food often proves in time to be deadly."

"No, not when one loves truly, as I do. Do you think that you will not love me so well after having possessed me?"

"No, it's because I think quite otherwise, that I dread to make the moment of parting so bitter."

"I see I must yield to your logic. I should like to see the food on which you feed your brain, otherwise your books. Will you let me come upstairs?"

"Certainly, but you will be caught."

"How?"

"Come and see."

We went to her room, and I found that all her books were Portuguese, with the exception of Milton, in English, Ariosto, in Italian, and Labruyère's "Characters," in French.

"Your selection gives me a high idea of your mental qualities," said I, "but tell me, why do you give such a preference to Camoens and all these Portuguese authors?"

"For a very good reason, I am Portuguese myself."

"You Portuguese? I thought you were Italian. And so you already know five languages, for you doubtless know Spanish."

"Yes, although Spanish is not absolutely necessary."

"What an education you have had!"

"I am twenty-two now, but I knew all these languages at eighteen."

"Tell me who you are, tell me all about yourself. I am worthy of your confidence."

"I think so too, and to give you a proof of my trust in you I am going to tell you my history, for since you love me you can only wish to do me good."

"What are all these manuscripts?"

"My history, which I have written down myself. Let us sit down."

CHAPTER IX

Pauline's Story—I Am Happy—Pauline Leaves Me

I AM the only daughter of the unfortunate Count X——o, whom Carvailho Oeiras killed in prison on suspicion of being concerned in the attempt on the king's life, in which the Jesuits were supposed to have had a hand. I do not know whether my father was innocent or guilty, but I do know that the tyrannical minister did not dare to have him tried, or to confiscate the estates, which remain in my possession, though I can only enjoy them by returning to my native land.

"My mother had me brought up in a convent where her sister was abbess. I had all kinds of masters, especially an Italian from Leghorn, who in six years taught me all that he thought proper for me to know. He would answer any questions I chose to put him, save on religious matters, but I must confess that his reserve made me all the fonder of him, for in leaving me to reflect on certain subjects by myself he did a great deal to form my judgment.

"I was eighteen when my grandfather removed me from the convent, although I protested that I would gladly stay there till I got married. I was fondly attached to my aunt, who did all in her power after my mother's death to make me forget the double loss I had sustained. My leaving the convent altered the whole course of my existence, and as it was not a voluntary action I have nothing to repent of.

239

"My grandfather placed me with his sister-in-law, the Marchioness X——o, who gave me up half her house. I had a governess, a companion, maids, pages, and foot-men, all of whom, though in my service, were under the orders of my governess, a well-born lady, who was happily honest and trustworthy.

"A year after I had left the convent my grandfather came and told me in the presence of my governess that Count Fl—— had asked my hand for his son, who was coming from Madrid and would arrive that day.

" 'What answer did you give him, dear grandfather?'

" 'That the marriage would be acceptable to the whole of the nobility, and also to the king and royal family.'

" 'But are you quite sure that the young count will like me and that I shall like the count?'

" 'That, my dear daughter, is a matter of course, and there need be no discussion on the subject.'

" 'But it is a question in which I am strongly in-terested, and I should like to consider it very carefully. We shall see how matters arrange themselves.'

" 'You can see each other before deciding, but you must decide all the same.'

" 'I hope so, but let us not be too certain. We shall see.'

"As soon as my grandfather had gone I told my gov-erness that I had made up my mind never to give my hand save where I had given my heart, and that I should only marry a man whose character and tastes I had carefully studied. My governess gave me no answer, and on my pressing her to give me her opinion, she replied that she thought her best course would be to keep silence on such a delicate question. This was as much as to tell me that she thought I was right; at least I persuaded myself that it was so.

"The next day I went to the convent, and told the story to my aunt, the abbess, who listened to me kindly and said it was to be hoped that I should fall in love with him and he with me, but that even if it were otherwise she was of opinion that the marriage would take place, as she had reasons for believing that the scheme came from the Princess of Brazil, who favoured Count Fl——.

"Though this information grieved me, I was still glad to hear it, and my resolution never to marry save for love was all the more strongly confirmed.

"In the course of a fortnight the count arrived, and my grandfather presented him to me, several ladies being in the company. Nothing was said about marrying, but there was a deal of talk about the strange lands and peoples the new arrival had seen. I listened with the greatest attention, not opening my mouth the whole time. I had very little knowledge of the world, so I could not make any comparisons between my suitor and other men, but my conclusion was that he could never hope to please any woman, and that he would certainly never be mine. He had an unpleasant sneering manner, joked in bad taste, was stupid, and a devotee, or rather a fanatic. Furthermore he was ugly and ill-shapen, and so great a fop that he was not ashamed to relate the story of his conquests in France and Italy.

"I went home hoping with all my heart that he had taken a dislike to me, and a week which passed away without my hearing anything on the subject confirmed me in this belief, but I was doomed to be disappointed. My great-aunt asked me to dinner, and when I went I found the foolish young man and his father present, together with my grandfather, who formally introduced him to me as my future husband, and begged me to fix the wedding day. I made up my mind that I would rather die than marry him, and answered politely but coldly that I would name the day when I had decided on marrying, but I should require time to think it over. The dinner went off silently, and I only opened my mouth to utter monosyllables in reply to questions which I could not avoid. After the coffee had been served I left the house, taking no notice of anyone besides my aunt and my grandfather.

"Some time elapsed, and I again began to hope that I had effectually disgusted my suitor, but one morning my governess told me that Father Freire was waiting to speak to me in the ante-chamber. I ordered him to be sent in. He was the confessor of the Princess of Brazil, and after some desultory conversation he said the princess had sent him to congratulate me on my approaching marriage with Count Fl——.

"I did not evince any surprise, merely replying that I was sensible of her highness's kindness, but that nothing had been decided so far, as I was not thinking of getting married.

"The priest, who was a perfect courtier, smiled in a manner, half kindly, half sardonic, and said that I was at that happy age when I had no need to think of anything, as my kind friends and relations did all my thinking for me.

"I only answered by an incredulous smile, which, for all his monastic subtlety, struck him as the expression of a young girl's coyness.

"Foreseeing the persecution to which I should be subjected, I went the next day to my aunt the abbess, who could not refuse me her advice. I began by stating my firm resolve to die rather than wed a being I detested.

"The worthy nun replied that the count had been introduced to her, and that to tell the truth she thought him insufferable; all the same, she said she was afraid I should be made to marry him.

"These words were such a shock to me that I turned the conversation, and spoke of other subjects for the remainder of my visit. But when I got back to my house I pursued an extraordinary course. I shut myself up in my closet and wrote a letter to the executioner of my unhappy father, the pitiless Oeiras, telling him the whole story, and imploring him to protect me and to speak to the king in my favour; 'for,' said I, 'as you have made me an orphan it is your duty before God to care for me.' I begged him to shelter me from the anger of the Princess of Brazil, and to leave me at liberty to dispose of my hand according to my pleasure.

"Though I did not imagine Oeiras to be a humane man, yet I thought he must have some sort of a heart; besides, by this extraordinary step and the firmness of my language, I hoped to appeal to his pride and to interest him in my favour. I felt sure that he would do me justice, if only to prove that he had not been unjust to my father. I was right, as will be seen, and although I was but an inexperienced girl my instinct served me well.

"Two days elapsed before I was waited on by a messenger from Oeiras, who begged the honour of a private interview with me. The messenger told me that the minister wished me to reply to all who pressed me to marry that I should not decide until I was assured that the princess desired the match. The minister begged me to excuse his not answering my letter, but he had good reasons for not doing so. The messenger assured me that I could count on his master's support.

"His message delivered, the gentleman took leave with

a profound bow, and went back without waiting for an answer. I must confess that the young man's looks had made a great impression on me. I cannot describe my feelings, but they have exerted great influence on my conduct, and will no doubt continue to do so for the rest of my life.

"This message put me quite at ease, for he would never have given me the instructions he did without being perfectly sure that the princess would not interfere any farther with my marriage; and so I gave myself up entirely to the new sentiments which possessed my heart. Though strong, the flame would no doubt soon have died down if it had not received fresh fuel every day, for when I saw the young messenger a week later in church I scarcely recognized him. From that moment, however, I met him everywhere; out walking, in the theatre, in the houses where I called, and especially when I was getting in or out of my carriage he was ever beside me, ready to offer his hand; and I got so used to his presence that when I missed his face I felt a void at my heart that made me unhappy.

"Almost every day I saw the two Counts Fl—— at my great-aunt's, but as there was no longer any engagement between us their presence neither joyed me nor grieved me. I had forgiven them but I was not happy. The image of the young messenger, of whom I knew nothing, was ever before me, and I blushed at my thoughts though I would not ask myself the reasons.

"Such was my state of mind, when one day I heard a voice, which was unknown to me, in my maid's room. I saw a quantity of lace on a table and proceeded to examine it without paying any attention to a girl who was standing near the table and curtsying to me. I did not like any of the lace, so the girl said that she would bring me some more to choose from the next day, and as I raised my eyes I was astonished to see that she had the face of the young man who was always in my thoughts. My only resource was to doubt their identity and to make myself believe that I had been deceived by a mere chance likeness. I was reassured on second thoughts; the girl seemed to me to be taller than the young man, whom I hesitated to believe capable of such a piece of daring. The girl gathered up her lace and went her way without raising her eyes to mine, and this made me feel suspicious again.

" 'Do you know that girl?' I said, coldly, to my maid, and she replied that she had never seen her before. I went away without another word, not knowing what to think.

"I thought it over and resolved to examine the girl when she came on the following day, and to unmask her if my suspicions proved to be well founded. I told myself that she might be the young man's sister, and that if it were otherwise it would be all the more easy to cure myself of my passion. A young girl who reasons on love falls into love, especially if she have no one in whom to confide.

"The pretended lace-seller duly came the next day with a box of lace. I told her to come into my room, and then speaking to her to force her to raise her eyes I saw before me the being who exerted such a powerful influence over me. It was such a shock that I had no strength to ask her any of the questions I had premeditated. Besides, my maid was in the room, and the fear of exposing myself operated, I think, almost as strongly as emotion. I set about choosing some pieces of lace in a mechanical way, and told my maid to go and fetch my purse. No sooner had she left the room than the lace-seller fell at my feet and exclaimed passionately,——

"'Give me life or death, madam, for I see you know who I am.'

"'Yes, I do know you, and I think you must have gone mad.'

"'Yes, that may be; but I am mad with love. I adore you.'

"'Rise, for my maid will come back directly.'

"'She is in my secret.'

"'What! you have dared——'

"He got up, and the maid came in and gave him his money with the utmost coolness. He picked up his lace, made me a profound bow, and departed.

"It would have been natural for me to speak to my maid, and still more natural if I had dismissed her on the spot. I had no courage to do so, and my weakness will only astonish those rigorous moralists who know nothing of a young girl's heart, and do not consider my painful position, passionately in love and with no one but myself to rely on.

"I did not follow at once the severe dictates of duty; afterwards it was too late, and I easily consoled myself with the thought that I could pretend not to be aware that the maid was in the secret. I determined to dissemble, hoping that I should never see the adventurous lover again, and that thus all would be as if it had never happened.

"This resolve was really the effect of anger, for a fortnight passed by without my seeing the young man in the theatre, the public walks, or in any of the public places he used to frequent, and I became sad and dreamy, feeling all the time ashamed of my own wanton fancies. I longed to know his name, which I could only learn from my maid, and it was out of the question for me to ask Oeiras. I hated my maid, and I blushed when I saw her, imagining that she knew all. I was afraid that she would suspect my honour, and at another time I feared lest she might think I did not love him; and this thought nearly drove me mad. As for the young adventurer I thought him more to be pitied than to be blamed, for I did not believe that he knew I loved him, and it seemed to me that the idea of my despising him was enough vengeance for his audacity. But my thoughts were different when my vanity was stronger than love, for then despair avenged itself on pride, and I fancied he would think no more of me, and perhaps had already forgotten me.

"Such a state cannot last long, for if nothing comes to put an end to the storm which tosses the soul to and fro, it ends at last by making an effort of itself to sail into the calm waters of peace.

"One day I put on a lace kerchief I had bought from him, and asked my maid,——

" 'What has become of the girl who sold me this kerchief?'

"I asked this question without premeditation; it was, as it were, an inspiration from my good or my evil genius.

"As crafty as I was simple, the woman answered that to be sure he had not dared to come again, fearing that I had found out his disguise.

" 'Certainly,' I replied, 'I found it out directly, but I was astonished to hear that you knew this lace-seller was a young man.'

" 'I did not think I should offend you, madam, I know him well.'

" 'Who is he?'

" 'Count d'Al——; you ought to know him, for he paid you a visit about four months ago.'

" 'True, and it is possible that I did not know him, but why did you tell a lie when I asked you, "Do you know that girl?" '

" 'I lied to spare your feelings, madam, and I was afraid you would be angry at the part I had taken.'

" 'You would have honoured me more by supposing the contrary. When you went out, and I told him he was mad, and that you would find him on his knees when you returned, he told me you were in the secret.'

" 'If it be a secret, but it seems to me a mere joke.'

" 'I wished to think so too, but nevertheless it seemed of such weight to me, that I resolved to be silent that I might not be obliged to send you away.'

" 'My idea was that you would have been amused, but as you take it seriously I am sorry that I have failed in my strict duty.'

"So weak is a woman in love that in this explanation which should have shewn me the servant's fault in all its enormity I only saw a full justification. In fact she had given peace to my heart, but my mind was still uneasy. I knew that there was a young Count d'Al—— belonging to a noble family, but almost penniless. All he had was the minister's patronage, and the prospect of good State employments. The notion that Heaven meant me to remedy the deficiencies in his fortune made me fall into a sweet reverie, and at last I found myself deciding that my maid who put it all down as a jest had more wit than I. I blamed myself for my scrupulous behaviour, which seemed no better than prudery. My love was stronger than I thought, and this is my best excuse, besides I had no one to guide or counsel me.

"But after sunshine comes shadow. My soul was like the ebb and tide of the sea, now in the heights and now in the depths. The resolve, which the count seemed to have taken, to see me no more, either shewed him to be a man of little enterprise or little love, and this supposition humiliated me. 'If,' I said to myself, 'the count is offended with me for calling him a madman, he can have no delicacy and no discretion; he is unworthy of my love.'

"I was in this dreadful state of uncertainty when my maid took upon herself to write to the count that he could come and see me under the same diguise. He followed her advice, and one fine morning the crafty maid came into my chamber laughing, and told me that the lace-seller was in the next room. I was moved exceedingly, but restraining myself I began to laugh also, though the affair was no laughing matter for me.

" 'Shall I shew her in?' said the maid.

" 'Are you crazy?'

" 'Shall I send her away?'

" 'No, I will go and speak to him myself.'

"This day was a memorable one. My maid left the room now and again, and we had plenty of time to disclose our feelings to one another. I frankly confessed that I loved him, but added that it were best that I should forget him, as it was not likely that my relations would consent to our marriage. In his turn he told me that the minister having resolved to send him to England, he would die of despair unless he carried with him the hope of one day possessing me, for he said he loved me too well to live without me. He begged me to allow him to come and see me under the same disguise, and though I could not refuse him anything I said that we might be discovered.

" 'It is enough for me,' he replied, tenderly, 'that you will incur no danger, my visits will be set down to the account of your maid.'

" 'But I am afraid for you,' I replied, 'your disguise is a crime in itself; your reputation will suffer, and that will not tend to bring the wish of your heart nearer.'

"In spite of my objections, my heart spoke in his favour, and he pleaded so well and promised to be so discreet that at last I said I would see him gladly whenever he liked to come.

"Count Al—— is twenty-two, and is shorter than I; he is small-boned, and in his disguise as a lace-seller it was hard to recognize him, even by his voice, which is very soft. He imitated the gestures and ways of women to perfection, and not a few women would be only too glad to be like him.

"Thus for nearly three months the disguised count came to see me three or four times a week, always in my maid's room, and mostly in her presence. But even if we had been perfectly alone his fear of my displeasure was too great to allow him to take the slightest liberties. I think now that this mutual restraint added fuel to our flames, for when we thought of the moment of parting it was with dumb sadness and with no idea of taking the opportunity of rendering one another happy. We flattered ourselves that Heaven would work some miracle in our favour, and that the day would never come wherein we should be parted.

"But one morning the count came earlier than usual, and, bursting into tears, told me that the minister had given him a letter for M. de Saa, the Portuguese ambassador at London, and another letter open for the captain of a ship which was shortly to sail for London. In this letter the minister ordered the captain to embark Count

Al——, to take him to London, and to treat him with distinction.

"My poor lover was overwhelmed, he was nearly choked with sobs, and his brain was all confusion. For his sake, and taking pity on his grief and my love, I conceived the plan of accompanying him as his servant, or rather to avoid disguising my sex, as his wife. When I told him, he was at once stupefied and dazzled. He was beyond reasoning, and left everything in my hands. We agreed to discuss the matter at greater length on the following day, and parted.

"Foreseeing that it would be difficult for me to leave the house in woman's dress, I resolved to disguise myself as a man. But if I kept to my man's dress I should be obliged to occupy the position of my lover's valet, and have to undertake tasks beyond my strength. This thought made me resolve to impersonate the master myself, but thinking that I should not care to see my lover degraded to the rank of a servant, I determined that he should be my wife, supposing that the captain of the ship did not know him by sight.

" 'As soon as we get to England,' I thought, 'we will get married, and can resume our several dresses. This marriage will efface whatever shame may be attached to our flight; they will say, perhaps, that the count carried me off; but a girl is not carried off against her will, and Oeiras surely will not persecute me for having made the fortune of his favourite. As to our means of subsistence, till I get my rents, I can sell my diamonds, and they will realize an ample sum.'

"The next day, when I told my lover of this strange plan, he made no objections. The only obstacle which he thought of was the circumstance that the sea-captain might know him by sight, and this would have been fatal; but as he did not think it likely we determined to run the risk, and it was agreed that he should get me the clothes for the new part I was to play.

"I saw my lover again after an interval of three days; it was nightfall when he came. He told me that the Admiralty had informed him that the ship was riding at the mouth of the Tagus, and that the captain would put out to sea as soon as he had delivered his dispatches and had received fresh instructions. Count Al—— was consequently requested to be at a certain spot at midnight, and a boat would be in waiting to take him on board.

"I had made up my mind, and this was enough for me; and after having fixed the time and place of meeting, I shut myself up, pretending to be unwell. I put a few necessaries into a bag, not forgetting the precious jewel-casket, and I dressed myself up as a man and left the house by a stair only used by the servants. Even the porter did not see me as I made my escape.

"Fearing lest I should go astray the count was waiting for me at a short distance, and I was pleasantly surprised when he took me by the arm, saying, ' 'Tis I.' From this careful action, simple though it was, I saw that he had intelligence; he was afraid to catch hold of me without making himself known. We went to a house where he had his trunk, and in half an hour his disguise was made. When all was ready a man came for our slight baggage, and we walked to the river where the count was waiting for us. It was eleven o'clock when we left land, and thinking my jewels would be safer in his pocket than in my bag, I gave them to him, and we anxiously awaited the arrival of the captain. He came aboard with his officers at midnight, and accosted me politely, saying he had received orders to treat me with distinction. I thanked him cordially, and introduced my wife to him, whom he greeted respectfully, saying he was delighted to have such a charming passenger, who would doubtless give us a fortunate voyage. He was too polite to be astonished that the minister had made no mention of the count's wife in his letter.

"We got to the frigate in less than an hour; she was three leagues from land, and as soon as we got on board the captain ordered the men to set sail. He took us to a room which was extremely comfortable, considering it was only a cabin, and after doing the honours left us to ourselves.

"When we were alone we thanked Heaven that everything had gone off so well, and far from going to sleep we spent the night in discussing the bold step we had taken, or rather, only just begun to take; however, we hoped it would have as fortunate an ending as beginning. When the day dawned our hearts were gladdened because Lisbon was no longer in sight, and as we were in need of rest I laid down on a seat, while the count got into a hammock, neither of us troubling to undress.

"We were just falling asleep, when we began to feel the approach of sea-sickness, and for three days we knew no peace.

"On the fourth day, scarcely being able to stand upright for weakness, we began to be hungry, and had to exercise a careful moderation, so as not to become seriously ill. Happily for us the captain had a store of good food, and our meals were delicate and well-served.

"My lover, whose sickness has been more severe than mine, used this as a pretext for not leaving his room. The captain only came to see us once; this must have been out of extreme politeness, for in Portugal one may be jealous and yet not ridiculous. As for me, I stood upon the bridge nearly all day; the fresh air did me good, and I amused myself by scanning the horizon with my telescope.

"The seventh day of the voyage my heart trembled as with a presentiment of misfortune, when the sailors said that a vessel which could be seen in the distance was a corvette which was due to sail a day after us, but being a swift sailor would probably reach England two or three days before us.

"Though the voyage from Lisbon to England is a long one we had a fair wind all the way, and in fourteen days we dropped anchor at day-break in the port of Plymouth.

"The officer sent ashore by the captain to ask leave to disembark passengers came on board in the evening with several letters. One the captain read with peculiar attention, and then called me to one side and said,——

" 'This letter comes from Count Oeiras, and enjoins me, on my life, not to let any Portuguese young lady land, unless she be known to me. I am to take her back to Lisbon after having executed my various commissions. There is neither wife nor maid on my frigate, except the countess your wife. If you can prove that she is really your wife she may land with you; otherwise, you see, I cannot disobey the minister's orders.'

" 'She is my wife,' I said, coolly; 'but as I could not foresee this accident I have no papers to prove the fact.'

" 'I am sorry to hear it, as in that case she must go back to Lisbon. You may be sure I will treat her with all possible respect.'

" 'But a wife may not be parted from her husband.'

" 'Quite so, but I cannot disobey orders. If you like you can return to Lisbon in the corvette; you will be there before us.'

" 'Why cannot I return in this frigate?'

" 'Because I have distinct orders to put you on land. And now I come to think of it, how was it that there was not a word about your wife in the letter you gave me when we started? If the lady is not the person meant by the minister, you may be sure she will be sent back to join you in London.'

" 'You will allow me to go and speak to her?'

" 'Certainly, but in my presence.'

"My heart was broken; nevertheless, I had to put a good face on the losing game I was playing. I went to the count, and addressing him as *my dear wife* communicated the order which was to part us.

"I was afraid he would betray himself, but he was strong-minded enough to restrain his emotion, and only replied that we must needs submit, and that we should see each other again in a couple of months.

"As the captain stood beside us, I could only utter common-places. I warned him, however, that I should write to the abbess directly I got to London, who was the first person he must go and see at Lisbon, as she would have my address. I took care not to ask for my jewel-case, as the captain might have thought that my false wife was some rich young lady whom I had seduced.

"We had to abandon ourselves to our destiny. We embraced each other and mingled our ears, and the captain wept, too, when he heard me say,——

" 'Trust in all things to the worthy captain, and let us not fear at all.'

"The count's trunk was lowered into the boat, and as I did not dare to take my bag I found myself loaded with nothing but a man's clothes, which would not have fitted me, even if I had intended to keep up my disguise.

"When I came to the custom-house I saw my possessions. There were books, letters, linen, some suits of clothes, a sword and two pairs of pistols, one pair of which I put in my pockets, and then I went to an inn where the host said that if I wanted to travel to London the next morning I should only have to pay for one horse.

" 'Who are the people,' said I, 'who desire a companion?'

" 'You shall sup with them if you like,' said he.

"I accepted the offer, and found the party consisted of a minister of religion and two ladies whose faces pleased me. I was fortunate enough to win their good graces, and early the next day we got to London and alighted in the Strand at an inn where I only dined, going out to seek a lodging appropriate to my means and the kind of life I wished to lead. Fifty Lisbon pieces and a ring of about the same value was all that I possessed in the world.

"I took a room on the third floor, being attracted by the honest and kindly expression of the landlady. I could only trust in God and confide my position to her. I agreed to pay her ten shillings a week, and begged her to get me some woman's clothes, for I was afraid to go out in my man's dress any longer.

"The next day I was clothed like a poor girl who desires to escape notice. I spoke English well enough to seem a native of the country, and I knew how I must behave if I wished to be let alone. Although the landlady was a worthy woman, her house was not exactly suitable for me; my stay in England might be protracted, and if I came to destitution I should be wretched indeed; so I resolved to leave the house. I received no visitors, but I could not prevent the inquisitive from hovering round my door, and the more it became known that I saw no one, the more their curiosity increased. The house was not quiet enough. It was near the Exchange, and the neighborhood swarmed with young men who came to dine on the first floor of the house, and did their best to cure me of my sadness, as they called it, though I had not shewn any signs of wishing to be cured.

"I made up my mind not to spend more than a guinea a week, and resolved to sell my ring if I could have the money paid to me at intervals. An old jeweler who lodged next door, and for whose honesty my landlady answered, told me it was worth a hundred and fifty guineas, and asked me to let him have it if I had no better offer. I had not thought it to be so valuable, and I sold it to him on condition that he would pay me four guineas a month, and that I should be at liberty to buy it back if I could do so before all the payments had been made.

"I wanted to keep my ready money, which I still have by me, so as to be able to go back to Lisbon by land when I can do so in safety, for I could not face the horrors of a sea voyage a second time.

"I told my case to my worthy landlady who still befriends me, and she helped me to get another lodging, but I had to procure a servant to fetch me my food; I could not summon up courage to have my meals in a coffee-house. However, all my servants turned out ill; they robbed me continually, and levied a tax on all their purchases.

"The temperance I observed—for I almost lived on bread and water—made me get thinner every day, still I saw no way of mending my existence till chance made me see your singular announcement. I laughed at it; and then drawn by some irresistible power, or perhaps by the curiosity that falls to the lot of most of us women,

I could not resist going in and speaking to you. Instinct thus pointed out the way to improve my lot without increasing my expenditure.

"When I got back I found a copy of the *Advertiser* on my landlady's table; it contained some editorial fun on the notice I had just read. The writer said that the master of the house was an Italian, and had therefore nothing to fear from feminine violence. On my side I determined to hazard everything, but I feel I have been too hasty, and that there are certain attacks which it is pleasant not to resist. I was brought up by an Italian, a clever and good man, and I have always had a great respect for your fellow-countrymen."

My fair Portuguese had finished her story, and I observed,——

"Really, your history has amused me very much; it has all the air of a romance."

"Quite so," said she; "but it is a strictly historical romance. But the most amusing thing to me is that you have listened to it without weariness."

"That is your modesty, madam; not only has your tale interested me, but now that I know you are a Portuguese I am at peace with the nation."

"Were you at war with us, then?"

"I have never forgiven you for letting your Portuguese Virgil die miserably two hundred years ago."

"You mean Camöens. But the Greeks treated Homer in the same way."

"Yes, but the faults of others are no excuse for our own."

"You are right; but how can you like Camöens so much if you do not know Portuguese?"

"I have read a translation in Latin hexameters so well done that I fancied I was reading Virgil."

"Is that truly so?"

"I would never lie to you."

"Then I make a vow to learn Latin."

"That is worthy of you, but it is of me that you must learn the language. I will go to Portugal and live and die there, if you will give me your heart.'

"My heart! I have only one, and that is given already. Since I have known you I have despised myself, for I am afraid I have an inconstant nature."

"It will be enough for me if you will love me as your father, provided I may sometimes take my daughter to my arms. But go on with your story, the chief part is yet untold. What became of your lover, and what did your relations do when they found out your flight?"

"Three days after I arrived in this vast city I wrote to the abbess, my aunt, and told her the whole story, begging her to protect my lover, and to confirm me in my resolution never to return to Lisbon till I could do so in security, and have no obstacles placed in the way of my marriage. I also begged her to write and inform me of all that happened, addressing her letters to 'Miss Pauline,' under cover of my landlady.

"I sent my letter by Paris and Madrid, and I had to wait three months before I got an answer. My aunt told me that the frigate had only returned a short time, and that the captain immediately on his arrival wrote to the minister informing him that the only lady who was in his ship when he sailed was still on board, for he had brought her back with him, despite the opposition of Count Al——, who declared she was his wife. The captain ended by asking his excellency for further orders with respect to the lady aforesaid.

"Oeiras, feeling sure that the lady was myself, told the captain to take her to the convent of which my aunt was abbess, with a letter he had written. In this letter he told my aunt that he sent her her niece, and begged her to keep the girl securely till further orders. My aunt was extremely surprised, but she would have been still more surprised if she had not got my letter a few days before. She thanked the captain for his care, and took the false niece to a room and locked her up. She then wrote to Oeiras, telling him that she had received into her convent a person supposed to be his niece, but as this person was really a man in woman's dress she begged his excellency to remove him as soon as possible.

"When the abbess had written this curious letter she paid a visit to the count, who fell on his knees before her. My good aunt raised him, and shewed him my letter. She said that she had been obliged to write to the minister, and that she had no doubt he would be removed from the convent in the course of a few hours. The count burst into tears, and begging the abbess to protect us both gave her my jewel-casket, which the worthy woman received with great pleasure. She left him, promising to write to me of all that happened.

"The minister was at one of his country estates, and did not receive the abbess's letter till the next day, but hastened to reply in person. My aunt easily convinced his excellency of the need for keeping the matter secret, for a man had been sent into the convent, which would be to her dishonour. She shewed the proud minister the letter she had had from me, and told him how the honest young man had given her my jewel-casket. He thanked her for her open dealing, and begged her pardon with a smile for sending a fine young man to her nunnery.

" 'The secret,' said he, 'is of the greatest importance; we must see that it goes no farther. I will relieve you of your false niece, and take her away in my carriage.'

"My aunt took him at his word and brought out the young recluse, who drove away with the minister. The abbess tells me that from that day she has heard nothing about him, but that all Lisbon is talking over the affair, but in a wholly distorted manner. They say that the minister first of all put me under the care of my aunt, but soon after took me away, and has kept me in some secret place ever since. Count Al—— is supposed to be in London, and I in the minister's power, and probably we are supposed to have entered into a tender relationship. No doubt his excellency is perfectly well informed of my doings here, for he knows my address and has spies everywhere.

"On the advice of my aunt I wrote to Oeiras a couple of months ago, telling him that I am ready to return to Lisbon, if I may marry Count Al—— and live in perfect liberty. Otherwise, I declared, I would stay in London, where the laws guaranteed my freedom. I am waiting for his answer every day, and I expect it will be a favourable one, for no one can deprive me of my estates, and Oeiras will probably be only too glad to protect me to lessen the odium which attaches to his name as the murderer of my father."

Pauline made no mystery of the names of the characters, but she may be still alive, and I respect her too well to run the risk of wounding her, though these Memoirs will not see the light of day during my lifetime. It is sufficient to say that the story is known to all the inhabitants of Lisbon, and that the persons who figure in it are public characters in Portugal.

I lived with dear Pauline in perfect harmony, feeling my love for her increase daily, and daily inspiring her with tenderer feelings towards myself. But as my love

increased in strength, I grew thin and feeble; I could
not sleep nor eat. I should have languished away if I
had not succeeded in gratifying my passion. On the
other hand, Pauline grew plumper and prettier every
day.

"If my sufferings serve to increase your charms," said
I, "you ought not to let me die, for a dead man has no
suffering."

"Do you think that your sufferings are due to your
love for me?"

"Certainly."

"There may be something in it, but, believe me, the
tender passion does not destroy the appetite nor take
away the power of sleep. Your indisposition is undoubtedly due to the sedentary life you have been leading
of late. If you love me, give me a proof of it; go out
for a ride."

"I cannot refuse you anything, dearest Pauline, but
what then?"

"Then you shall find me grateful to you, you will
have a good appetite, and will sleep well."

"A horse, a horse! Quick! My boots!" I kissed
her hand—for I had not got any farther than that—
and began to ride towards Kingston. I did not care
for the motion of trotting, so I put my horse at a gallop,
when all of a sudden he stumbled, and in an instant
I was lying on the ground in front of the Duke of Kingston's house. Miss Chudleigh happened to be at the
window, and seeing me thrown to the ground uttered
a shriek. I raised my head and she recognized me, and
hastened to send some of her people to help me. As
soon as I was on my feet I wanted to go and thank her,
but I could not stir, and a valet who knew something
of surgery examined me, and declared that I had put

out my collar-bone and would require a week's rest.

The young lady told me that if I liked to stay in her house the greatest care should be taken of me. I thanked her warmly, but begged her to have me taken home, as I should not like to give her so much trouble. She immediately gave the necessary orders, and I was driven home in a comfortable carriage. The servants in charge would not acept any money, and I saw in the incident a proof of that hospitality for which the English are famed, although they are at the same time profoundly egotistic.

When I got home I went to bed, and sent for a surgeon, who laughed when I told him that I had put out a bone.

"I'll wager it is nothing more than a sprain. I only wish it was put out that I might have some chance of shewing my skill."

"I am delighted," I said, "not to be in a position to call for that amount of talent, but I shall have a high opinion of you if you set me up in a short time."

I did not see Pauline, much to my astonishment. I was told she had gone out in a sedan-chair, and I almost felt jealous. In two hours she came in looking quite frightened, the old house-keeper having told her that I had broken my leg, and that the doctor had been with me already.

"Unhappy wretch that I am!" she exclaimed as she came to my bedside, " 'tis I that have brought you to this."

With these words she turned pale and almost fell in a swoon beside me.

"Divine being!" I cried, as I pressed her to my breast, "it is nothing; only a sprain."

"What pain that foolish old woman has given me!

God be praised that it is no worse! Feel my heart."

"Oh, yes! I felt it with delight. It was a happy fall for me."

Fastening my lips on hers, I felt with delight that our transports were mutual, and I blessed the sprain that had brought me such bliss.

After these ectasies I felt that Pauline was laughing.

"What are you laughing at, sweetheart?"

"At the craft of love, which always triumphs at last."

"Where have you been?"

"I went to my old jeweler's to redeem my ring, that you might have a souvenir of me; here it is."

"Pauline! Pauline! a little love would have been much more precious to me than this beautiful ring."

"You shall have both. Till the time of my departure, which will come only too soon, we will live together like man and wife; and to-night shall be our wedding night, and the bed the table for the feast."

"What sweet news you give me, Pauline! I cannot believe it till my happiness is actually accomplished."

"You may doubt, if you like; but let it be a slight doubt, or else you will do me wrong. I am tired of living with you as a lover and only making you wretched, and the moment I saw you on horseback I determined to belong to you. Consequently I went to redeem the ring directly you left, and I do not intend to leave you until I receive the fatal message from Lisbon. I have dreaded its arrival every day for the last week."

"May the messenger that brings it be robbed on the way."

"No such luck, I am afraid."

As Pauline was standing, I asked her to come to my arms, for I longed to give her some palpable signs of my love.

"No, dearest, one can love and yet be wise; the door is open."

She got down Ariosto and began to read to me the adventure of Ricciardetto with Fiordespina, an episode which gives its beauty to the twenty-ninth canto of that beautiful poem which I knew by heart. She imagined that she was the princess, and I Ricciardetto. She liked to fancy,——

> *Che il ciel l'abbia concesso,*
> *Bradamante cangiata in miglior sesso.*

When she came to the lines,——

> *Le belle braccia al collo indi mi getta,*
> *E dolcemente stringe, e baccia in bocca:*
> *Tu puoi pensar se allora la saetta*
> *Dirizza Amor, se in mezzo al cor mi tocca.*

She wanted some explanations on the expression *baccia in bocca,* and on the love which made Ricciardetto's arrow so stiff, and I, only too ready to comment on the text, made her touch an arrow as stiff as Ricciardetto's. Of course, she was angry at that, but her wrath did not last long. She burst out laughing when she came to the lines,——

> *Io il veggo, io il sento, e a pena vero parmi:*
> *Sento in maschio in femina matarsi.*

And then,——

> *Cosi le dissi, e feci ch'ella stessa*
> *Trovo con man la veritade expressa.*

She expressed her wonder that this poem abounding in obscenities had not been put on the "Index" at Rome.

"What you call obscenity is mere license, and there is plenty of that at Rome."

"That's a joke which should bring the censures of the Church upon you. But what do you call obscenities, if Ariosto is not obscene?"

"Obscenity disgusts, and never gives pleasure."

"Your logic is all your own, but situated as I am I cannot reargue your proposition. I am amused at Ariosto's choosing a Spanish woman above all others to conceive that strange passion for Bradamante."

"The heat of the Spanish climate made him conclude that the Spanish temperament was also ardent, and consequently whimsical in its tastes."

"Poets are a kind of madmen who allow themselves to give utterance to all their fancies."

The reading was continued, and I thought my time had come when she read the verses:

> Io senza scale in su la rocca salto,
> E lo stendardo piantovi di botto,
> E la nemica mia mi caccio sotto.*

*I scaled the rock without a ladder, I planted my standard suddenly, and held my enemy beneath me.

I wanted to give her a practical illustration of the lines, but with that sensibility so natural to women, and which they can use so well as a goad to passion, she said,——

"Dearest, you might make yourself worse; let us wait till your sprain is cured."

"Are we to wait till I am cured for the consummation of our marriage?"

"I suppose so, for if I am not mistaken the thing can't be done without a certain movement."

"You are wrong, dear Pauline, but it would make no

difference to me even if it were so. You may be sure I would not put it off till to-morrow, even if it cost me my leg. Besides, you shall see that there are ways and means of satisfying our passions without doing me any harm. Is that enough for you?"

"Well, well, as it is written that a wife should obey her husband, you will find me docile."

"When?"

"After supper."

"Then we will have no supper. We shall dine with all the better appetite to-morrow. Let us begin now."

"No, for the suspicions of the servants might be aroused. Love has its rules of decency like everything else."

"You talk as wisely as Cato, and I am obliged to confess that you are right in all you say."

Supper was served as usual; it was delicate enough, but the thought of approaching bliss had taken away our appetites, and we ate only for form's sake. At ten o'clock we were at liberty, and could indulge our passion without any fear of being disturbed.

But this delightful woman, who had so plainly told me a few hours before that when I was cured we would live together as man and wife, was now ashamed to undress before me. She could not make up her mind, and told me so, laughing at herself. From this circumstance I gathered that the decency of the body is more tenacious in its grasp than the purity of the soul.

"But, sweetheart," said I, "you dressed and undressed for a fortnight before your betrothed."

"Yes, but he was always lying in his hammock with his back towards me at night, and in the morning he never turned round and wished me good day till he knew I was dressed."

"What, he never turned?"

"I never let him take any liberties."

"Such virtue is incomprehensible to me."

"You see the count was to be my husband, and I was to be his wife, and in such cases a young woman is careful. Besides, I believe that if one will but refrain from taking the first step, continence is easy. Then the count was naturally timid, and would never have taken any liberties without my encouraging him, which I took care not to do. For this once, you will allow me to sleep with you in my clothes."

"Certainly, if you wish me to be dressed also, otherwise it would be unbearable for both of us."

"You are very cruel."

"But, dearest, are you not ashamed of these foolish scruples?"

"Well, well, put out the candles, and in a minute I will be beside you."

"Very good; though the want of light will deprive me of a great pleasure. Quick, out with them!"

My charming Portuguese did not reflect that the moon shone full into the room, and that the muslin curtains would not prevent my seeing her exquisite figure, which shewed to greater advantage in the position she happened to take. If Pauline had been a coquette I should have considered her scruples as mere artifice calculated to increase my ardour; but she had no need to use such stratagems. At last she was within my arms, and we clasped each other closely and in silence that was only broken by the murmur of our kisses. Soon our union became closer, and her sighs and the ardour of her surrender shewed me that her passion was more in need of relief than mine. I was sufficiently master of myself to remember that I must have a care for her honour, greatly to her astonishment, for she confessed she had never thought of such a thing, and had given herself up freely, resolved to brave the consequences which she believed to be inevitable. I explained the mystery and made her happy.

Till this moment love alone had swayed me, but now that the bloody sacrifice was over I felt full of respect and gratitude. I told her effusively that I knew how great was my happiness, and that I was ready to sacrifice my life to her to prove my love.

The thought that our embraces would have no dangerous result had put Pauline at her ease, and she gave reins to her ardent temperament, while I did valiant service, till at last we were exhausted and the last sacrifice was not entirely consummated. We abandoned ourselves to a profound and peaceful sleep. I was the first to awake; the sun was shining in through the window, and I gazed on Pauline. As I looked at this woman, the first beauty in Portugal, the only child of an illustrious family, who had given herself to me all for love, and whom I should possess for so short a time, I could not restrain a profound sigh.

Pauline awoke, and her gaze, as bright as the rising sun in springtime, fixed itself on me truthfully and lovingly.

"What are you thinking of, dearest?"

"I am trying to convince myself that my happiness is not a dream, and if it be real I want it to last for ever. I am the happy mortal to whom you have given up your great treasure, of which I am unworthy, though I love you tenderly."

"Sweetheart, you are worthy of all my devotion and affection, if you have not ceased to respect me."

"Can you doubt it, Pauline?"

"No, dearest, I think you love me, and that I shall never repent having trusted in you."

The sweet sacrifice was offered again, and Pauline rose and laughed to find that she was no longer ashamed of her nakedness before me. Then, passing from jest to earnest, she said,——

"If the loss of shame is the result of knowledge, how was it that our first parents were not ashamed till they had acquired knowledge?"

"I don't know, dearest, but tell me, did you ever ask your learned Italian master that same question?"

"Yes, I did."

"What did he say?"

"That their shame arose not from their enjoyment, but from disobedience; and that in covering the parts which had seduced them, they discovered, as it were, the sin they had committed. Whatever may be said on the subject, I shall always think that Adam was much more to blame than Eve."

"How is that?"

"Because Adam had received the prohibition from God, while Eve had only received it from Adam."

"I thought that both of them received the prohibition directly from God."

"You have not read Genesis, then."

"You are laughing at me."

"Then you have read it carelessly, because it is distinctly stated that God made Eve after he had forbidden Adam to eat of the fruit."

"I wonder that point has not been remarked by our commentators; it seems a very important one to me."

"They are a pack of knaves, all sworn enemies of women."

"No, no, they give proofs of quite another feeling only too often."

"We won't say anything more about it. My teacher was an honest man."

"Was he a Jesuit?"

"Yes, but of the short robe."

"What do you mean?"

"We will discuss the question another time."

"Very good; I should like to have it proved to me that a man can be a Jesuit and honest at the same time."

"There are exceptions to all rules."

My Pauline was a profound thinker, and strongly attached to her religion. I should never have discovered that she possessed this merit if I had not slept with her. I have known several women of the same stamp; if you wish to know the elevation of their souls, you must begin by damning them. When this is done, one enjoys their confidence, for they have no secrets for the happy victor. This is the reason why the charming though feeble sex loves the brave and despises the cowardly. Sometimes they appear to love cowards, but always for their physical beauty. Women amuse themselves with such fellows, but are the first to laugh if they get caned.

After the most delicious night I had ever passed, I resolved not to leave my house till Pauline had to return to Portugal. She did not leave me for a moment, save to hear mass on Sundays. I shut my door to everybody, even to the doctor, for my sprain disappeared of itself. I did not fail to inform Miss Chudleigh of my rapid cure; she had sent twice a day ever since the accident to learn how I was.

Pauline went to her room after our amorous conflict,

and I did not see her again till dinner-time; but when I did see her I thought her an angel. Her face had caught the hues of the lily and the rose, and had an air of happiness I could not help admiring.

As we both wanted to have our portraits taken, I asked Martinelli to send me the best miniature-painter in London. He sent a Jew, who succeeded admirably. I had my miniature mounted in a ring and gave it to Pauline; and this was the only present she would accept from me, who would have thought myself all the richer if she had accepted all I had.

We spent three weeks in a happy dream which no pen can describe. I was quite well again, and we tasted all the sweets of love together. All day and all night we were together, our desires were satisfied only to be renewed; we enjoyed the extremest bliss. In a word, it is difficult to form a just idea of the state of two individuals who enjoy all the range of physical and mental pleasures together, whose life is for the present without thought of the future; whose joys are mutual and continual; such, nevertheless, was the position of myself and my divine Pauline.

Every day I discovered in her some fresh perfection which made me love her more; her nature was inexhaustible in its treasures, for her mental qualities even surpassed her physical beauties, and an excellent education had wonderfully increased the powers of her intelligence. With all the beauty and grace of a woman she had that exalted character which is the lot of the best of men. She began to flatter herself that the fatal letter would never come, and the count was little more than a dream of the past. Sometimes she would say that she could not understand how a pretty face could exercise such a strong influence over us in spite of our reason.

"I have found out too late," she added, "that chance alone can make a marriage, contracted for such physical reasons, happy."

The 1st of August was a fatal day for both of us. Pauline received a letter from Lisbon, which summoned her home without delay, and I had a letter from Paris announcing the death of Madame d'Urfé. Madame du Rumain told me that on the evidence of her maid the doctors had pronounced her death to be due to an overdose of the liquid she called "The Panacea." She added that a will had been found which savoured of a lunatic asylum, for she had left all her wealth to the son or daughter that should be born of her, declaring that she was with child. I was to be the governor of the infant; this vexed me exceedingly, as I knew I should be the laughing-stock of Paris for a week at least. Her daughter, the Comtesse de Chatelet, had taken possession of all her real estate and of her pocket-book, which contained, to my surprise, four hundred thousand francs. It was a great shock for me, but the contents of the two letters Pauline had received was a greater blow. One was from her aunt, and the other from Oeiras, who begged her to return to Lisbon as soon as possible, and assured her that she should be put in possession of her property on her arrival, and would be at liberty to marry Count Al—— in the sight of all the world. He sent her a cheque for twenty million reis. I was not aware of the small value of the coin, and was in an ecstasy; but Pauline laughed, and said it only came to two thousand pounds, which was a sufficient sum, however, to allow her to travel in the style of a duchess. The minister wanted her to come by sea, and all she had to do was to communicate with the Portuguese ambassador, who had orders to give her a passage on a Portuguese frigate which happened to be riding in an English port. Pauline would not hear of the voyage, or of applying to the ambassador, for she did not want anyone to think that she had been obliged to return. She was angry with the minister for having sent her a cheque, thinking that he must be aware that she had been in need, but I soon brought her to see reason on this point, telling her that it was a very thoughtful and delicate proceeding on the part of Oeiras, and that he had merely lent her the money, and not given it to her.

Pauline was rich, and she was a high-minded woman. Her generosity may be estimated by her giving me her ring when she was in want, and she certainly never counted on my purse, though she may have felt sure that I would not abandon her. I am sure she believed me to be very rich, and my conduct was certainly calculated to favour that idea.

The day and even the night passed sadly. The next day Pauline addressed me as follows:

"We must part, dear friend, and try to forget one another, for my honour obliges me to become the wife of the count as soon as I arrive in Lisbon. The first fancy of my heart, which you have almost effaced, will regain all its old force when I see you no longer, and I am sure I shall love my husband, for he is a good-hearted, honest, and pleasant young man; that much I know from the few days we lived together.

"Now I have a favour to ask of you, which I am sure you will grant. Promise me never to come to Lisbon without my permission. I hope you will not seek to know my reasons; you would not, I am sure, come

to trouble my peace, for if I sinned I should be unhappy, and you would not desire that for me. I have
dreamed we have lived together as man and wife, and
now we are parted I shall fancy myself a widow about
to undertake another marriage."

I burst into tears, and pressing her to my breast
promised I would do as she wished.

Pauline wrote to her aunt and Oeiras that she would
be in Lisbon in October, and that they should have
further news of her when she reached Spain. She had
plenty of money, and bought a carriage and engaged a
maid, and these arrangements took up her time during
the last week she spent with me. I made her promise
me to let Clairmont accompany her as far as Madrid.
She was to send me back my faithful servant when she
reached the Spanish capital, but fate had decreed that
I should see his face no more.

The last few days were spent partly in sorrow and
partly in delight. We looked at each other without
speaking, and spoke without knowing what we said.
We forgot to eat, and went to bed hoping that love and
anguish would keep us awake, but our exhausted bodies
fell into a heavy sleep, and when we awoke we could
only sigh and kiss again.

Pauline allowed me to escort her as far as Calais, and
we started on the 10th of August, only stopping at Dover
to embark the carriage on the packet, and four hours
afterwards we disembarked at Calais, and Pauline, considering her widowhood had begun, begged me to sleep
in another room. She started on the 12th of August,
preceded by my poor Clairmont, and resolved only to
travel by day-time.

The analogy between my parting with Pauline and
my parting with Henriette fifteen years before, was

exceedingly striking; the two women were of very similar character, and both were equally beautiful, though
their beauty was of a different kind. Thus I fell as
madly in love with the second as with the first, both
being equally intelligent. The fact that one had more
talent and less prejudices than the other must have
been an effect of their different educations. Pauline
had the fine pride of her nation, her mind was a serious
cast, and her religion was more an affair of the heart
than the understanding. She was also a far more ardent mistress than Henriette. I was successful with
both of them because I was rich; if I had been a poor
man I should never have known either of them. I
have half forgotten them, as everything is forgotten
in time, but when I recall them to my memory I find
that Henriette made the profounder impression on me,
no doubt because I was twenty-five when I knew her,
while I was thirty-seven in London.

The older I get the more I feel the destructive effects
of old age; and I regret bitterly that I could not discover the secret of remaining young and happy for ever.
Vain regrets! we must finish as we began, helpless and
devoid of sense.

I went back to England the same day, and had a
troublesome passage. Nevertheless, I did not rest at
Dover; and as soon as I got to London I shut myself
up with a truly English attack of the spleen, while I
thought of Pauline and strove to forget her. Jarbe put
me to bed, and in the morning, when he came into my
room, he made me shudder with a speech at which I
laughed afterwards.

"Sir," said he, "the old woman wants to know whether
she is to put up the notice again."

"The old hag! Does she want me to choke her?"

"Good heavens—no, sir! She is very fond of you, seeing you seemed so sad, she thought. . . ."

"Go and tell her never to think such things again, and as for you. . . ."

"I will do as you wish, sir."

"Then leave me."

CHAPTER X

Eccentricity of the English — Castelbajac — Count Schwerin—Sophie at School—My Reception at the Betting Club—the Charpillon

I PASSED a night which seemed like a never-ending nightmare, and I got up sad and savage, feeling as if I could kill a man on the smallest provocation. It seemed as if the house, which I had hitherto thought so beautiful, was like a millstone about my neck. I went out in my travelling clothes, and walked into a coffee-house, where I saw a score of people reading the papers.

I sat down, and, not understanding English, passed my time in gazing at the goers and comers. I had been there some time when my attention was attracted by the voice of a man speaking as follows in French:

"Tommy has committed suicide, and he was wise, for he was in such a state that he could only expect unhappiness for the rest of his life."

"You are quite mistaken," said the other, with the greatest composure. "I was one of his creditors myself, and on making an inventory of his effects I feel satisfied that he has done a very foolish and a very childish thing; he might have lived on comfortably, and not killed himself for fully six months."

At any other time this calculation would have made me laugh, and, as it was, I felt as if the incident had done me good.

I left the coffee-house without having said a word or

spent a penny, and I went towards the Exchange to get
some money. Bosanquet gave me what I wanted directly, and as I walked out with him I noticed a curi-
ous-looking individual, whose name I asked.

"He's worth a hundred thousand," said the banker.

"And who is that other man over there?"

"He's not worth a ten-pound note."

"But I don't want to hear what they are worth; it's
their names I want."

"I really don't know."

"How can you tell how much they are worth, not
knowing their names?"

"Names don't go for anything here. What we want
to know about a man is *how much he has got?* Besides,
what's in a name? Ask me for a thousand pounds and
give me a proper receipt, and you can do it under the
name of Socrates or Attila, for all I care. You will
pay me back my money as Socrates or Attila, and not
as Seingalt; that is all."

"But how about signing bills of exchange?"

"That's another thing; I must use the name which
the drawer gives me."

"I don't understand that."

"Well, you see, you are not English, nor are you a
business man."

On leaving him I walked towards the park, but wishing to change a twenty-pound note before going in I
went to a fat merchant, an epicure whose acquaintance
I had made at the tavern, and put down the note on his
counter, begging him to cash it for me.

"Come again in an hour," said he, "I have no money
by me just now."

"Very good; I will call again when I come from the
park."

"Take back your note; you shall give it to me when I hand you the money."

"Never mind; keep it. I don't doubt your honesty."

"Don't be so foolish. If you left me the note I should certainly decline to hand over the money, if only for the sake of giving you a lesson."

"I don't believe you are capable of such dishonesty."

"Nor am I, but when it comes to such a simple thing as putting a bank note in your pocket, the most honest man in the world would never dream of having such a thing in his possession without having paid the money for it, and the least slip of memory might lead to a dispute in which you would infallibly come off second best."

"I feel the force of your arguments, especially in a town where so much business is carried on."

When I got into the park I met Martinelli and thanked him for sending me a copy of the *Decameron*, while he congratulated me on my re-appearance in society, and on the young lady of whom I had been the happy possessor and no doubt the slave.

"My Lord Pembroke has seen her," said he, "and thought her charming."

"What? Where could he have seen her?"

"In a carriage with you driving fast along the Rochester road. It is three or four days ago."

"Then I may tell you that I was taking her to Calais; I shall never see her face again."

"Will you let the room again in the same way?"

"No, never again, though the god of love has been propitious to me. I shall be glad to see you at my house whenever you like to come."

"Shall I send you a note to warn you?"

"Not at all."

We walked on talking about literature, manners, and so forth, in an aimless way. All at once, as we approached Buckingham House, I saw five or six persons, relieving nature amidst the bushes, with their hinder parts facing the passers-by. I thought this a disgusting piece of indecency, and said as much to Martinelli, adding that the impudent rascals might at least turn their faces towards the path.

"Not at all," he exclaimed, "for then they might be recognized; whereas in exposing their posteriors they run no such risk; besides the sight makes squeamish persons turn away."

"You are right, but you will confess that the whole thing strikes a stranger as very revolting."

"Yes, there is nothing so ineradicable as national prejudice. You may have noticed that when an Englishman wants to ease his sluices in the street, he doesn't run up an alley or turn to the wall like we do."

"Yes, I have noticed them turning towards the middle of the street, but if they thus escape the notice of the people in the shops and on the pavement they are seen by everybody who is driving in a carriage, and that is as bad."

"The people in the carriages need not look."

"That is true."

We walked on to the Green Park, and met Lord Pembroke on horseback. He stopped and burst into exclamations on seeing me. As I guessed the cause of his surprise, I hastened to tell him that I was a free man once more, to my sorrow, and felt lonely amidst my splendour.

"I feel rather curious about it, and perhaps I may come and keep you company to-day."

We parted, and reckoning on seeing him at dinner I

went back to tell my cook that dinner was to be served in the large room. Martinelli had an engagement and could not come to dinner, but he led me out of the park by a door with which I was not acquainted, and sent me on my way.

As we were going along we saw a crowd of people who seemed to be staring at something. Martinelli went up to the crowd, and then returned to me, saying,——

"That's a curious sight for you; you can enter it amidst your remarks on English manners."

"What is it?"

"A man at the point of death from a blow he has received in boxing with another sturdy fellow."

"Cannot anything be done?"

"There is a surgeon there who would bleed him, if he were allowed."

"Who could prevent him?"

"That's the curious part of it. Two men have betted on his death or recovery. One says, 'I'll bet twenty guineas he dies,' and the other says, 'Done.' Number one will not allow the surgeon to bleed him, for if the man recovered his twenty guineas would be gone."

"Poor man! what pitiless betters!"

"The English are very strange in their betting proclivities; they bet about everything. There is a Betting Club to which I will introduce you, if you like."

"Do they speak French there?"

"Most certainly, for it is composed of men of wit and mark."

"What do they do?"

"They talk and argue, and if one man brings forward a proposition which another denies, and one backs his opinion, the other has to bet too, on pain of a fine which goes to the common fund."

"Introduce me to this delightful club, by all means; it will make my fortune, for I shall always take care to be on the right side."

"You had better be careful; they are wary birds."

"But to return to the dying man; what will be done to his antagonist?"

"His hand will be examined, and if it is found to be just the same as yours or mine it will be marked, and he will be let go."

"I don't understand that, so kindly explain. How do they recognize a dangerous hand?"

"If it is found to be marked already, it is a proof that he has killed his man before and has been marked for it, with the warning, 'Take care not to kill anyone else, for if you do you will be hanged.'"

"But supposing such a man is attacked?"

"He ought to shew his hand, and then his adversary would let him alone."

"But if not?"

"Then he is defending himself; and if he kills his man he is acquitted, provided he can bring witnesses to swear that he was obliged to fight."

"Since fighting with the fist may cause death, I wonder it is allowed."

"It is only allowed for a wager. If the combatants do not put one or more pieces of money on the ground before the fight, and there is a death, the man is hanged."

"What laws! What manners!"

In such ways I learnt much concerning the manner and customs of this proud nation, at once so great and so little.

The noble lord came to dinner, and I treated him in a manner to make him wish to come again. Although there were only the two of us, the meal lasted a long time, as I was anxious for additional information on what I had heard in the morning, especially on the Betting Club. The worthy Pembroke advised me not to have anything to do with it, unless I made up my mind to keep perfect silence for four or five weeks.

"But supposing they ask me a question?"

"Evade it."

"Certainly, if I am not in a position to give my opinion; but if I have an opinion, the powers of Satan could not shut my mouth."

"All the worse for you."

"Are the members knaves?"

"Certainly not. They are noblemen, philosophers, and epicures; but they are pitiless where a bet is concerned."

"Is the club treasury rich?"

"Far from it; they are all ashamed to pay a fine, and prefer to bet. Who will introduce you?"

"Martinelli."

"Quite so; through Lord Spencer, who is a member. I would not become one."

"Why not?"

"Because I don't like argument."

"My taste runs the other way, so I shall try to get in."

"By the way, M. de Seingalt, do you know that you are a very extraordinary man?"

"For what reason, my lord?"

"You shut yourself up for a whole month with a woman who spent fourteen months in London without anybody making her acquaintance or even discovering her nationality. All the amateurs have taken a lively interest in the affair."

"How did you find out that she spent fourteen months in London?"

"Because several persons saw her in the house of a worthy widow where she spent the first month. She would never have anything to say to any advances, but the bill in your window worked wonders."

"Yes, and all the worse for me, for I feel as if I could never love another woman."

"Oh, that's childish indeed! You will love another woman in a week—nay, perhaps to-morrow, if you will come and dine with me at my country house. A perfect French beauty has asked me to dine with her. I have told some of my friends who are fond of gaming."

"Does the charming Frenchwoman like gaming?"

"No, but her husband does."

"What's his name?"

"He calls himself Count de Castelbajac."

"Ah! Castelbajac?"

"Yes."

"He is a Gascon?"

"Yes."

"Tall, thin, and dark, and marked with the small-pox?"

"Exactly! I am delighted to find you know him. You will agree with me that his wife is very pretty?"

"I really can't say. I knew Castelbajac, as he calls himself, six years ago, and I never heard he was married. I shall be delighted to join you, however. I must warn you not to say anything if he seems not to know me; he may possibly have good reasons for acting in that manner. Before long I will tell you a story which does not represent him in a very advantageous manner. I did not know he played. I shall take care to be on my guard at the Betting Club, and I advise you, my lord, to be on your guard in the society of Castelbajac."

"I will not forget the warning."

When Pembroke had left me I went to see Madame Cornelis, who had written a week before to tell me my daughter was ill, and explained that she had been turned from my doors on two occasions though she felt certain I was in. To this I replied that I was in love, and so happy within my own house that I had excluded all strangers, and with that she had to be contented, but the state in which I found little Sophie frightened me. She was lying in bed with high fever, she had grown much thinner, and her eyes seemed to say that she was dying of grief. Her mother was in despair, for she was passionately fond of the child, and I thought she would have torn my eyes out when I told her that if Sophie died she would only have herself to reproach. Sophie, who was very good-hearted, cried out, "No, no! papa dear;" and quieted her mother by her caresses.

Nevertheless, I took the mother aside, and told her that the disease was solely caused by Sophie's dread of her severity.

"In spite of your affection," said I, "you treat her with insufferable tyranny. Send her to a boarding-school for a couple of years, and let her associate with girls of good family. Tell her this evening that she is to go to school, and see if she does not get better."

"Yes," said she, "but a good boarding-school costs a hundred guineas a year, including masters."

"If I approve of the school you select I will pay a year in advance."

On my making this offer the woman, who seemed to be living so luxuriously, but was in reality poverty-stricken, embraced me with the utmost gratitude.

"Come and tell the news to your daughter now," said she, "I should like to watch her face when she hears it."

"Certainly."

"My dear Sophie," I said, "your mother agrees with me that if you had a change of air you would get better, and if you would like to spend a year or two in a good school I will pay the first year in advance."

"Of course, I will obey my dear mother," said Sophie.

"There is no question of obedience. Would you like to go to school? Tell me truly."

"But would my mother like me to go?"

"Yes, my child, if it would please you."

"Then, mamma, I should like to go very much."

Her face flushed as she spoke, and I knew that my diagnosis had been correct. I left her saying I should hope to hear from her soon.

At ten o'clock the next day Jarbe came to ask if I had forgotten my engagement.

"No," said I, "but it is only ten o'clock."

"Yes, but we have twenty miles to go."

"Twenty miles?"

"Certainly, the house is at St. Albans."

"It's very strange Pembroke never told me; how did you find out the address?"

"He left it when he went away."

"Just like an Englishman."

I took a post-chaise, and in three hours I had reached my destination. The English roads are excellent, and the country offers a smiling prospect on every side. The vine is lacking, for though the English soil is fertile it will not bear grapes.

Lord Pembroke's house was not a particularly large one, but twenty masters and their servants could easily be accommodated in it.

The lady had not yet arrived, so my lord shewed me his gardens, his fountains, and his magnificent hot-houses; also a cock chained by the leg, and of a truly ferocious aspect.

"What have we here, my lord?"

"A cock."

"I see it is, but why do you chain it?"

"Because it is savage. It is very amorous, and if it were loose it would go after the hens, and kill all the cocks on the country-side."

"But why do you condemn him to celibacy?"

"To make him fiercer. Here, this is the list of his conquests."

He gave me a list of his cock's victories, in which he had killed the other bird; this had happened more than thirty times. He then shewed me the steel spurs, at the sight of which the cock began to ruffle and crow. I could not help laughing to see such a martial spirit in so small an animal. He seemed possessed by the demon of strife, and lifted now one foot and now the other, as if to beg that his arms might be put on.

Pembroke then exhibited the helmet, also of steel.

"But with such arms," said I, "he is sure of conquest."

"No; for when he is armed *cap-à-pie* he will not fight with a defenceless cock."

"I can't believe it, my lord."

"It's a well-known fact. Here, read this."

He then gave me a piece of paper with this remarkable biped's pedigree. He could prove his thirty-two quarters more easily than a good many noblemen, on the father's side, be it understood, for if he could have proved pure blood on the mother's side as well, Lord Pembroke would have decorated him with the Order of the Golden Fleece at least.

"The bird cost me a hundred guineas," said he, "but I would not sell him for a thousand."

"Has he any offspring?"

"He tries his best, but there are difficulties."

I do not remember whether Lord Pembroke explained what these difficulties were. Certainly the English offer more peculiarities to the attentive observer than any other nation.

At last a carriage containing a lady and two gentlemen drove up to the door. One of the gentlemen was the rascally Castelbajac and the other was introduced as Count Schwerin, nephew of the famous marshal of that name who fell on what is commonly called the field of glory. General Bekw—— an Englishman who was in the service of the King of Prussia, and was one of Pembroke's guests, received Schwerin politely, saying that he had seen his uncle die; at this the modest nephew drew the Order of the Black Eagle from his breast, and shewed it to us all covered with blood.

"My uncle wore it on the day of his death, and the King of Prussia allowed me to keep it as a noble memorial of my kinsman."

"Yes," said an Englishman who was present, "but the coat-pocket is not the place for a thing like that."

Schwerin made as if he did not understand, and this enabled me to take his measure.

Lord Pembroke took possession of the lady, whom I did not think worthy of being compared to Pauline. She was paler and shorter, and utterly deficient in Pauline's noble air; besides, when she smiled it spoiled her face, and this is a defect in a woman, to whom laughter should always be becoming.

Lord Pembroke introduced us all to each other, and when he came to me Castelbajac said he was delighted to see me again, although he might easily have pretended not to know me under my name of Seingalt.

We had a good English dinner, and afterwards the lady proposed a game of faro. My lord never played, so the general consented to amuse the company by holding the bank, and placed a hundred guineas and several bank notes on the table. There might be a thousand guineas in all. He then gave twenty counters to each punter, saying that every counter was worth ten shillings. As I only staked gold against gold I would not accept them. By the third deal Schwerin had lost his twenty counters and asked for twenty more; but the banker told him he must pay for them, and the self-styled field-marshal's nephew lapsed into silence and played no more.

At the following deal Castelbajac was in the same position as his friend, and being on my side he begged to be allowed to take ten pieces.

"You will bring me ill-luck," I said, coldly, warding off his hand; and he went out to the garden, no doubt to swallow the affront he had received. The lady said her husband had forgotten his pocket-book. An hour afterwards the game came to an end, and I took my leave, after inviting Lord Pembroke and the rest of the company to dine with me the next day.

I got home at eleven o'clock without meeting any highwaymen as I had expected, indeed I had put up six guineas in a small purse for their special use and benefit. I woke up my cook to tell him that the next day I should have twelve people to dinner, and that I hoped he would do me honour. I found a letter from Madame Cornelis on my table telling me that she and her daughter would drive with me on the following Sunday, and that we could go and see the boarding-school she had selected.

Next day Lord Pembroke and the fair Frenchwoman were the first to arrive. They drove in a carriage with two rather uncomfortable seats, but this discomfort is favourable to love. The Gascon and the Prussian were the last to come.

We sat down to table at two and left it at four, all of us well pleased with the cook, and still more so with the wine merchant; for though we had emptied forty bottles of wine, not one of us was at all intoxicated.

After coffee had been served the general invited us all to sup with him, and Madame Castelbajac begged me to hold a bank. I did not wait to be pressed but placed a thousand guineas on the table, and as I had no counters of any kind I warned the company that I would only play gold against gold, and that I should stop playing whenever I thought fit.

Before the game began the two counts paid their losses of the day before to the general in bank notes, which he begged me to change. I also changed two other notes presented to me by the same gentleman, and put them all under my snuff-box. Play began. I had no croupier, so I was obliged to deal slowly and keep an eye on the two counts, whose method of play was very questionable. At last both of them were dried up, and Castelbajac gave me a bill of exchange for two hundred guineas, begging me to discount it for him.

"I know nothing about business," I replied.

An Englishman took the bill, and after a careful examination said he neither knew the drawer, the accepter, nor the backer.

"I am the backer," said Castelbajac, "and that ought to be enough, I think."

Everybody laughed, besides myself, and I gave it him back courteously, saying politely that he could get it discounted on 'Change the next day. He got up in a bad temper, and left the room, murmuring some insolent expressions. Schwering followed him.

After these two worthy gentlemen had left us, I went on dealing till the night was far advanced, and then left off, though I was at a loss. However, the general had a run of luck, and I thought it best to stop. Before leaving he took me and Lord Pembroke aside, and begged me to contrive that the two knaves should not come to his house the following day. "For," said he, "if that Gascon were to be half as insolent to me as he was to you, I should shew him out by the window."

Pembroke said he would tell the lady of the general's wishes.

"Do you think," said I, "that those four notes of theirs can be forgeries?"

"It's very possible."

"What would you advise my doing to clear the matter up?"

"I would send them to the bank."

"And if they should be forgeries?"

"I would have patience, or I would arrest the rascals."

The next day I went to the bank myself, and the person to whom I gave the notes gave me them back, saying, coldly,——

"These notes are bad, sir."

"Be kind enough to examine them closely."

"It's no good, they are evident forgeries. Return them to the person from whom you got them, and he will be only too glad to cash them."

I was perfectly aware that I could put the two knaves under lock and key, but I did not want to do so. I went to Lord Pembroke to find out their address, but he was still in bed, and one of his servants took me to them. They were surprised to see me. I told them coolly enough that the four notes were forged, and that I should feel much obliged if they would give me forty guineas and take their notes back.

"I haven't got any money," said Castelbajac, "and what you say astonishes me very much. I can only return them to the persons who gave them to me, if they are really the same notes that we gave you yesterday."

At this suggestion the blood rushed to my face, and with a withering glance and an indignant apostrophe I left them. Lord Pembroke's servant took me to a magistrate who, having heard my statement on oath, gave me a paper authorizing me to arrest two counts. I gave the document to an alderman, who said he would see it was carried out, and I went home ill pleased with the whole business.

Martinelli was waiting for me; he had come to ask me to give him a dinner. I told him my story, without adding that the knaves were to be arrested, and his advice delivered with philosophic calm was to make an *auto-da-fé* of the four notes. It was very good advice, but I did not take it.

The worthy Martinelli, thinking to oblige me, told me that he had arranged with Lord Spencer the day on which I was to be introduced to the club, but I answered that my fancy for going there was over. I ought to have treated this learned and distinguished man with more politeness, but who can sound human weakness to its depths? One often goes to a wise man for advice which one has not the courage to follow.

In the evening I went to the general's, and found the self-styled Countess Castelbajac seated on Lord Pem-

broke's knees. The supper was a good one, and passed
off pleasantly; the two rascals were not there, and their
absence was not remarked. When we left the table we
went into another room, and played till day-break. I left
the board with a loss of two or three hundred guineas.

I did not wake till late the next morning, and when I
did my man told me that a person wanted to speak to
me. I had him shewn in, and as he only spoke English
the negro had to be our interpreter. He was the chief of
the police, and told me that if I would pay for the journey he would arrest Castelbajac at Dover, for which
town he had started at noon. As to the other he was
sure of having him in the course of the night. I gave
him a guinea, and told him it would be enough to catch
the one, and that the other could go where he liked.

The next day was Sunday, the only day on which Ma-
dame Cornelis could go abroad without fear of the bailiff.
She came to dine with me, and brought her daughter,
whom the prospect of leaving her mother had quite cured.
The school which Madame Cornelis had chosen was at
Harwich, and we went there after dinner.

The head-mistress was a Catholic, and though she must
have been sixty, she looked keen, witty, and as if she
knew the ways of the world. She had received an introduction from Lady Harrington, and so welcomed the
young lady in the most cordial manner. She had about
fifteen young boarders of thirteen or fourteen years of
age. When she presented Sophie to them as a new companion, they crowded round her and covered her with
caresses. Five or six were perfect angels of beauty, and
two or three were hideously ugly; and such extremes are
more common in England than anywhere else. My
daughter was the smallest of them all, but as far as
beauty went she had nothing to fear by comparison, and

her talents placed her on a par with the eldest, while she responded to their caresses with that ease which later in life is only acquired with great difficulty.

We went over the house, and all the girls followed us, and those who could speak French or Italian spoke to me, saying how much they would love my daughter, while those who could not speak sufficiently well held off as if ashamed of their ignorance. We saw the bedrooms, the dining-room, the drawing-room, the harps and the pianos —in fact, everything, and I decided that Sophie could not be better placed. We went into the head-mistress's private room, and Madame Cornelis paid her a hundred guineas in advance, and obtained a receipt. We then agreed that Sophie should be received as a boarder as soon as she liked to come, that she was to bring her bed with her, and all the necessary linen. Madame Cornelis made the final arrangements on the ensuing Sunday.

Next day the alderman told me that Count Schwerin was a prisoner, and wanted to speak to me. I declined at first, but as the alderman's messenger told me, through Jarbe, that the poor devil had not a farthing in his pocket, I was moved with compassion. As he was charged with uttering forged notes he had been taken to Newgate, and was in danger of being hanged.

I followed the magistrate's messenger, and cannot say how the woeful aspect, the tears and supplications for mercy of the poor wretch, moved my heart. He swore that Castelbajac had given him the notes, but he added that he knew where they came from originally, and would tell me if I would release him.

A little bitterness still remained in my breast, so I told him that if he knew who forged the notes he could certainly escape the gallows, but that I should keep him prisoner till I got my money back. At this threat his tears and supplications began over again and with renewed force, and telling me that he was in utter poverty he emptied his pockets one after the other to shew me that he had no money, and at last offered me the blood-stained badge of his uncle. I was delighted to be able to relieve him without any appearance of weakness, and accepted the bauble as a pledge, telling him that he should have it back on payment of forty pounds.

I wrote out a formal release, and in his presence and in that of the alderman I burnt the four notes and set him free.

Two days afterwards the so-called countess came to my house, saying that now Castelbajac and Schewirin were gone, she knew not where to lay her head. She complained bitterly of Lord Pembroke, who deserted her after making her give him the clearest proofs of her affection. By way of consolation I told her that it would be very foolish of him to have abandoned her before instead of after.

To get rid of her I was obliged to give her the money to pay her journey to Calais. She told me she did not want to rejoin the Gascon, who was not really her husband. We shall hear more of these persons in the course of three years.

Two or three days later an Italian called on me, and gave me a letter from my friend Baletti, which recommended the bearer, Constantini, a native of Vicenza, to my good offices. He had come to London on a matter of importance in which I could help him.

I assured M. Constantini that I was only too happy to do anything to justify the confidence placed in my by one of my best friends, and he said that the long journey had almost exhausted his purse; but he added,——

"I know that my wife lives here, and that she is rich. I shall easily find out where she lives, and you know that as I am her husband all that is hers is mine."

"I was not aware of that."

"Then you don't know the laws of this country?"

"Not at all."

"I am sorry to hear it, but such is the case. I am going to her house, and I shall turn her out of doors with nothing else than the dress on her back, for the furniture, clothes, jewels, linen—in fact, all her possessions, belong to me. May I ask you to be with me when I perform this exploit?"

I was astonished. I asked him if he had told Baletti what he intended to do.

"You are the first person to whom I have disclosed my intentions."

I could not treat him as a madman, for he did not look like one, and, concluding that there really might be the law he had alleged, I replied that I did not feel inclined to join him in his enterprise, of which I disapproved very strongly, unless his wife had actually robbed him of what she possessed.

"She has only robbed me of my honour, sir, and she left me, taking her talents with her. She must have made a great fortune here, and have I not a right to take it from her, were it only for vengeance sake?"

"That may be, but I ask you what you would think of me if I agreed to join you in an undertaking which seems a cruel one to me, however good your reasons may be. Besides I may know your wife, she may even be a friend of mine."

"I will tell you her name."

"No, I beg of you not to do so, although I do not know any Madame Constantini."

"She has changed her name to Calori, and she sings at the 'Haymarket.'"

"I know who she is now. I am sorry you have told me."

"I have no doubt you will keep my secret, and I am now going to find out where she lives; for that is the principal thing."

He left me weeping, and I pitied him, but at the same time I was sorry that he had made me the depositary of his secret. A few hours after I called on Madame Binetti, and she told me the histories of all the artistes in London. When she came to the Calori she told me that she had had several lovers out of whom she had made a great deal, but at present she had no lover, unless it were the violinist Giardini, with whom she was in love in earnest.

"Where does she come from?"

"From Vicenza."

"Is she married?"

"I don't think so."

I thought no more of this wretched business, but three or four days later I had a letter from King's Bench Prison. It was from Constantini. The poor wretch said I was the only friend he had in London, and that he hoped I would come and see him, were it only to give him some advice.

I thought it my duty to accede to his request, and I went to the prison, where I found the poor man in a wretched state, with an old English attorney, who spoke a little bad Italian, and was known to me.

Constantini had been arrested the day before on account of several bills drawn by his wife which had not been taken up. By these bills she appeared in debt to the amount of a thousand guineas. The attorney had got the five bills, and he was trying to make some arrangements with the husband.

I saw at once that the whole thing was a scandalous swindle, for Madame Binetti had told me that the Calori was very rich. I begged the attorney to leave me alone with the prisoner, as I wanted to have some private conversation with him.

"They have arrested me for my wife's debts," said he, "and they tell me I must pay them because I am her husband."

"It's a trick your wife has played on you; she must have found out you were in London."

"She saw me through the window."

"Why did you delay putting your project into execution?"

"I meant to carry it out this morning, but how was I to know that she had debts?"

"Nor has she any debts; these bills are shams. They must have been ante-dated, for they were really executed yesterday. It's a bad business, and she may have to pay dearly for it."

"But in the meanwhile I am in prison."

"Never mind, trust to me, I will see you again to-morrow."

This scurvy trick had made me angry, and I made up my mind to take up the poor man's cause. I went to Bosanquet, who told me that the device was a very common one in London, but that people had found out the way to defeat it. Finally, he said that if the prisoner interested me he would put the case into the hands of a barrister who would extricate him from his difficulty, and make the wife and the lover, who had probably helped her, repent of their day's work. I begged him to act as if my interests were at stake, and promised to guarantee all expenses.

"That's enough," said he; "don't trouble yourself any more about it."

Some days after Mr. Bosanquet came to tell me that Constantini had left the prison and England as well, according to what the barrister who had charge of the case told him.

"Impossible!"

"Not at all. The lover of his wife, foreseeing the storm that was about to burst over their heads, got round the fellow, and made him leave the country by means of a sum more or less large."

The affair was over, but it was soon in all the newspapers, garnished with all the wit imaginable, and Giardini was warmly praised for the action he had taken.

As for me I was glad enough to have the matter over, but I felt vexed with Constantini for having fled without giving the lovers a lesson. I wrote an account of the circumstances to Baletti, and I heard from Madame Binetti that the Calori had given her husband a hundred guineas to leave the country. Some years later I saw the Calori at Prague.

A Flemish officer, the man whom I had helped at Aix-la-Chapelle, had called on me several times, and had even dined three or four times with me. I reproached myself for not having been polite enough to return his call, and when we met in the street, and he reproached me for not having been to see him, I was obliged to blush. He had his wife and daughter with him, and some feeling of shame and a good deal of curiosity made me call on him.

When he saw me he threw his arms about my neck,

calling me his preserver. I was obliged to receive all the compliments which knaves make to honest men when they hope to take them in. A few moments after, an old woman and a girl came in, and I was introduced as the Chevalier de Seingalt, of whom he had spoken so often. The girl, affecting surprise, said she had known a M. Casanova, who was very like me. I answered that Casanova was my name as well as Seingalt, but that I had not the happiness of recollecting her.

"My name was Anspergher when I saw you," she replied, "but now it is Charpillon; and considering that we only met once, and that I was only thirteen at the time, I do not wonder at your not recollecting me. I have been in London with my mother and aunts for the last four years."

"But where had I the pleasure of speaking to you?"

"At Paris."

"In what part of Paris?"

"In the Bazaar. You were with a charming lady, and you gave me these buckles" (she shewed me them on her shoes), "and you also did me the honour to kiss me."

I recollected the circumstance, and the reader will remember that I was with Madame Baret, the fair stocking-seller.

"Now I remember you," said I; "but I do not recognize your aunt."

"This is the sister of the one you saw, but if you will take tea with us you will see her."

"Where do you live?"

"In Denmark Street, Soho."

CHAPTER XI

The Charpillon—Dreadful Consequences of My Acquaintance With Her

THE name Charpillon reminded me that I was the bearer of a letter for her, and drawing it from my pocket-book I gave it her, saying that the document ought to cement our acquaintance.

"What!" she exclaimed, "a letter from the dear ambassador Morosini. How delighted I am to have it! And you have actually been all these months in London without giving it me?"

"I confess I am to blame, but, as you see, the note has no address on it. I am grateful for the chance which has enabled me to discharge my commission to-day."

"Come and dine with us to-morrow."

"I cannot do so, as I am expecting Lord Pembroke to dinner."

"Will you be alone?"

"I expect so."

"I am glad to hear it; you will see my aunt and myself appearing on the scene."

"Here is my address; and I shall be delighted if you will come and see me."

She took the address, and I was surprised to see her smile as she read it.

"Then you are the Italian," she said, "who put up that notice that amused all the town?"

"I am."

302

"They say the joke cost you dear."

"Quite the reverse; it resulted in the greatest happiness."

"But now that the beloved object has left you, I suppose you are unhappy?"

"I am; but there are sorrows so sweet that they are almost joys."

"Nobody knows who she was, but I suppose you do?"

"Yes."

"Do you make a mystery of it?"

"Surely, and I would rather die than reveal it."

"Ask my aunt if I may take some rooms in your house; but I am afraid my mother would not let me."

"Why do you want to lodge cheaply?"

"I don't want to lodge cheaply, but I should like to punish the audacious author of that notice."

"How would you punish me?"

"By making you fall in love with me, and then tormenting you. It would have amused me immensely."

"Then you think that you can inspire me with love, and at the same time form the dreadful plan of tyrannising over the victim of your charms. Such a project is monstrous, and unhappily for us poor men, you do not look a monster. Nevertheless, I am obliged to you for your frankness, and I shall be on my guard."

"Then you must take care never to see me, or else all your efforts will be in vain."

As the Charpillon had laughed merrily through the whole of this dialogue, I took it all as a jest, but I could not help admiring her manner, which seemed made for the subjugation of men. But though I knew it not, the day I made that woman's acquaintance was a luckless one for me, as my readers will see.

It was towards the end of the month of September,

1763, when I met the Charpillon, and from that day I began to die. If the lines of ascent and declination are equal, now, on the first day of November, 1797, I have about four more years of life to reckon on, which will pass by swiftly, according to the axiom *Motus in fine velocior*.

The Charpillon, who was well known in London, and I believe is still alive, was one of those beauties in whom it is difficult to find any positive fault. Her hair was chestnut coloured, and astonishingly long and thick, her blue eyes were at once languorous and brilliant, her skin, faintly tinged with a rosy hue, was of a dazzling whiteness; she was tall for her age, and seemed likely to become as tall as Pauline. Her breast was perhaps a little small, but perfectly shaped, her hands were white and plump, her feet small, and her gait had something noble and gracious. Her features were of that exquisite sensibility which gives so much charm to the fair sex, but nature had given her a beautiful body and a deformed soul. This siren had formed a design to wreck my happiness even before she knew me, and as if to add to her triumph she told me as much.

I left Malingan's house not like a man who, fond of the fair sex, is glad to have made the acquaintance of a beautiful woman, but in a state of stupefaction that the image of Pauline, which was always before me, was not strong enough to overcome the influence of a creature like the Charpillon, whom in my heart I could not help despising.

I calmed myself by saying that this strong impression was due to novelty, and by hoping that I should soon be disenchanted.

"She will have no charm," said I, "when I have once

possessed her, and that will not be long in coming."

Perhaps the reader will think that I was too presump-
tuous, but why should I suppose that there would be
any difficulty? She had asked me to dinner herself, she
had surrendered herself entirely to Morosini, who was
not the man to sigh for long at any woman's feet, and
must have paid her, for he was not young enough nor
handsome enough to inspire her with a fancy for him.
Without counting my physical attractions, I had plenty
of money, and I was not afraid of spending it; and so I
thought I could count on an easy victory.

Pembroke had become an intimate friend of mine
since my proceedings with regard to Schwerin. He admired my conduct in not making any claim on the
general for half my loss. He had said we would make a
pleasant day of it together, and when he saw that my
table was laid for four he asked who the other guests
were to be. He was extremely surprised when he heard
that they were the Charpillon and her aunt, and that the
girl had invited herself when she heard he was to dine
with me.

"I once took a violent fancy for the little hussy," said
he. "It was one evening when I was at Vauxhall, and I
offered her twenty guineas if she would come and take a
little walk with me in a dark alley. She said she would
come if I gave her the money in advan'ce, which I was
fool enough to do. She went with me, but as soon as we
were alone she ran away, and I could not catch her again,
though I looked for her all the evening."

"You ought to have boxed her ears before everybody."

"I should have got into trouble, and people would have
laughed at me besides. I preferred to despise her and
the money too. Are you in love with her?"

"No; but I am curious, as you were."

"Take care! she will do all in her power to entrap you."

She came in and went up to my lord with the most perfect coolness, and began to chatter away to him without taking any notice of me. She laughed, joked, and reproached him for not having pursued her at Vauxhall. Her stratagem, she said, was only meant to excite him the more.

"Another time," she added, "I shall not escape you."

"Perhaps not, my dear, for another time I shall take care not to pay in advance."

"Oh, fie! you degrade yourself by talking about paying."

"I suppose I honour you."

"We never talk of such things."

Lord Pembroke laughed at her impertinences, while she made a vigorous assault on him, for his coolness and indifference piqued her.

She left us soon after dinner, making me promise to dine with her the day after next.

I passed the next day with the amiable nobleman who initiated me into the mysteries of the English bagnio, an entertainment which I shall not describe, for it is well known to all who care to spend six guineas.

On the day appointed, my evil destiny made me go to the Charpillon's; the girl introduced me to her mother, whom I at once recollected, although she had aged and altered since I had seen her.

In the year 1759 a Genevan named Bolomé had persuaded me to sell her jewels to the extent of six thousand francs, and she had paid me in bills drawn by her and her two sisters on this Bolomé, but they were then known as Anspergher. The Genevan became bankrupt before the bills were due, and the three sisters disappeared. As may be imagined, I was surprised to find them in England, and especially to be introduced to them by the Charpillon, who, knowing nothing of the affair of the jewels, had not told them that Seingalt was the same as Casanova, whom they had cheated of six thousand francs.

"I am delighted to see you again," were the first words I addressed to her.

"I recollect you, sir; that rascal Bolomé . . . ."

"We will discuss that subject another time. I see you are ill."

"I have been at death's door, but I am better now. My daughter did not tell me your proper name."

"Yes, she did. My name is Seingalt as well as Casanova. I was known by the latter name at Paris when I made your daughter's acquaintance, though I did not know then that she was your daughter."

Just then the grandmother, whose name was also Anspergher, came in with the two aunts, and a quarter of an hour later three men arrived, one of whom was the Chevalier Goudar, whom I had met at Paris. I did not know the others who were introduced to me under the names of Rostaing and Caumon. They were three friends of the household, whose business it was to bring in dupes.

Such was the infamous company in which I found myself, and though I took its measure directly, yet I did not make my escape, nor did I resolve never to go to the house again. I was fascinated; I thought I would be on my guard and be safe, and as I only wanted the daughter I looked on all else as of little moment.

At table I led the conversation, and thought that my prey would soon be within my grasp. The only thing which annoyed me was that the Charpillon, after apologizing for having made me sit down to such a poor dinner, invited herself and all the company to sup with me on any day I liked to mention. I could make no opposition, so I begged her to name the day herself, and she did so, after a consultation with her worthy friends.

After coffee had been served we played four rubbers of whist, at which I lost, and at midnight I went away ill pleased with myself, but with no purpose of amendment, for this sorceress had got me in her toils.

All the same I had the strength of mind to refrain from seeing her for two days, and on the third, which was the day appointed for the cursed supper, she and her aunt paid me a call at nine o'clock in the morning.

"I have come to breakfast with you, and to discuss a certain question," said she, in the most engaging manner.

"Will you tell me your business now, or after breakfast?"

"After breakfast; for we must be alone."

We had our breakfast, and then the aunt went into another room, and the Charpillon, after describing the monetary situation of the family, told me that it would be much relieved if her aunt could obtain a hundred guineas.

"What would she do with the money?"

"She would make the Balm of Life, of which she possesses the secret, and no doubt she would make her fortune, too."

She then began to dilate on the marvellous properties of the balm, on its probable success in a town like London, and on the benefits which would accrue to myself, for of course I should share in the profits. She added that her mother and aunt would give me a written promise to repay the money in the course of six years.

"I will give you a decided answer after supper."

I then began to caress her, and to make assaults in the style of an amorous man, but it was all in vain, though I succeeded in stretching her on a large sofa. She made her escape, however, and ran to her aunt, while I followed her, feeling obliged to laugh as she did. She gave me her hand, and said,——

"Farewell, till this evening."

When they were gone, I reflected over what had passed and thought this first scene of no bad augury. I saw that I should get nothing out of her without spending a hundred guineas, and I determined not to attempt to bargain, but I would let her understand that she must make up her mind not to play prude. The game was in my hands, and all I had to do was to take care not to be duped.

In the evening the company arrived, and the girl asked me to hold a bank till supper was ready; but I declined, with a burst of laughter that seemed to puzzle her.

"At least, let us have a game of whist," said she.

"It seems to me," I answered, "that you don't feel very anxious to hear my reply."

"You have made up your mind, I suppose?"

"I have, follow me."

She followed me into an adjoining room, and after she had seated herself on a sofa, I told her that the hundred guineas were at her disposal.

"Then please to give the money to my aunt, otherwise these gentlemen might think I got it from you by some improper means."

"I will do so."

I tried to get possession of her, but in vain; and I ceased my endeavours when she said,——

"You will get nothing from me either by money or

violence; but you can hope for all when I find you really nice and quiet."

I re-entered the drawing-room, and feeling my blood boiling I began to play to quiet myself. She was as gay as ever, but her gaiety tired me. At supper I had her on my right hand, but the hundred impertinences which, under other circumstances, would have amused me, only wearied me, after the two rebuffs I had received from her.

After supper, just as they were going, she took me aside, and told me that if I wanted to hand over the hundred guineas she would tell her aunt to go with me into the next room.

"As documents have to be executed," I replied, "it will take some time; we will talk of it again."

"Won't you fix the time?"

I drew out my purse full of gold, and shewed it her, saying,——

"The time depends entirely on you."

When my hateful guests were gone, I began to reflect, and came to the conclusion that this young adventuress had determined to plunder me without giving me anything in return. I determined to have nothing more to do with her, but I could not get her beauty out of my mind.

I felt I wanted some distraction, something that would give me new aims and make me forget her. With this idea I went to see my daughter, taking with me an immense bag of sweets.

As soon as I was in the midst of the little flock, the delight became general, Sophie distributing the sweetmeats to her friends, who received them gratefully.

I spent a happy day, and for a week or two I paid several visits to Harwich. The mistress treated me with the utmost politeness and my daughter with boundless affection, always calling me "dear papa."

In less than three weeks I congratulated myself on having forgotten the Charpillon, and on having replaced her by innocent amours, though one of my daughter's schoolmates pleased me rather too much for my peace of mind.

Such was my condition when one morning the favourite aunt of the Charpillon paid me a call, and said that they were all mystified at not having seen me since the supper I had given them, especially herself, as her niece had given her to understand that I would furnish her with the means of making the Balm of Life.

"Certainly; I would have given you the hundred guineas if your niece had treated me as a friend, but she refused me favours a vestal might have granted, and you must be aware that she is by no means a vestal."

"Don't mind my laughing. My niece is an innocent, giddy girl; she loves you, but she is afraid you have only a passing whim for her. She is in bed now with a bad cold, and if you will come and see her I am sure you will be satisfied."

These artful remarks, which had no doubt been prepared in advance, ought to have aroused all my scorn, but instead of that they awakened the most violent desires. I laughed in chorus with the old woman, and asked what would be the best time to call.

"Come now, and give one knock."

"Very good, then you may expect me shortly."

I congratulated myself on being on the verge of success, for after the explanation I had had with the aunt, and having, as I thought, a friend in her, I did not doubt that I should succeed.

I put on my great coat, and in less than a quarter of

an hour I knocked at their door. The aunt opened to me, and said,——

"Come back in a quarter of an hour; she has been ordered a bath, and is just going to take it."

"This is another imposture. You're as bad a liar as she is."

"You are cruel and unjust, and if you will promise to be discreet, I will take you up to the third floor where she is bathing."

"Very good; take me." She went upstairs, I following on tiptoe, and pushed me into a room, and shut the door upon me. The Charpillon was in a huge bath, with her head towards the door, and the infernal coquette, pretending to think it was her aunt, did not move, and said,——

"Give me the towels, aunt."

She was in the most seductive posture, and I had the pleasure of gazing on her exquisite proportions, hardly veiled by the water.

When she caught sight of me, or rather pretended to do so, she gave a shriek, huddled her limbs together, and said, with affected anger,——

"Begone!"

"You needn't exert your voice, for I am not going to be duped."

"Begone!"

"Not so, give me a little time to collect myself."

"I tell you, go!"

"Calm yourself, and don't be afraid of my shewing you any violence; that would suit your game too well."

"My aunt shall pay dearly for this."

"She will find me her friend. I won't touch you, so shew me a little more of your charms."

"More of my charms?"

"Yes; put yourself as you were when I came in."

"Certainly not. Leave the room."

"I have told you I am not going, and that you need not fear for your . . . well, for your virginity, we will say."

She then shewed me a picture more seductive than the first, and pretending kindliness, said,——

"Please, leave me; I will not fail to shew my gratitude."

Seeing that she got nothing, that I refrained from touching her, and that the fire she had kindled was in a fair way to be put out, she turned her back to me to give me to understand that it was no pleasure to her to look at me. However, my passions were running high, and I had to have recourse to self-abuse to calm my senses, and was glad to find myself relieved, as this proved to me that the desire went no deeper than the senses.

The aunt came in just as I had finished, and I went out without a word, well pleased to find myself despising a character wherein profit and loss usurped the place of feeling.

The aunt came to me as I was going out of the house, and after enquiring if I were satisfied begged me to come into the parlour.

"Yes," said I, "I am perfectly satisfied—to know you and your niece. Here is the reward."

With these words I drew a bank-note for a hundred pounds from my pocket-book, and was foolish enough to give it her, telling her that she could make her balm, and need not trouble to give me any document as I knew if would be of no value. I had not the strength to go away without giving her anything, and the procuress was sharp enough to know it.

When I got home I reflected on what had happened,

and pronounced myself the conqueror with great triumph. I felt well at ease, and felt sure that I should never set foot in that house again. There were seven of them altogether, including servants, and the need of subsisting made them do anything for a living; and when they found themselves obliged to make use of men, they summoned the three rascals I have named, who were equally dependent on them.

Five or six days afterwards, I met the little hussy at Vauxhall in company with Goudar. I avoided her at first, but she came up to me reproaching me for my rudeness. I replied coolly enough, but affecting not to notice my manner, she asked me to come into an arbour with her and take a cup of tea.

"No, thank you," I replied, "I prefer supper."

"Then I will take some too, and you will give it me, won't you, just to shew that you bear no malice?"

I ordered supper for four and we sat down together as if we had been intimate friends.

Her charming conversation combined with her beauty gradually drew me under her charm, and as the drink began to exercise its influence over me, I proposed a turn in one of the dark walks, expressing a hope that I should fare better than Lord Pembroke. She said gently, and with an appearance of sincerity that deceived me, that she wanted to be mine, but by day and on the condition that I would come and see her every day.

"I will do so, but first give me one little proof of your love."

"Most certainly not."

I got up to pay the bill, and then I left without a word, refusing to take her home. I went home by myself and went to bed.

The first thought when I awoke was that I was glad she had not taken me at my word; I felt very strongly that it was to my interest to break off all connection between that creature and myself. I felt the strength of her influence over me, and that my only way was to keep away from her, or to renounce all pretension to the possession of her charms.

The latter plan seemed to me impossible, so I determined to adhere to the first; but the wretched woman had resolved to defeat all my plans. The manner in which she succeeded must have been the result of a council of the whole society.

A few days after the Vauxhall supper Goudar called on me, and began by congratulating me on my resolution not to visit the Ansperghers any more, "for," said he, "the girl would have made you more and more in love with her, and in the end she would have seduced you to beggary."

"You must think me a great fool. If I had found her kind I should have been grateful, but without squandering all my money; and if she had been cruel, instead of ridiculous, I might have given her what I have already given her every day, without reducing myself to beggary."

"I congratulate you; it shews that you are well off. But have you made up your mind not to see her again?"

"Certainly."

"Then you are not in love with her?"

"I have been in love, but I am so no longer; and in a few days she will have passed completely out of my memory. I had almost forgotten her when I met her with you at Vauxhall."

"You are not cured. The way to be cured of an amour

does not lie in flight, when the two parties live in the same town. Meetings will happen, and all the trouble has to be taken over again."

"Then do you know a better way?"

"Certainly; you should satiate yourself. It is quite possible that the creature is not in love with you, but you are rich and she has nothing. You might have had her for so much, and you could have left her when you found her to be unworthy of your constancy. You must know what kind of a woman she is."

"I should have tried this method gladly, but I found her out."

"You could have got the best of her, though, if you had gone to work in the proper way. You should never have paid in advance. I know everything."

"What do you mean?"

"I know she has cost you a hundred guineas, and that you have not won so much as a kiss from her. Why, my dear sir, you might have had her comfortably in your own bed for as much! She boasts that she took you in, though you pride yourself on your craft."

"It was an act of charity towards her aunt."

"Yes, to make her Balm of Life; but you know if it had not been for the niece the aunt would never have had the money."

"Perhaps not, but how come you who are of their party to be talking to me in this fashion?"

"I swear to you I only speak out of friendship for you, and I will tell you how I came to make the acquaintance of the girl, her mother, her grandmother and her two aunts, and then you will no longer consider me as of their party.

"Sixteen months ago I saw M. Morosini walking

about Vauxhall by himself. He had just come to England to congratulate the king on his accession to the
throne, on behalf of the Republic of Venice. I saw
how enchanted he was with the London beauties, and
I went up to him and told him that all these beauties
were at his service. This made him laugh, and on my
repeating that it was not a jest he pointed out one of
the girls, and asked if she would be at his service. I
did not know her, so I asked him to wait awhile, and
I would bring him the information he required. There
was no time to be lost, and I could see that the girl was
not a vestal virgin, so I went up to her and told her
that the Venetian ambassador was amorous of her, and
that I would take her to him if she would receive his
visits. The aunt said that a nobleman of such an exalted rank could only bring honour to her niece. I took
their address, and on my way back to the ambassador
I met a friend of mine who is learned in such com-
modities, and after I had shewed him the address he
told me it was the Charpillon."

"And it was she?"

"It was. My friend told me she was a young Swiss
girl who was not yet in the general market, but who
would soon be there, as she was not rich, and had a
numerous train to support.

"I rejoined the Venetian, and told him that his business was done, and asked him at what time I should
introduce him the next day, warning him that as she
had a mother and aunts she would not be alone.

" 'I am glad to hear it,' said he, 'and also that she is
not a common woman.' He gave me an appointment
for the next day, and we parted.

"I told the ladies at what hour I should have the

pleasure of introducing the great man to them, and after warning them that they must appear not to know him I went home.

"The following day I called on M. de Morosini, and took him to Denmark Street incognito. We spent an hour in conversation, and then went away without anything being settled. On the way back the ambassador told me that he should like to have the girl on conditions which he would give me in writing at his residence.

"These conditions were that she should live in a furnished house free of rent, without any companion, and without receiving any visitors. His excellency would give her fifty guineas a month, and pay for supper whenever he came and spent the night with her. He told me to get the house if his conditions were received. The mother was to sign the agreement.

"The ambassador was in a hurry, and in three days the agreement was signed; but I obtained a document from the mother promising to let me have the girl for one night as soon as the Venetian had gone; it was known he was only stopping in London for a year."

Goudar extracted the document in question from his pocket, and gave it to me. I read it and re-read it with as much surprise as pleasure, and he then proceeded with his story.

"When the ambassador had gone, the Charpillon, finding herself at liberty once more, had Lord Baltimore, Lord Grosvenor, and M. de Saa, the Portuguese ambassador, in turn, but no titular lover. I insisted on having my night with her according to agreement, but both mother and daughter laughed at me when I spoke of it. I cannot arrest her, because she is a minor, but I will have the mother imprisoned on the first opportunity, and you will see how the town will laugh. Now you know why I go to their house; and I assure you you are wrong if you think I have any part in their councils. Nevertheless, I know they are discussing how they may catch you, and they will do so if you do not take care."

"Tell the mother that I have another hundred guineas at her service if she will let me have her daughter for a single night."

"Do you mean that?"

"Assuredly, but I am not going to pay in advance."

"That's the only way not to be duped. I shall be glad to execute your commission."

I kept the rogue to dinner, thinking he might be useful to me. He knew everything and everybody, and told me a number of amusing ancedotes. Although a good-for-nothing fellow, he had his merits. He had written several works, which, though badly constructed, shewed he was a man of some wit. He was then writing his "Chinese Spy," and every day he wrote five or six news-letters from the various coffee-houses he frequented. I wrote one or two letters for him, with which he was much pleased. The reader will see how I met him again at Naples some years later.

The next morning, what was my surprise to see the Charpillon, who said with an air that I should have taken for modesty in any other woman,——

"I don't want you to give me any breakfast, I want an explanation, and to introduce Miss Lorenzi to you."

I bowed to her and to her companion, and then said,——

"What explanation do you require?"

At this, Miss Lorenzi, whom I had never seen before, thought proper to leave us, and I told my man that I was not at home to anybody. I ordered breakfast to be served to the companion of the nymph, that she might not find the waiting tedious.

"Sir," said the Charpillon, "is it a fact that you charged the Chevalier Goudar to tell my mother that you would give a hundred guineas to spend the night with me?"

"No, not to spend a night with you, but after I had passed it. Isn't the price enough?"

"No jesting, sir, if you please. There is no question of bargaining; all I want to know is whether you think you have a right to insult me, and that I am going to bear it?"

"If you think yourself insulted, I may, perhaps, confess I was wrong; but I confess I did not think I should have to listen to any reproaches from you. Goudar is one of your intimate friends, and this is not the first proposal he has taken to you. I could not address you directly, as I know your arts only too well."

"I shall not pay any attention to your abuse of myself; I will only remind you of what I said—'that neither money nor violence were of any use,' and that your only way was to make me in love with you by gentle means. Shew me where I have broken my word! It is you that have foresworn yourself in coming into my bath-room, and in sending such a brutal message to my mother. No one but a rascal like Goudar would have dared to take such a message."

"Goudar a rascal, is he? Well, he is your best friend. You know he is in love with you, and that he only got you for the ambassador in the hope of enjoying you himself. The document in his possession proves that you have behaved badly towards him. You are in his debt, discharge it, and then call him a rascal if you have the conscience to do so. You need not trouble to weep, for I knew the source of those tears; it is defiled."

"You know nothing of it. I love you, and it is hard to have you treat me so."

"You love me? You have not taken the best way to prove it."

"As good a way as yours. You have behaved to me as if I were the vilest of prostitutes, and yesterday you seemed to think I was a brute beast, the slave of my mother. You should have written to me in person, and without the intervention of so vile an agent; I should have replied in the same way, and you need not have been afraid that you would be deceived."

"Supposing I had written, what would your answer have been?"

"I should have put all money matters out of question. I should have promised to content you on the condition that you would come and court me for a fortnight without demanding the slightest favour. We should have lived a pleasant life; we should have gone to the theatre and to the parks. I should have become madly in love with you. Then I should have given myself up to you for love, and nothing but love. I am ashamed to say that hitherto I have only given myself out of mere complaisance. Unhappy woman that I am! but I think nature meant me to love, and I thought when I saw you that my happy star had sent you to England that I might know the bliss of true affection. Instead of this you have only made me unhappy. You are the first man that has seen me weep; you have troubled my peace at home, for my mother shall never have the sum you promised her were it for nothing but a kiss."

"I am sorry to have injured you, though I did not intend to do so; but I really don't know what I can do."

"Come and see us, and keep your money, which I

despise. If you love me, come and conquer me like a reasonable and not a brutal lover; and I will help you, for now you cannot doubt that I love you."

All this seemed so natural to me that I never dreamed it contained a trap. I was caught, and I promised to do what she wished, but only for a fortnight. She confirmed her promise, and her countenance became once more serene and calm. The Charpillon was a born actress.

She got up to go, and on my begging a kiss as a pledge of our reconciliation she replied, with a smile, the charm of which she well knew, that it would not do to begin by breaking the term of our agreement, and she left me more in love than ever, and full of repentance for my conduct.

CHAPTER XII

Goudar's Chair

IF SHE had written all this to me instead of coming
and delivering it *vivâ voce*, it would probably have
produced no effect; there would have been no tears, no
ravishing features. She probably calculated all this, for
women have a wonderful instinct in these matters.

That very evening I began my visits, and judged from
my welcome that my triumph was nigh at hand. But
love fills our minds with idle visions, and draws a veil
over the truth.

The fortnight went by without my even kissing her
hand, and every time I came I brought some expensive
gift, which seemed cheap to me when I obtained such
smiles of gratitude in exchange. Besides these presents,
not a day passed without some excursion to the country
or party at the theatre; that fortnight must have cost
me four hundred guineas at the least.

At last it came to an end, and I asked her in the
presence of her mother where she would spend the night
with me, there or at my house. The mother said that
we would settle it after supper, and I made no objection,
not liking to tell her that in my house the supper would
be more succulent, and a better prelude for the kind
of exercise I expected to enjoy.

When we had supped the mother took me aside, and
asked me to leave with the company and then to come
back. I obeyed, laughing to myself at this foolish

mystery, and when I came back I found the mother and the daughter in the parlour, in which a bed had been laid on the floor.

Though I did not much care for this arrangement, I was too amorous to raise any objection at a moment when I thought my triumph was at hand; but I was astonished when the mother asked me if I would like to pay the hundred guineas in advance.

"Oh, fie!" exclaimed the girl; and her mother left the room, and we locked the door.

My amorous feelings, so long pent up within my breast, would soon find relief. I approached her with open arms; but she avoided my caress, and gently begged me to get into bed while she prepared to follow me. I watched her undress with delight, but when she had finished she put out the candles. I complained of this act of hers, but she said she could not sleep with the light shining on her. I began to suspect that I might have some difficulties thrown in my way to sharpen the pleasure, but I determined to be resigned and to overcome them all.

When I felt her in the bed I tried to clasp her in my arms, but found that she had wrapped herself up in her long night-gown; her arms were crossed, and her head buried in her chest. I entreated, scolded, cursed, but all in vain; she let me go on, and answered not a word.

At first I thought it was a joke, but I soon found out my mistake; the veil fell from my eyes and I saw myself in my true colours, the degraded dupe of a vile prostitute.

Love easily becomes fury. I began to handle her roughly, but she resisted and did not speak. I tore her night-gown to rags, but I could not tear it entirely off her. My rage grew terrible, my hands became talons, and I treated her with the utmost cruelty; but all for nothing. At last, with my hand on her throat, I felt tempted to strangle her; and then I knew it was time for me to go.

It was a dreadful night. I spoke to this monster of a woman in every manner and tone—with gentleness, with argument, rage, remonstrance, prayers, tears, and abuse, but she resisted me for three hours without abandoning her painful position, in spite of the torments I made her endure.

At three o'clock in the morning, feeling my mind and body in a state of exhaustion, I got up and dressed myself by my sense of touch. I opened the parlour door, and finding the street door locked I shook it till a servant came and let me out. I went home and got into bed, but excited nature refused me the sleep I needed so. I took a cup of chocolate, but it would not stay on my stomach, and soon after a shivering fit warned me that I was feverish. I continued to be ill till the next day, and then the fever left me in a state of complete exhaustion.

As I was obliged to keep to my bed for a few days, I knew that I should soon get my health again; but my chief consolation was that at last I was cured. My shame had made me hate myself.

When I felt the fever coming on I told my man not to let anybody come to see me, and to place all my letters in my desk; for I wanted to be perfectly well before I troubled myself with anything.

On the fourth day I was better, and I told Jarbe to give me my letters. I found one from Pauline, dated from Madrid, in which she informed me that Clairmont had saved her life while they were fording a river, and she had determined to keep him till she got to Lisbon, and would then send him back by sea. I congratulated myself at the time on her resolve; but it was a fatal one for Clairmont, and indirectly for me also. Four months after, I heard that the ship in which he had sailed had been wrecked, and as I never heard from him again I could only conclude that my faithful servant had perished amidst the waves.

Amongst my London letters I found two from the infamous mother of the infamous Charpillon, and one from the girl herself. The first of the mother's letters, written before I was ill, told me that her daughter was ill in bed, covered with bruises from the blows I had given her, so that she would be obliged to institute legal proceedings against me. In the second letter she said she had heard I too was ill, and that she was sorry to hear it, her daughter having informed her that I had some reason for my anger; however, she would not fail to justify herself on the first opportunity. The Charpillon said in her letter that she knew she had done wrong, and that she wondered I had not killed her when I took her by the throat. She added that no doubt I had made up my mind to visit her no more, but she hoped I would allow her one interview as she had an important communication to make to me. There was also a note from Goudar, saying that he wanted to speak to me, and that he would come at noon. I gave orders that he should be admitted.

This curious individual began by astonishing me; he told me the whole story of what had taken place, the mother having been his informant.

"The Charpillon," he added, "has not got a fever, but is covered with bruises. What grieves the old woman most is that she has not got the hundred guineas."

"She would have had them the next morning," I said, "if her daughter had been tractable."

"Her mother had made her swear that she would not be tractable, and you need not hope to possess her without the mother's consent."

"Why won't she consent?"

"Because she thinks that you will abandon the girl as soon as you have enjoyed her."

"Possibly, but she would have received many valuable presents, and now she is abandoned and has nothing."

"Have you made up your mind not to have anything more to do with her?"

"Quite."

"That's your wisest plan, and I advise you to keep to it, nevertheless I want to shew you something which will surprise you. I will be back in a moment."

He returned, followed by a porter, who carried up an arm-chair covered with a cloth. As soon as we were alone, Goudar took off the covering and asked me if I would buy it.

"What should I do with it? It is not a very attractive piece of furniture."

"Nevertheless, the price of it is a hundred guineas."

"I would not give three."

"This arm-chair has five springs, which come into play all at once as soon as anyone sits down in it. Two springs catch the two arms and hold them tightly, two others separate the legs, and the fifth lifts up the seat."

After this description Goudar sat down quite naturally in the chair and the springs came into play and forced him into the position of a woman in labour.

"Get the fair Charpillon to sit in this chair," said he, "and your business is done."

I could not help laughing at the contrivance, which struck me as at once ingenious and diabolical, but I could not make up my mind to avail myself of it.

"I won't buy it," said I, "but I shall be obliged if you will leave it here till to-morrow."

"I can't leave it here an hour unless you will buy it; the owner is waiting close by to hear your answer."

"Then take it away and come back to dinner."

He shewed me how I was to release him from his ridiculous position, and then after covering it up again he called the porter and went away.

There could be no doubt as to the action of the machinery, and it was no feeling of avarice which hindered me from buying the chair. As I have said, it seemed rather a diabolical idea, and besides it might easily have sent me to the gallows. Furthermore, I should never have had the strength of mind to enjoy the Charpillon forcibly, especially by means of the wonderful chair, the mechanism of which would have frightened her out of her wits.

At dinner I told Goudar that the Charpillon had demanded an interview, and that I had wished to keep the chair so as to shew her that I could have her if I liked. I shewed him the letter, and he advised me to accede to her request, if only for curiosity's sake.

I was in no hurry to see the creature while the marks on her face and neck were still fresh, so I spent seven or eight days without making up my mind to receive her. Goudar came every day, and told me of the confabulations of these women who had made up their minds not to live save by trickery.

He told me that the grandmother had taken the name of Anspergher without having any right to it, as she was merely the mistress of a worthy citizen of Berne, by whom she had four daughters; the mother of the Charpillon was the youngest of the family, and, as she was pretty and loose in her morals, the Government had exiled her with her mother and sisters. They had then betaken themselves to Franche-Comté, where they lived for some time on the Balm of Life. Here it was that the Charpillon came into the world, her mother attributing her to a Count de Boulainvilliers. The child grew up pretty, and the family removed to Paris under the impression that it would be the best market for such a commodity, but in the course of four years the income from the Balm having dwindled greatly, the Charpillon being still too young to be profitable, and debtors closing round them on every side, they resolved to come to London.

He then proceeded to tell me of the various tricks and cheats which kept them all alive. I found his narrative interesting enough then, but the reader would find it dull, and I expect will be grateful for my passing it over.

I felt that it was fortunate for me that I had Goudar, who introduced me to all the most famous courtezans in London, above all to the illustrious Kitty Fisher, who was just beginning to be fashionable. He also introduced me to a girl of sixteen, a veritable prodigy of beauty, who served at the bar of a tavern at which we took a bottle of strong beer. She was an Irishwoman and a Catholic, and was named Sarah. I should have liked to get possession of her, but Goudar had views of his own on the subject, and carried her off in the course of the next year. He ended by marrying her, and she was the Sara Goudar who shone at Naples, Florence, Venice, and elsewhere. We shall hear of her in four or five years, still with her husband. Goudar had conceived the plan of making her take the place of Dubarry, mistress of Louis XV., but a *lettre de cachet* compelled him to try elsewhere. Ah! happy days of *lettres de cachet,* you have gone never to return!

The Charpillon waited a fortnight for me to reply, and then resolved to return to the charge in person. This was no doubt the result of a conference of the most secret kind, for I heard nothing of it from Goudar.

She came to see my by herself in a sedan-chair, and I decided on seeing her. I was taking my chocolate and I let her come in without rising or offering her any breakfast. She asked me to give her some with great modesty, and put up her face for me to give her a kiss, but I turned my head away. However, she was not in the least disconcerted.

"I suppose the marks of the blows you gave me make my face so repulsive?"

"You lie; I never struck you."

"No, but your tiger-like claws have left bruises all over me. Look here. No, you needn't be afraid that what you see may prove too seductive; besides, it will have no novelty for you."

So saying the wretched creature let me see her body, on which some livid marks were still visible.

Coward that I was! Why did I not look another way? I will tell you: it was because she was so beautiful, and because a woman's charms are unworthy of the name if they cannot silence reason. I affected only to look at the bruises, but it was an empty farce. I blush for myself; here was I conquered by a simple girl, ignorant of well nigh everything. But she knew well enough that I was inhaling the poison at every pore. All at once she dropped her clothes and came and sat beside me, feeling sure that I should have relished a continuance of the spectacle.

However, I made an effort and said, coldly, that it was all her own fault.

"I know it is," said she, "for if I had been tractable as I ought to have been, you would have been loving instead of cruel. But repentance effaces sin, and I am come to beg pardon. May I hope to obtain it?"

"Certainly; I am angry with you no longer, but I cannot forgive myself. Now go, and trouble me no more."

"I will if you like, but there is something you have not heard, and I beg you will listen to me a moment."

"As I have nothing to do you can say what you have got to say, I will listen to you."

In spite of the coldness of my words, I was really profoundly touched, and the worst of it was that I began to believe in the genuineness of her motives.

She might have relieved herself of what she had to say in a quarter of an hour, but by dint of tears, sighs, groans, digressions, and so forth, she took two hours to tell me that her mother had made her swear to pass the night as she had done. She ended by saying that she would like to be mine as she had been M. Morosini's, to live with me, and only to go out under my escort, while I might allow her a monthly sum which she would hand over to her mother, who would, in that case, leave her alone.

She dined with me, and it was in the evening that she made this proposition. I suppose because she thought me ripe for another cheat. I told her that it might be arranged, but that I should prefer to settle with her mother, and that she would see me at their house the following day, and this seemed to surprise her.

It is possible that the Charpillon would have granted me any favour on that day, and then there would have been no question of deception or resistance for the future. Why did I not press her? Because sometimes love stupefies instead of quickens, and because I had been in a way her judge, and I thought it would be base of me to revenge myself on her by satisfying my amorous desires, and possibly because I was a fool, as I have often been in the course of my existence.

She must have left me in a state of irritation, and no doubt she registered a vow to revenge herself on me for the half-contemptuous way in which I had treated her.

Goudar was astonished when he heard of her visit, and of the way in which I had spent the day. I begged him to get me a small furnished house, and in the evening I went to see the infamous woman in her own house.

She was with her mother, and I laid my proposal before them.

"Your daughter will have a house at Chelsea," said I to the mother, "where I can go and see her whenever I like, and also fifty guineas a month to do what she likes with."

"I don't care what you give her a month," she replied, "but before I let her leave my house she must give me the hundred guineas she was to have had when she slept with you."

"It is your fault that she didn't have them; however, to cut the matter short, she shall give them to you."

"And in the meanwhile, till you have found the house, I hope you will come and see me."

"Yes."

The next day Goudar shewed me a pretty house at Chelsea, and I took it, paying ten guineas, a month's rent, in advance, for which I received a receipt. In the afternoon I concluded the bargain with the mother, the

Charpillon being present. The mother asked me to give her the hundred guineas, and I did so, not fearing any treachery, as nearly the whole of the girl's clothing was already at Chelsea.

In due course we went to our country house. The Charpillon liked the house immensely, and after a short talk we supped merrily together. After supper we went to bed, and she granted me some slight preliminary favours, but when I would have attained my end I found an obstacle which I had not expected. She gave me some physiological reasons for the circumstances, but not being a man to stop for so little, I would have gone on, but she resisted, and yet with such gentleness that I left her alone and went to sleep. I awoke sooner than she did, and determined to see whether she had imposed on me; so I raised her night-gown carefully, and took off her linen only to find that I had been duped once more. This roused her, and she tried to stop me, but it was too late. However, I gently chid her for the trick, and feeling disposed to forgive it set about making up for lost time, but she got on the high horse, and pretended to be hurt at my taking her by surprise. I tried to calm her by renewed tenderness, but the wretched creature only got more furious, and would give me nothing. I left her alone, but I expressed my opinion of her in pretty strong terms. The impudent slut honoured me with a smile of disdain, and then beginning to dress herself she proceeded to indulge in impertinent repartees. This made me angry, and I gave her a box on the ears which stretched her at full length on the floor. She shrieked, stamped her feet, and made a hideous uproar; the landlord came up, and she began to speak to him in English, while the blood gushed from her nose.

The man fortunately spoke Italian, and told me that

she wanted to go away, and advised me to let her do so, or she might make it awkward for me, and he himself would be obliged to witness against me.

"Tell her to begone as fast as she likes," said I, "and to keep out of my sight for ever."

She finished dressing, staunched the blood, and went off in a sedan-chair, while I remained petrified, feeling that I did not deserve to live, and finding her conduct utterly outrageous and incomprehensible.

After an hour's consideration I decided on sending her back her trunk, and then I went home and to bed, telling my servants I was not at home to anyone.

I spent twenty-four hours in pondering over my wrongs, and at last my reason told me that the fault was mine; I despised myself. I was on the brink of suicide, but happily I escaped that fate.

I was just going out when Goudar came up and made me go in with him, as he said he wanted to speak to me. After telling me that the Charpillon had come home with a swollen cheek which prevented her shewing herself, he advised me to abandon all claims on her or her mother, or the latter would bring a false accusation against me which might cost me my life. Those who know England, and especially London will not need to be informed as to the nature of this accusation, which is so easily brought in England; it will suffice to say that through it Sodom was overwhelmed.

"The mother has engaged me to mediate," said Goudar, "and if you will leave her alone, she will do you no harm."

I spent the day with him, foolishly complaining, and telling him that he could assure the mother that I would take no proceedings against her, but that I should

like to know if she had the courage to receive this assurance from my own lips.

"I will carry your message," said he, "but I pity you;
for you are going into their nets again, and will end in
utter ruin."

I fancied they would be ashamed to see me; but I was
very much mistaken, for Goudar came back laughing,
and said the mother expressed a hope that I should always be the friend of the family. I ought to have refused to have anything more to do with them, but I had
not the strength to play the man. I called at Denmark
Street the same evening, and spent an hour without uttering a syllable. The Charpillon sat opposite to me,
with eyes lowered to a piece of embroidery, while from
time to time she pretended to wipe away a tear as she
let me see the ravages I had worked on her cheek.

I saw her every day and always in silence till the fatal
mark had disappeared, but during these mad visits the
poison of desire was so instilled into my veins that if
she had known my state of mind she might have de-
spoiled me of all I possessed for a single favour.

When she was once more as beautiful as ever I felt as
if I must die if I did not hold her in my arms again,
and I bought a magnificent pier-glass and a splendid
breakfast service in Dresden china, and sent them to her
with an amorous epistle which must have made her think
me either the most extravagant or the most cowardly
of men. She wrote in answer that she would expect me
to sup with her in her room, that she might give me the
tenderest proofs of her gratitude.

This letter sent me completely mad with joy, and in
a paroxysm of delight I resolved to surrender to her
keeping the two bills of exchange which Bolomeé had

given me, and which gave me power to send her mother
and aunts to prison.

Full of the happiness that awaited me, and enchanted
with my own idiotic heroism, I went to her in the evening. She received me in the parlour with her mother,
and I was delighted to see the pier-glass over the mantel, and the china displayed on a little table. After a
hundred words of love and tenderness she asked me to
come up to her room, and her mother wished us good
night. I was overwhelmed with joy. After a delicate
little supper I took out the bills of exchange, and after
telling her their history gave them up to her, to shew
that I had no intention of avenging myself on her mother
and aunts. I made her promise that she would never
part with them, and she said she would never do so,
and with many expressions of gratitude and wonder at
my generosity she locked them up with great care.

Then I thought it was time to give her some marks
of my passion, and I found her kind; but when I would
have plucked the fruit, she clasped me to her arms,
crossed her legs, and began to weep bitterly.

I made an effort, and asked her if she would be the
same when we were in bed. She sighed, and after a moment's pause, replied, "Yes."

For a quarter of an hour I remained silent and motionless, as if petrified. At last I rose with apparent coolness, and took my cloak and sword.

"What!" said she, "are you not going to spend the
night with me?"

"No."

"But we shall see each other to-morrow?"

"I hope so. Good night."

I left that infernal abode, and went home to bed.

CHAPTER XIII

The End of the Story Stranger Than the Beginning

A T EIGHT o'clock the next morning Jarbe told me
that the Charpillon wanted to see me, and that she
had sent away her chairmen.

"Tell her that I can't see her."

But I had hardly spoken when she came in, and Jarbe
went out. I addressed her with the utmost calmness,
and begged her to give me back the two bills of exchange
I had placed in her hands the night before.

"I haven't got them about me; but why do you want
me to return them to you?"

At this question I could contain myself no longer,
and launched a storm of abuse at her. It was an explosion which relieved nature, and ended with an involuntary shower of tears. My infamous seductress stood as
calmly as Innocence itself; and when I was so choked
with sobs that I could not utter a word, she said she
had only been cruel because her mother had made her
swear an oath never to give herself to anyone in her
own house, and that she had only come now to convince
me of her love, to give herself to me without reserve,
and never to leave me any more if I wished it.

The reader who imagines that at these words rage
gave place to love, and that I hastened to obtain the
prize, does not know the nature of the passion so well
as the vile woman whose plaything I was. From hot
love to hot anger is a short journey, but the return is

slow and difficult. If there be only anger in a man's breast it may be subdued by tenderness, by submission, and affection; but when to anger is added a feeling of indignation at having been shamefully deceived, it is impossible to pass suddenly to thoughts of love and voluptuous enjoyment. With me mere anger has never been of long duration, but when I am indignant the only cure is forgetfulness.

The Charpillon knew perfectly well that I would not take her at her word, and this kind of science was inborn in her. The instinct of women teaches them greater secrets than all the philosophy and the research of men.

In the evening this monster left me, feigning to be disappointed and disconsolate, and saying,——

"I hope you will come and see me again when you are once more yourself."

She had spent eight hours with me, during which time she had only spoken to deny my suppositions, which were perfectly true, but which she could not afford to let pass. I had not taken anything all day, in order that I might not be obliged to offer her anything or to eat with her.

After she had left me I took some soup and then enjoyed a quiet sleep, for which I felt all the better. When I came to consider what had passed the day before I concluded that the Charpillon was repentant, but I seemed no longer to care anything about her.

Here I may as well confess, in all humility, what a change love worked on me in London, though I had attained the age of thirty-eight. Here closed the first act of my life; the second closed when I left Venice in 1783, and probably the third will close here, as I amuse myself by writing these memoirs. Thus, the three-act comedy will finish, and if it be hissed, as may possibly be the case, I shall not hear the sounds of disapproval. But as yet the reader has not seen the last and I think the most interesting scene of the first act.

I went for a walk in the Green Park and met Goudar. I was glad to see him, as the rogue was useful to me.

"I have just been at the Charpillons," he began; "they were all in high spirits. I tried in vain to turn the conversation on you, but not a word would they utter."

"I despise them entirely," I rejoined, "I don't want to have anything more to do with them."

He told me I was quite right, and advised me to persevere in my plan. I made him dine with me, and then we went to see the well-known procuress, Mrs. Wells, and saw the celebrated courtezan, Kitty Fisher, who was waiting for the Duke of —— to take her to a ball. She was magnificently dressed, and it is no exaggeration to say that she had on diamonds worth five hundred thousand francs. Goudar told me that if I liked I might have her then and there for ten guineas. I did not care to do so, however, for, though charming, she could only speak English, and I liked to have all my senses, including that of hearing, gratified. When she had gone, Mrs. Wells told us that Kitty had eaten a bank-note for a thousand guineas, on a slice of bread and butter, that very day. The note was a present from Sir —— Akins, brother of the fair Mrs. Pitt. I do not know whether the bank thanked Kitty for the present she had made it.

I spent an hour with a girl named Kennedy, a fair Irishwoman, who could speak a sort of French, and behaved most extravagantly under the influence of champagne; but the image of the Charpillon was still before me, though I knew it not, and I could not enjoy anything. I went home feeling sad and ill pleased with myself. Common sense told me to drive all thoughts of that wretched woman out of my head, but something I called honour bade me not leave her the triumph of having won the two bills of exchange from me for nothing, and made me determine to get them back by fair means or foul.

M. Malingan, at whose house I had made the acquaintance of this creature, came and asked me to dinner. He had asked me to dine with him several times before, and I had always refused, and now I would not accept until I had heard what guests he had invited. The names were all strange to me, so I agreed to come.

When I arrived I found two young ladies from Liège, in one of whom I got interested directly. She introduced me to her husband, and to another young man who seemed to be the cavalier of the other lady, her cousin.

The company pleased me, and I was in hopes that I should spend a happy day, but my evil genius brought the Charpillon to mar the feast. She came into the room in high glee, and said to Malingan,——

"I should not have come to beg you to give me a dinner if I had known that you would have so many guests, and if I am at all in the way I will go."

Everybody welcomed her, myself excepted, for I was on the rack. To make matters worse, she was placed at my left hand. If she had come in before we sat down to dinner I should have made some excuse and gone away, but as we had begun the soup a sudden flight would have covered me with ridicule. I adopted the plan of not looking at her, reserving all my politeness for the lady on my right. When the meal was over Malingan took me apart, and swore to me that he had not invited the Charpillon, but I was not convinced, though I pretended to be for politeness' sake.

The two ladies from Liège and their cavaliers were embarking for Ostend in a few days, and in speaking of their departure the one to whom I had taken a fancy said that she was sorry to be leaving England without having seen Richmond. I begged her to give me the pleasure of shewing it her, and without waiting for an answer I asked her husband and all the company to be present, excepting the Charpillon, whom I pretended not to see.

The invitation was accepted.

"Two carriages," I said, "holding four each, shall be ready at eight o'clock, and we shall be exactly eight."

"No, nine, for I am coming," said the Charpillon, giving me an impudent stare, "and I hope you will not drive me away."

"No, that would be impolite, I will ride in front on horseback."

"Oh, not at all! Emilie shall sit on my lap."

Emilie was Malingan's daughter, and as everybody seemed to think the arrangement an extremely pleasant one I had not the courage to resist. A few moments after, I was obliged to leave the room for a few moments, and when I came back I met her on the landing. She told me I had insulted her grievously, and that unless I made amends I should feel her vengeance.

"You can begin your vengeance," I said, "by returning my bills of exchange."

"You shall have them to-morrow, but you had better try and make me forget the insult you have put on me."

I left the company in the evening, having arranged that we should all breakfast together the next day.

At eight o'clock the two carriages were ready, and

Malingan, his wife, his daughter, and the two gentlemen got into the first vehicle, and I had to get into the second with the ladies from Liège and the Charpillon, who seemed to have become very intimate with them. This made me ill-tempered, and I sulked the whole way. We were an hour and a quarter on the journey, and when we arrived I ordered a good dinner, and then we proceeded to view the gardens; the day was a beautiful one, though it was autumn.

Whilst we were walking the Charpillon came up to me and said she wanted to return the bills in the same place in which I had given her them. As we were at some distance from the others I pelted her with abuse, telling her of her perfidy and of her corruption at an age when she should have retained some vestiges of innocence calling her by the name she deserved, as I reminded her how often she had already prostituted herself; in short I threatened her with my vengeance if she pushed me to extremities. But she was as cold as ice, and opposed a calm front to the storm of invective I rained in her ears. However, as the other guests were at no great distance, she begged me to speak more softly, but they heard me and I was very glad of it.

At last we sat down to dinner, and the wretched woman contrived to get a place beside me, and behaved all the while as if I were her lover, or at any rate as if she loved me. She did not seem to care what people thought of my coldness, while I was in a rage, for the company must either have thought me a fool or else that she was making game of me.

After dinner we returned to the garden, and the Charpillon, determined to gain the victory, clung to my arm and after several turns led me towards the maze where she wished to try her power. She made me sit down on the grass beside her and attacked me with passionate words and tender caresses, and by displaying the most interesting of her charms she succeeded in seducing me, but still I do not know whether I were impelled by love or vengeance, and I am inclined to think that my feelings were a compound of both passions.

But at the moment she looked the picture of voluptuous *abandon*. Her ardent eyes, her fiery cheeks, her wanton kisses, her swelling breast, and her quick sighs, all made me think that she stood as much in need of defeat as I of victory; certainly I should not have judged that she was already calculating on resistance.

Thus I once more became tender and affectionate; I begged pardon for what I had said and done. Her fiery kisses replied to mine, and I thought her glance and the soft pressure of her body were inviting me to gather the delicious fruit; but just as my hand opened the door of the sanctuary, she gave a sudden movement, and the chance was lost.

"What! you would deceive me again?"

"No, no but we have done enough now. I promise to spend the night in your arms in your own house."

For a moment I lost my senses. I only saw the deceitful wretch who had profited by my foolish credulity so many times, and I resolved to enjoy or take vengeance. I held her down with my left arm, and drawing a small knife from my pocket I opened it with my teeth and pricked her neck, threatening to kill her if she resisted me.

"Do as you like," she said with perfect calm, "I only ask you to leave me my life, but after you have satisfied yourself I will not leave the spot; I will not enter your carriage unless you carry me by force, and everybody shall know the reason."

This threat had no effect, for I had already got back my senses, and I pitied myself for being degraded by a creature for whom I had the greatest contempt, in spite of the almost magical influence she had over me, and the furious desires she knew how to kindle in my breast. I rose without a word, and taking my hat and cane I hastened to leave a place where unbridled passion had brought me to the brink of ruin.

My readers will scarcely believe me (but it is nevertheless the exact truth) when I say that the impudent creature hastened to rejoin me, and took my arm again as if nothing had happened. A girl of her age could not have played the part so well unless she had been already tried in a hundred battles. When we rejoined the company I was asked if I were ill, while nobody noticed the slightest alteration in her.

When we got back to London I excused myself under the plea of a bad headache, and returned home.

The adventure had made a terrible impression on me, and I saw that if I did not avoid all intercourse with this girl I should be brought to ruin. There was something about her I could not resist. I therefore resolved to see her no more, but feeling ashamed of my weakness in giving her the bills of exchange I wrote her mother a note requesting her to make her daughter return them, or else I should be compelled to take harsh measures.

In the afternoon I received the following reply:

"Sir,—I am exceedingly surprised at your addressing yourself to me about the bills you handed to my daughter. She tells me she will give you them back in person when you shew more discretion, and have learnt to respect her."

This impudent letter so enraged me that I forgot my vow of the morning. I put two pistols in my pocket and proceeded to the wretched woman's abode to compel her to return me my bills if she did not wish to be soundly caned.

I only took the pistols to overawe the two male rascals who supped with them every evening. I was furious when I arrived, but I passed by the door when I saw a handsome young hairdresser, who did the Charpillon's hair every Saturday evening, going into the house.

I did not want a stranger to be present at the scene I meant to make, so I waited at the corner of the street for the hairdresser to go. After I had waited half an hour Rostaing and Couman, the two supports of the house, came out and went away, much to my delight. I waited on; eleven struck, and the handsome barber had not yet gone. A little before midnight a servant came out with a lamp, I suppose to look for something that had fallen out of the window. I approached noiselessly, stepped in and opened the parlour-door, which was close to the street, and saw . . . the Charpillon and the barber stretched on the sofa and doing the beast with two backs, as Shakespeare calls it.

When the slut saw me she gave a shriek and unhorsed her gallant, whom I caned soundly until he escaped in the confusion consequent on the servants, mother, and aunts all rushing into the room. While this was going on the Charpillon, half-naked, remained crouched behind the sofa, trembling lest the blows should begin to descend on her. Then the three hags set upon me like furies; but their abuse only irritated me, and I broke the pier-glass, the china, and the furniture, and as they still howled and shrieked I roared out that if they did not cease I would break their heads. At this they began to calm.

I threw myself upon the fatal sofa, and bade the

mother to return me the bills of exchange; but just then the watchman came in.

There is only one watchman to a district, which he perambulates all night with a lantern in one hand and a staff in the other. On these men the peace of the great city depends. I put three or four crowns into his hand and said "Go away," and so saying shut the door upon him. Then I sat down once more and asked again for the bills of exchange.

"I have not got them; my daughter keeps them."

"Call her."

The two maids said that whilst I was breaking the china she had escaped by the street door, and that they did not know what had become of her. Then the mother and aunts began to shriek, weep, and exclaim,——

"My poor daughter alone in the streets of London at midnight! My dear niece, alas! alas! she is lost. Cursed be the hour when you came to England to make us all unhappy!"

My rage had evaporated, and I trembled at the thought of this young frightened girl running about the streets at such an hour.

"Go and look for her at the neighbours' houses," I said to the servants, "no doubt you will find her. When you tell me she is safe, you shall have a guinea apiece."

When the three Gorgons saw I was interested, their tears, complaints, and invectives began again with renewed vigor, while I kept silence as much as to say that they were in the right. I awaited the return of the servants with impatience, and at last at one o'clock they came back with looks of despair.

"We have looked for her everywhere," said they, "but we can't find her."

I gave them the two guineas as if they had succeeded, whilst I sat motionless reflecting on the terrible consequences of my anger. How foolish is man when he is in love!

I was idiot enough to express my repentance to the three old cheats. I begged them to seek for her everywhere when dawn appeared, and to let me know of her return that I might fall at her feet to beg pardon, and never see her face again. I also promised to pay for all the damage I had done, and to give them a full receipt for the bills of exchange. After these acts, done to the everlasting shame of my good sense, after this apology made to procuresses who laughed at me and my honour, I went home, promising two guineas to the servant who should bring me tidings that her young mistress had come home.

On leaving the house I found the watchman at the door; he had been waiting to see me home. It was two o'clock. I threw myself on my bed, and the six hours of sleep I obtained, though troubled by fearful dreams, probably saved me from madness.

At eight o'clock I heard a knock at the door, and on opening the window found it was one of the servants from the house of my foes. I cried out to let her in, and I breathed again on hearing that Miss Charpillon had just arrived in a sedan-chair in a pitiable condition, and that she had been put to bed.

"I made haste to come and tell you," said the cunning maid, "not for the sake of your two guineas, but because I saw you were so unhappy."

This duped me directly. I gave her the two guineas, and made her sit down on my bed, begging her to tell me all about her mistress's return. I did not dream that she had been schooled by my enemies; but during the whole of this period I was deprived of the right use of my reason.

The slut began by saying that her young mistress loved me, and had only deceived me in accordance with her mother's orders.

"I know that," I said, "but where did she pass the night?"

"At a shop which she found open, and where she was known from having bought various articles there. She is in bed with a fever, and I am afraid it may have serious consequences as she is in her monthly period."

"That's impossible, for I caught her in the act with her hairdresser."

"Oh, that proves nothing! the poor young man does not look into things very closely."

"But she is in love with him."

"I don't think so, though she has spent several hours in his company."

"And you say that she loves me!"

"Oh, that has nothing to do with it! It is only a whim of hers with the hairdresser."

"Tell her that I am coming to pass the day beside her bed, and bring me her reply."

"I will send the other girl if you like."

"No, she only speaks English."

She went away, and as she had not returned by three o'clock I decided on calling to hear how she was. I knocked at the door, and one of the aunts appeared and begged me not to enter as the two friends of the house were there in a fury against me, and her niece lay in a delirium, crying out "There's Seingalt, there's Seingalt! He's going to kill me. Help! help!" "For God's sake, sir, go away!"

I went home desperate, without the slightest suspicion that it was all a lie. I spent the whole day without eating anything; I could not swallow a mouthful. All night I kept awake, and though I took several glasses of strong waters I could obtain no rest.

At nine o'clock the next morning I knocked at the Charpillon's door, and the old aunt came and held it half open as before. She forbade me to enter, saying that her niece was still delirious, continually calling on me in her transports, and that the doctor had declared that if the disease continued its course she had not twenty-four hours to live. "The fright you gave her has arrested her periods; she is in a terrible state."

"O, fatal hairdresser!" I exclaimed.

"That was a mere youthful folly; you should have pretended not to have seen anything."

"You think that possible, you old witch, do you? Do not let her lack for anything; take that."

With these words I gave her a bank note for ten guineas and went away, like the fool I was. On my way back I met Goudar, who was quite frightened at my aspect. I begged him to go and see how the Charpillon really was, and then to come and pass the rest of the day with me. An hour after he came back and said he had found them all in tears and that the girl was *in extremis*.

"Did you see her?"

"No, they said she could see no one."

"Do you think it is all true?"

"I don't know what to think; but one of the maids, who tells me the truth as a rule, assured me that she had become mad through her courses being stopped, while she has also a fever and violent convulsions. It is all credible enough, for these are the usual results of a shock when a woman is in such a situation. The girl told me it was all your fault."

I then told him the whole story. He could only pity me, but when he heard that I had neither eaten nor slept for the last forty-eight hours he said very wisely that if I did not take care I should lose my reason or my life. I knew it, but I could find no remedy. He spent the day with me and did me good. As I could not eat I drank a good deal, and not being able to sleep I spent the night in striding up and down my room like a man beside himself.

On the third day, having heard nothing positive about the Charpillon, I went out at seven o'clock in the morning to call on her. After I had waited a quarter of an hour in the street, the door was partly opened, and I saw the mother all in tears, but she would not let me come in. She said her daughter was in the last agony. At the same instant a pale and thin old man came out, telling the mother that we must resign ourselves to the will of God. I asked the infamous creature if it were the doctor.

"The doctor is no good now," said the old hypocrite, weeping anew, "he is a minister of the Gospel, and there is another of them upstairs. My poor daughter! In another hour she will be no more."

I felt as if an icy hand had closed upon my heart. I burst into tears and left the woman, saying,——

"It is true that my hand dealt the blow, but her death lies at your door."

As I walked away my knees seemed to bend under me, and I entered my house determined to commit suicide.

With this fearful idea, I gave orders that I was not at home to anyone. As soon as I got to my room I put

my watches, rings, snuff-boxes, purse and pocket-book
in my casket, and shut it up in my escritoire. I then
wrote a letter to the Venetian ambassador, informing
him that all my property was to go to M. de Bragadin
after my death. I sealed the letter and put it with the
casket, and took the key with me, and also silver to
the amount of a few guineas. I took my pistols and
went out with the firm intention of drowning myself in
the Thames, near the Tower of London.

Pondering over my plan with the utmost coolness, I
went and bought some balls of lead as large as my
pockets would hold, and as heavy as I could bear, to
carry to the Tower, where I intended to go on foot. On
my way I was strengthened in my purpose by the reflection, that if I continued to live I should be tormented
for the remainder of my days by the pale shade of the
Charpillon reproaching me as her murderer. I even congratulated myself on being able to carry out my purpose without any effort, and I also felt a secret pride in
my courage.

I walked slowly on account of the enormous weight I
bore, which would assure me a speedy passage to the
bottom of the river.

By Westminster Bridge my good fortune made me
meet Sir Edgar ——, a rich young Englishman, who lived
a careless and joyous life. I had made his acquaintance
at Lord Pembroke's, and he had dined with me several
times. We suited one another, his conversation was
agreeable, and we had passed many pleasant hours together. I tried to avoid him, but he saw me, and came
up and took me by the arm in a friendly manner.

"Where are you going? Come with me, unless you
are going to deliver some captive. Come along, we shall
have a pleasant party."

"I can't come, my dear fellow, let me go."

"What's the matter? I hardly recognized you, you looked so solemn."

"Nothing is the matter."

"Nothing? You should look at your face in the glass. Now I feel quite sure that you are going to commit a foolish action."

"Not at all."

"It's no good denying it."

"I tell you there's nothing the matter with me. Good bye, I shall see you again."

"It's no good, I won't leave you. Come along, we will walk together."

His eyes happening to fall on my breeches pocket, he noticed my pistol, and putting his hand on the other pocket he felt the other pistol, and said,——

"You are going to fight a duel; I should like to see it. I won't interfere with the affair, but neither will I leave you."

I tried to put on a smile, and assured him that he was mistaken, and that I was only going for a walk to pass the time.

"Very good," said Edgar, "then I hope my society is as pleasant to you as yours is to me; I won't leave you. After we have taken a walk we will go and dine at the 'Canon.' I will get two girls to come and join us, and we shall have a gay little party of four."

"My dear friend, you must excuse me; I am in a melancholy mood, and I want to be alone to get over it."

"You can be alone to-morrow, if you like, but I am sure you will be all right in the next three hours, and if not, why I will share your madness. Where did you think of dining?"

"Nowhere; I have no appetite. I have been fasting for the last three days, and I can only drink."

"Ah! I begin to see daylight. Something has crossed you, and you are going to let it kill you as it killed one of my brothers. I must see what can be done."

Edgar argued, insisted, and joked till at last I said to myself, "A day longer will not matter, I can do the deed when he leaves me, and I shall only have to bear with life a few hours longer."

When Edgar heard that I had no particular object in crossing the bridge he said that we had better turn back, and I let myself be persuaded; but in half an hour I begged him to take me somewhere where I could wait for him, as I could not bear the weight of the lead any longer. I gave him my word of honour that I would meet him at the "Canon."

As soon as I was alone I emptied my pockets, and put the leaden balls into a cupboard. Then I lay down and began to consider whether the good-natured young man would prevent me committing suicide, as he had already made me postpone it.

I reasoned, not as one that hopes, but rather as one that foresaw that Edgar would hinder me from shortening my days. Thus I waited in the tavern for the young Englishman, doubtful whether he was doing me a service or an injury.

He came back before long, and was pleased to find me.

"I reckoned on your keeping your word," said he.

"You did not think that I would break my word of honour."

"That's all right; I see you are on the way to recovery."

The sensible and cheerful talk of the young man did

me good, and I began to feel better, when the two young wantons, one of whom was a Frenchwoman, arrived in high spirits. They seemed intended for pleasure, and Nature had dowered them with great attractions. I appreciated their charms, but I could not welcome them in the manner to which they were accustomed. They began to think me some poor valetudinarian; but though I was in torments, a feeling of vanity made me endeavour to behave sensibly. I gave them some cold kisses and begged Edgar to tell his fellow-countrywoman that if I were not three parts dead I would prove how lovely and charming I thought her. They pitied me. A man who has spent three days without eating or sleeping is almost incapable of any voluptuous excitement, but mere words would not have convinced these priestesses of Venus if Edgar had not given them my name. I had a reputation, and I saw that when they heard who I was they were full of respect. They all hoped that Bacchus and Comus would plead the cause of Love, and I let them talk, knowing that their hopes were vain.

We had an English dinner; that is, a dinner without the essential course of soup, so I only took a few oysters and a draught of delicious wine, but I felt better, and was pleased to see Edgar amusing himself with the two nymphs.

The young madcap suddenly proposed that the girls should dance a hornpipe in the costume of Mother Eve, and they consented on the condition that we would adopt the dress of Father Adam, and that blind musicians were summoned. I told them that I would take off my clothes to oblige them, but that I had no hopes of being able to imitate the seductive serpent. I was allowed to retain my dress, on the condition that if I felt the prick of the flesh I should immediately undress. I agreed to do so, and the blind musicians were sent for, and while they tuned their instruments toilettes were made, and the orgy began.

It taught me some useful lessons. I learnt from it that amorous pleasures are the effect and not the cause of gaiety. I sat gazing at three naked bodies of perfect grace and beauty, the dance and the music were ravishing and seductive, but nothing made any impression on me. After the dance was over the male dancer treated the two females, one after the other, until he was forced to rest. The French girl came up to ascertain whether I shewed any signs of life, but feeling my hopeless condition she pronounced me useless.

When it was all over I begged Edgar to give the French girl four guineas, and to pay my share, as I had very little money about me.

What should I have said if I had been told in the morning that instead of drowning myself I should take part in so pleasant an entertainment?

The debt I had contracted with the young Englishman made me resolve to put off my suicide to another day. After the nymphs had gone I tried to get rid of Edgar, but in vain; he told me I was getting better, that the oysters I had taken shewed my stomach was improving, and that if I came with him to Ranelagh I should be able to make a good dinner the next day. I was weak and indifferent and let myself be persuaded, and got into a coach with Edgar in obedience to the Stoic maxim I had learnt in the happy days of my youth: *Sequere Deum.*

We entered the fine rotunda with our hats off, and began to walk round and round, our arms behind our backs—a common custom in England, at least in those days.

A minuet was being danced, and I was so attracted by a lady who danced extremely well that I waited for her to turn round. What made me notice her more particularly was that her dress and hat were exactly like those I had given to the Charpillon a few days before, but as I believed the poor wretch to be dead or dying the likeness did not inspire me with any suspicion. But the lady turned round, lifted her face, and I saw—the Charpillon herself!

Edgar told me afterwards that at that moment he thought to see me fall to the ground in an epileptic fit; I trembled and shuddered so terribly.

However, I felt so sure she was ill that I could not believe my own eyes, and the doubt brought me to my senses.

"She can't be the Charpillon," I said to myself, "she is some other girl like her, and my enfeebled senses have led me astray." In the meanwhile the lady, intent on her dancing, did not glance in my direction, but I could afford to wait. At last she lifted her arms to make the curtsy at the end of the minuet, I went up instinctively as if I were about to dance with her; she looked me in the face, and fled.

I constrained myself; but now that there could be no doubt my shuddering fit returned, and I made haste to sit down. A cold sweat bedewed my face and my whole body. Edgar advised me to take a cup of tea but I begged him to leave me alone for a few moments.

I was afraid that I was on the point of death; I trembled all over, and my heart beat so rapidly that I could not have stood up had I wished.

At last, instead of dying, I got new life. What a wonderful change I experienced! Little by little my peace of mind returned, and I could enjoy the glitter of the multitudinous wax lights. By slow degrees I passed through all the shades of feeling between despair and an ecstasy of joy. My soul and mind were so astonished by the shock that I began to think I should never see Edgar again.

"This young man," I said to myself, "is my good genius, my guardian angel, my familiar spirit, who has taken the form of Edgar to restore me to my senses again."

I should certainly have persisted in this idea if my friend had not reappeared before very long.

Chance might have thrown him in the way of one of those seductive creatures who make one forget everything else; he might have left Ranelagh without having time to tell me he was going, and I should have gone back to London feeling perfectly certain that I had only seen his earthly shape. Should I have been disabused if I had seen him a few days after? Possibly; but I am not sure of it. I have always had a hankering after superstition, of which I do not boast; but I confess the fact, and leave the reader to judge me.

However, he came back in high spirits, but anxious about me. He was surprised to find me full of animation, and to hear me talking in a pleasant strain on the surrounding objects and persons.

"Why, you are laughing!" said he, "your sadness has departed, then?"

"Yes, good genius, but I am hungry, and I want you to do me a favour, if you have no other pressing engagements."

"I am free till the day after to-morrow, and till then you can do what you like with me."

"I owe my life to you, but to make your gift complete

I want you to spend this night and the whole of the next day with me."

"Done."

"Then let us go home."

"With all my heart; come along."

I did not tell him anything as we were in the coach, and when we got home I found nothing fresh, except a note from Goudar, which I put in my pocket, intending to reserve all business for the next day.

It was an hour after midnight. A good supper was served to us, and we fell to; for my part I devoured my food like a wild beast. Edgar congratulated me, and we went to bed, and I slept profoundly till noon. When I awoke I breakfasted with Edgar, and told him the whole story, which would have ended with my life if he had not met me on Westminster Bridge, and he had not been keen enough to mark my condition. I took him to my room, and shewed him my escritoire, my casket, and my will. I then opened Goudar's letter, and read,——

"I am quite sure that the girl you know of is very far from dying, as she has gone to Ranelagh with Lord Grosvenor."

Although Edgar was a profligate, he was a sensible man, and my story made him furious. He threw his arms around my neck, and told me he should always think the day on which he rescued me from death for so unworthy an object the happiest in his life. He could scarcely credit the infamy of the Charpillon and her mother. He told me I could have the mother arrested, though I had not got the bills of exchange, as her mother's letter acknowledging her daughter's possession of the bills was sufficient evidence.

Without informing him of my intention, I resolved that moment to have her arrested. Before we parted we swore eternal friendship, but the reader will see before long what a penance the kind Englishman had to do for befriending me.

The next day I went to the attorney I had employed against Count Schwerin. After hearing my story he said that I had an undoubted claim, and that I could arrest the mother and the two aunts.

Without losing time I went before a magistrate, who took my sworn information and granted me a warrant. The same official who had arrested Schwerin took charge of the affair; but as he did not know the women by sight it was necessary that someone who did should go with him, for though he was certain of surprising them there might be several other women present, and he might not arrest the right ones.

As Goudar would not have undertaken the delicate task of pointing them out, I resolved on accompanying him myself.

I made an appointment with him at an hour when I knew they would be all in the parlour. He was to enter directly the door was opened, and I would come in at the same instant and point out the women he had to arrest. In England all judicial proceedings are conducted with the utmost punctuality, and everything went off as I had arranged. The bailiff and his subaltern stepped into the parlour and I followed in their footsteps. I pointed out the mother and the two sisters and then made haste to escape, for the sight of the Charpillon, dressed in black, standing by the hearth, made me shudder. I felt cured, certainly; but the wounds she had given me were not yet healed, and I cannot say what might have happened if the Circe had had the presence of mind to throw her arms about my neck and beg for mercy.

As soon as I had seen these women in the hands of justice I fled, tasting the sweets of vengeance, which are very great, but yet a sign of unhappiness. The rage in which I had arrested the three procuresses, and my terror in seeing the woman who had well-nigh killed me, shewed that I was not really cured. To be so I must fly from them and forget them altogether.

The next morning Goudar came and congratulated me on the bold step I had taken, which proved, he said, that I was either cured or more in love than ever. "I have just come from Denmark Street," he added, "and I only saw the grandmother, who was weeping bitterly, and an attorney, whom no doubt she was consulting."

"Then you have heard what has happened?"

"Yes, I came up a minute after you had gone and I stayed till the three old sluts made up their minds to go with the constable. They resisted and said he ought to leave them till the next day, when they would be able to find someone to bail them. The two bravos drew their swords to resist the law, but the other constable disarmed them one after the other, and the three women were led off. The Charpillon wanted to accompany them, but it was judged best that she should remain at liberty, in order to try and set them free."

Goudar concluded by saying that he should go and see them in prison, and if I felt disposed to come to an arrangement he would mediate between us. I told him that the only arrangement I would accept was the payment of the six thousand francs, and that they might think themselves very lucky that I did not insist on having my interest, and thus repaying myself in part for the sums they had cheated out of me.

A fortnight elapsed without my hearing any more of the matter. The Charpillon dined with them every day, and in fact, kept them. It must have cost her a good deal, for they had two rooms, and their landlord would not allow them to have their meals prepared outside the prison. Goudar told me that the Charpillon said she would never beg me to listen to her mother, though she knew she had only to call on me to obtain anything she wanted. She thought me the most abominable of men. If I feel obliged to maintain that she was equally abominable, I must confess that on this occasion she shewed more strength of mind than I; but whereas I had acted out of passion, her misdeeds were calculated, and tended solely to her own interests.

For the whole of this fortnight I had sought for Edgar in vain, but one morning he came to see me, looking in high spirits.

"Where have you been hiding all this time?" said I, "I have been looking for you everywhere."

"Love has been keeping me a prisoner," said he, "I have got some money for you."

"For me? From what quarter?"

"On behalf of the Ansperghers. Give me a receipt and the necessary declaration, for I am going to restore them myself to the poor Charpillon, who has been weeping for the last fortnight."

"I daresay she has, I have seen her weep myself; but I like the way in which she has chosen the being who delivered me from her chains as a protector. Does she know that I owe my life to you?"

"She only knew that I was with you at Ranelagh when you saw her dancing instead of dying, but I have told her the whole story since."

"No doubt she wants you to plead with me in her favour."

"By no means. She has just been telling me that you

are a monster of ingratitude, for she loved you and gave you several proofs of her affection, but now she hates you."

"Thank Heaven for that! The wretched woman! It's curious she should have selected you as her lover by way of taking vengeance on me, but take care! she will punish you."

"It may be so, but at all events it's a pleasant kind of punishment."

"I hope you may be happy, but look to yourself; she is a mistress in all sorts of deceit."

Edgar counted me out two hundred and fifty guineas, for which I gave him a receipt and the declaration he required, and with these documents he went off in high spirits.

After this I might surely flatter myself that all was at an end between us, but I was mistaken.

Just about this time the Crown Prince of Brunswick, now the reigning duke, married the King of England's sister. The Common Council presented him with the freedom of the City, and the Goldsmith's Company admitted him into their society, and gave him a splendid box containing the documents which made him a London citizen. The prince was the first gentleman in Europe, and yet he did not disdain to add this new honour to a family illustrious for fourteen hundred years.

On this occasion Lady Harrington was the means of getting Madame Cornelis two hundred guineas. She lent her room in Soho Square to a confectioner who gave a ball and supper to a thousand persons at three guineas each. I paid my three guineas, and had the honour of standing up all the evening with six hundred others, for the table only seated four hundred, and there were several ladies who were unable to procure seats.

That evening I saw Lady Grafton seated beside the Duke of Cumberland. She wore her hair without any powder, and all the other ladies were exclaiming about it, and saying how very unbecoming it was. They could not anathematize the innovator too much, but in less than six months Lady Grafton's style of doing the hair became common, crossed the Channel, and spread all over Europe, though it has been given another name. It is still in fashion, and is the only method that can boast the age of thirty years, though it was so unmercifully ridiculed at first.

The supper for which the giver of the feast had received three thousand guineas, or sixty-five thousand francs, contained a most varied assortment of delicacies, but as I had not been dancing, and did not feel taken with any of the ladies present, I left at one in the morning. It was Sunday, a day on which all persons, save criminals, are exempt from arrest; but, nevertheless, the following adventure befell me:

I was dressed magnificently, and was driving home in my carriage, with my negro and another servant seated behind me; and just as we entered Pall Mall I heard a voice crying, "Good night, Seingalt." I put my head out of the window to reply, and in an instant the carriage was surrounded by men armed with pistols, and one of them said,——

"In the king's name!"

My servant asked what they wanted, and they answered,——

"To take him to Newgate, for Sunday makes no difference to criminals."

"And what crime have I committed?"

"You will hear that in prison."

"My master has a right to know his crime before he goes to prison," said the negro.

"Yes, but the magistrate's abed."

The negro stuck to his position, however, and the people who had come up declared with one consent that he was in the right.

The head-constable gave in, and said he would take me to a house in the city.

"Then drive to the city," said I, "and have done with it."

We stopped before the house, and I was placed in a large room on the ground floor, furnished solely with benches and long tables. My servant sent back the carriage, and came to keep me company. The six constables said they could not leave me, and told me I should send out for some meat and drink for them. I told my negro to give them what they wanted, and to be as amicable with them as was possible.

As I had not committed any crime, I was quite at ease; I knew that my arrest must be the effect of a slander, and as I was aware that London justice was speedy and equitable, I thought I should soon be free. But I blamed myself for having transgressed the excellent maxim, never to answer anyone in the night time; for if I had not done so I should have been in my house, and not in prison. The mistake, however, had been committed, and there was nothing to be done but to wait patiently. I amused myself by reflecting on my rapid passage from a numerous and exalted assemblage to the vile place I now occupied, though I was still dressed like a prince.

At last the day dawned, and the keeper of the tavern came to see who the prisoner was. I could not helping laughing at him when he saw me, for he immediately began to abuse the constables for not awaking him when I came; he had lost the guinea I should have paid for a private room. At last news was brought that the magistrate was sitting, and that I must be brought up.

A coach was summoned, and I got into it, for if I had dared to walk along the streets in my magnificent attire the mob would have pelted me.

I went into the hall of justice, and all eyes were at once attracted towards me; my silks and satins appeared to them the height of impertinence.

At the end of the room I saw a gentleman sitting in an arm-chair, and concluded him to be my judge. I was right, and the judge was blind. He wore a broad band round his head, passing over his eyes. A man beside me, guessing I was a foreigner, said in French,——

"Be of good courage, Mr. Fielding is a just and equitable magistrate."

I thanked the kindly unknown, and was delighted to see before me this famous and estimable writer, whose works are an honour to the English nation.

When my turn came, the clerk of the court told Mr. Fielding my name, at least, so I presume.

"Signor Casanova," said he, in excellent Italian, "be kind enough to step forward. I wish to speak to you."

I was delighted to hear the accents of my native tongue, and making my way through the press I came up to the bar of the court, and said,——

"*Eccomi, Signore.*"

He continued to speak Italian, and said,——

"Signor de Casanova, of Venice, you are condemned to perpetual confinement in the prisons of His Majesty the King of Great Britain."

"I should like to know, sir, for what crime I am condemned. Would you be kind enough to inform me as to its nature?"

"Your demand is a reasonable one, for with us no one is condemned without knowing the cause of his condemnation. You must know, then, that the accusation (which is supported by two witnesses) charges you with intending to do grievous bodily harm to the person of a pretty girl; and as this pretty girl aforesaid goes in dread of you, the law decrees that you must be kept in prison for the rest of your days."

"Sir, this accusation is a groundless calumny; to that I will take my oath! It is very possible indeed that the girl may fear my vengeance when she comes to consider her own conduct, but I can assure you that I have had no such designs hitherto, and I don't think I ever shall."

"She has two witnesses."

"Then they are false ones. But may I ask your worship the name of my accuser?"

"Miss Charpillon."

"I thought as much; but I have never given her aught but proofs of my affection."

"Then you have no wish to do her any bodily harm?"

"Certainly not."

"Then I congratulate you. You can dine at home; but you must find two sureties. I must have an assurance from the mouths of two householders that you will never commit such a crime."

"Whom shall I find to do so?"

"Two well-known Englishmen, whose friendship you have gained, and who know that you are incapable of such an action. Send for them, and if they arrive before I go to dinner I will set you at liberty."

The constable took me back to prison, where I had passed the night, and I gave my servants the addresses of all the householders I recollected, bidding them explain my situation, and to be as quick as possible. They ought to have come before noon, but London is such a large place! They did not arrive, and the magistrate went to dinner. I comforted myself by the thought that he would sit in the afternoon, but I had to put up with a disagreeable experience.

The chief constable, accompanied by an interpreter, came to say that I must go to Newgate. This is a prison where the most wretched and abject criminals are kept.

I signified to him that I was awaiting bail, and that he could take me to Newgate in the evening if it did not come, but he only turned a deaf ear to my petition. The interpreter told me in a whisper that the fellow was certainly paid by the other side to put me to trouble, but that if I liked to bribe him I could stay where I was.

"How much will he want?"

The interpreter took the constable aside, and then told me that I could stay where I was for ten guineas.

"Then say that I should like to see Newgate."

A coach was summoned, and I was taken away.

When I got to this abode of misery and despair, a hell, such as Dante might have conceived, a crowd of wretches, some of whom were to be hanged in the course of the week, greeted me by deriding my elegant attire. I did not answer them, and they began to get angry and to amuse me. The gaoler quieted them by saying that I was a foreigner and did not understand English, and then took me to a cell, informing me how much it would cost me, and of the prison rules, as if he felt certain that I should make a long stay. But in the course of half an hour, the constable who had tried to get ten guineas out of me told me that bail had arrived and that my carriage was at the door.

I thanked God from the bottom of my heart, and soon found myself in the presence of the blind magistrate. My bail consisted of Pegu, my tailor, and Maisonneuve, my wine merchant, who said they were happy to be able to render me this slight service. In another part of the court I noticed the infamous Charpillon, Rostaing, Goudar, and an attorney. They made no impression on me, and I contented myself with giving them a look of profound contempt.

My two sureties were informed of the amount in which they were to bail me, and signed with a light heart, and then the magistrate said, politely,——

"Signor Casanova, please to sign your name for double the amount, and you will then be a free man again."

I went towards the clerk's table, and on asking the sum I was to answer for was informed that it was forty guineas, each of my sureties signing for twenty. I signed my name, telling Goudar that if the magistrate could have seen the Charpillon he would have valued her beauty at ten thousand guineas. I asked the names of the two witnesses, and was told that they were Rostaing and Bottarelli. I looked contemptuously at Rostaing, who was as pale as death, and averting my face from the Charpillon out of pity, I said,——

"The witnesses are worthy of the charge."

I saluted the judge with respect, although he could not see me, and asked the clerk if I had anything to pay. He replied in the negative, and a dispute ensued between him and the attorney of my fair enemy, who was disgusted on hearing that she could not leave the court without paying the costs of my arrest.

Just as I was going, five or six well-known Englishmen appeared to bail me out, and were mortified to hear that they had come too late. They begged me to forgive the laws of the land, which are only too often converted into a means for the annoyance of foreigners.

At last, after one of the most tedious days I have ever spent, I returned home and went to bed, laughing at the experience I had undergone.

CHAPTER XIV

Bottarelli—A Letter from Pauline—The Avenging Parrot—Pocchini—Guerra, the Venetian—I Meet Sara Again; My Idea of Marrying Her and Settling in Switzerland—The Hanoverians

THUS ended the first act of the comedy; the second began the next morning. I was just getting up, when I heard a noise at the street door, and on putting my head out of the window I saw Pocchini, the scoundrel who had robbed me at Stuttgart trying to get into my house. I cried out wrathfully that I would have nothing to do with him, and slammed down my window.

A little later Goudar put in an appearance. He had got a copy of the *St. James's Chronicle*, containing a brief report of my arrest, and of my being set a liberty under a bail of eighty guineas. My name and the lady's were disguised, but Rostaing and Bottarelli were set down plainly, and the editor praised their conduct. I felt as if I should like to know Bottarelli, and begged Goudar to take me to him, and Martinelli, happening to call just then, said he would come with us.

We entered a wretched room on the third floor of a wretched house, and there we beheld a picture of the greatest misery. A woman and five children clothed in rags formed the foreground, and in the background was Bottarelli, in an old dressing-gown, writing at a table worthy of Philemon and Baucis. He rose as we came in, and the sight of him moved me to compassion. I said,——

"Do you know me, sir?"

"No, sir, I do not."

"I am Casanova, against whom you bore false witness; whom you tried to cast into Newgate."

"I am very sorry, but look around you and say what choice have I? I have no bread to give my children. I will do as much in your favour another time for nothing."

"Are you not afraid of the gallows?"

"No, for perjury is not punished with death; besides it is very difficult to prove."

"I have heard you are a poet."

"Yes. I have lengthened the *Didone* and abridged the *Demetrio*."

"You are a great poet, indeed!"

I felt more contempt than hatred for the rascal, and gave his wife a guinea, for which she presented me with a wretched pamphlet by her husband: "The Secrets of the Freemasons Displayed." Bottarelli had been a monk in his native city, Pisa, and had fled to England with his wife, who had been a nun.

About this time M. de Saa surprised me by giving me a letter from my fair Portuguese, which confirmed the sad fate of poor Clairmont. Pauline said she was married to Count Al——. I was astonished to hear M. de Saa observe that he had known all about Pauline from the moment she arrived in London. That is the hobby of all diplomatists; they like people to believe that they are omniscient. However, M. de Saa was a man of worth and talent, and one could excuse this weakness as an incident inseparable from his profession; while most diplomatists only make themselves ridiculous by their assumption of universal knowledge.

M. de Saa had been almost as badly treated by the

Charpillon as myself, and we might have condoled with one another, but the subject was not mentioned.

A few days afterwards, as I was walking idly about, I passed a place called the Parrot Market. As I was amusing myself by looking at these curious birds, I saw a fine young one in a cage, and asked what language it spoke. They told me that it was quite young and did not speak at all yet, so I bought it for ten guineas. I thought I would teach the bird a pretty speech, so I had the cage hung by my bed, and repeated dozens of times every day the following sentence: *"The Charpillon is a bigger wh—e than her mother."*

The only end I had in view was my private amusement, and in a fortnight the bird had learnt the phrase with the utmost exactness; and every time it uttered the words it accompanied them with a shriek of laughter which I had not taught it, but which made me laugh myself.

One day Goudar heard the bird, and told me that if I sent it to the Exchange I should certainly get fifty guineas for it. I welcomed the idea, and resolved to make the parrot the instrument of my vengeance against the woman who had treated me so badly. I secured myself from fear of the law, which is severe in such cases, by entrusting the bird to my negro, to whom such merchandise was very suitable.

For the first two or three days my parrot did not attract much attention, its observations being in French; but as soon as those who knew the subject of them had heard it, its audience increased and bids were made. Fifty guineas seemed rather too much, and my negro wanted me to lower the price, but I would not agree, having fallen in love with this odd revenge.

In the course of a week Goudar came to inform me

of the effect the parrot's criticism had produced in the Charpillon family. As the vendor was my negro, there could be no doubt as to whom it belonged, and who had been its master of languages. Goudar said that the Charpillon thought my vengeance very ingenious, but that the mother and aunts were furious. They had consulted several counsel, who agreed in saying that a parrot could not be indicted for libel, but that they could make me pay dearly for my jest if they could prove that I had been the bird's instructor. Goudar warned me to be careful of owning to the fact, as two witnesses would suffice to undo me.

The facility with which false witnesses may be produced in London is something dreadful. I have myself seen the word *evidence* written in large characters in a window; this is as much as to say that false witnesses may be procured within.

The *St. James's Chronicle* contained an article on my parrot, in which the writer remarked that the ladies whom the bird insulted must be very poor and friendless, or they would have bought it at once, and have thus prevented the thing from becoming the talk of the town. He added,——

"The teacher of the parrot has no doubt made the bird an instrument of his vengeance, and has displayed his wit in doing so; he ought to be an Englishman."

I met my good friend Edgar, and asked him why he had not bought the little slanderer.

"Because it delights all who know anything about the object of the slander," said he.

At last Jarbe found a purchaser for fifty guineas, and I heard afterwards that Lord Grosvenor had bought it to please the Charpillon, with whom he occasionally diverted himself.

Thus my relations with that girl came to an end. I have seen her since with the greatest indifference, and without any renewal of the old pain.

One day, as I was going into St. James's Park, I saw two girls drinking milk in a room on the ground floor of a house. They called out to me, but not knowing them I passed on my way. However, a young officer of my acquaintance came after me and said they were Italians, and being curious to see them I retracted my steps.

When I entered the room I was accosted by the scoundrelly Pocchini, dressed in a military uniform, who said he had the honour of introducing me to his daughters.

"Indeed," said I, "I remember two other daughters of yours robbing me of a snuff-box and two watches at Stuttgart."

"You lie!" said the impudent rascal.

I gave him no verbal answer, but took up a glass of milk and flung it in his face, and then left the room without more ado.

I was without my sword. The young officer who had brought me into the place followed me and told me I must not go without giving his friend some satisfaction.

"Tell him to come out, and do you escort him to the Green Park, and I shall have the pleasure of giving him a caning in your presence, unless you would like to fight for him; if so, you must let me go home and get my sword. But do you know this man whom you call your friend?"

"No, but he is an officer, and it is I that brought him here."

"Very good, I will fight to the last drop of my blood;

but I warn you your friend is a thief. But go; I will await you."

In the course of a quarter of an hour they all came out, but the Englishman and Pocchini followed me alone. There were a good many people about, and I went before them till we reached Hyde Park. Pocchini attempted to speak to me, but I replied, lifting my cane,——

"Scoundrel, draw your sword, unless you want me to give you a thrashing!"

"I will never draw upon a defenceless man."

I gave him a blow with my cane by way of answer, and the coward, instead of drawing his sword, began to cry out that I wished to draw him into a fight. The Englishman burst out laughing and begged me to pardon his interference, and then, taking me by the arm, said,——

"Come along, sir, I see you know the gentleman."

The coward went off in another direction, grumbling as he went.

On the way I informed the officer of the very good reasons I had for treating Pocchini as a rogue, and he agreed that I had been perfectly right. "Unfortunately," he added, "I am in love with one of his daughters."

When we were in the midst of St. James's Park we saw them, and I could not help laughing when I noticed Goudar with one of them on each side.

"How did you come to know these ladies?" said I.

"Their father the captain," he answered, "has sold me jewels; he introduced me to them."

"Where did you leave our father?" asked one.

"In Hyde Park, after giving him a caning."

"You served him quite right."

The young Englishman was indignant to hear them approving my ill-treatment of their father, and shook my hand and went away, swearing to me that he would never be seen in their company again.

A whim of Goudar's, to which I was weak enough to consent, made me dine with these miserable women in a tavern on the borders of London. The rascally Goudar made them drunk, and in this state they told some terrible truths about their pretended father. He did not live with them, but paid them nocturnal visits in which he robbed them of all the money they had earned. He was their pander, and made them rob their visitors instructing them to pass it off as a joke if the theft was discovered. They gave him the stolen articles, but he never said what he did with them. I could not help laughing at this involuntary confession, remembering what Goudar had said about Pocchini selling him jewels.

After this wretched meal I went away leaving the duty of escorting them back to Goudar. He came and saw me the next day, and informed me that the girls had been arrested and taken to prison just as they were entering their house.

"I have just been to Pocchini's," said he, "but the landlord tells me he has not been in since yesterday."

The worthy and conscientious Goudar added that he did not care if he never saw him again, as he owed the fellow ten guineas for a watch, which his daughters had probably stolen, and which was well worth double.

Four days later I saw him again, and he informed me that the rascal had left London with a servant-maid, whom he had engaged at a registry office where any number of servants are always ready to take service with the first comer. The keeper of the office answers for their fidelity.

"The girl he has gone with is a pretty one, from what the man tells me, and they have taken ship from London. I am sorry he went away before I could pay him for the watch; I am dreading every moment to meet the individual from whom it was stolen."

I never heard what became of the girls, but Pocchini will re-appear on the scene in due course.

I led a tranquil and orderly life, which I should have been pleased to continue for the remainder of my days; but circumstances and my destiny ordered it otherwise, and against these it is not becoming in a Christian philosopher to complain. I went several times to see my daughter at her school, and I also frequented the British Museum, where I met Dr. Mati. One day I found an Anglican minister with him, and I asked the clergyman how many different sects there were in England.

"Sir," he replied in very tolerable Italian, "no one can give a positive answer to that question, for every week some sect dies and some new one is brought into being. All that is necessary is for a man of good faith, or some rogue desirous of money or notoriety, to stand in some frequented place and begin preaching. He explains some texts of the Bible in his own fashion, and if he pleases the gapers around him they invite him to expound next Sunday, often in a tavern. He keeps the appointment and explains his new doctrines in a spirited manner. Then people begin to talk of him; he disputes with ministers of other sects; he and his followers give themselves a name, and the thing is done. Thus, or almost thus, are all the numerous English sects produced."

About this time M. Steffano Guerra, a noble Venetian who was travelling with the leave of his Government, lost a case against an English painter who had executed a miniature painting of one of the prettiest ladies in Lon-

don, Guerra having given a written promise to pay
twenty-five guineas. When it was finished Guerra did
not like it, and would not take it or pay the price. The
Englishman, in accordance with the English custom,
began by arresting his debtor; but Guerra was released
on bail, and brought the matter before the courts, which
condemned him to pay the twenty-five guineas. He appealed, lost again, and was in the end obliged to pay.
Guerra contented that he had ordered a portrait, that a
picture bearing no likeness to the lady in question was
not a portrait, and that he had therefore a right to refuse payment. The painter replied that it was a portrait as it had been painted from life. The judgment
was that the painter must live by his trade, and that as
Guerra had given him painting to do he must therefore
provide him with the wherewithal to live, seeing that
the artist swore he had done his best to catch the likeness. Everybody thought this sentence just, and so did
I; but I confess it also seemed rather hard, especially to
Guerra, who with costs had to pay a hundred guineas
for the miniature.

Malingan's daughter died just as her father received
a public box on the ear from a nobleman who liked
piquet, but did not like players who corrected the ca-
prices of fortune. I gave the poor wretch the wherewithal to bury his daughter and to leave England. He
died soon after at Liège, and his wife told me of the circumstance, saying that he had expired regretting his
inability to pay his debts.

M. M—— F—— came to London as the representative of the canton of Berne, and I called, but was not
received. I suspected that he had got wind of the liberties I had taken with pretty Sara, and did not want me
to have an opportunity for renewing them. He was a

somewhat eccentric man, so I did not take offence, and
had almost forgotten all about it when chance led me
to the Marylebone Theatre one evening. The spectators
sat at little tables, and the charge for admittance was
only a shilling, but everyone was expected to order something, were it only a pot of ale.

On going into the theatre I chanced to sit down beside
a girl whom I did not notice at first, but soon after I
came in she turned towards me, and I beheld a ravishing profile which somehow seemed familiar; but I attributed that to the idea of perfect beauty that was
graven on my soul. The more I looked at her the surer
I felt that I had never seen her before, though a smile
of inexpressible slyness had begun to play about her
lips. One of her gloves fell, and I hastened to restore it
to her, whereupon she thanked me in a few well-chosen
French sentences.

"Madam is not English, then?" said I, respectfully.

"No, sir, I am a Swiss, and a friend of yours."

At this I looked round, and on my right hand sat
Madame M—— F——, then her eldest daughter, then
her husband. I got up, and after bowing to the lady,
for whom I had a great esteem, I saluted her husband,
who only replied by a slight movement of the head. I
asked Madame M—— F—— what her husband had
against me, and she said that Possano had written to
him telling some dreadful stories about me.

There was not time for me to explain and justify
myself, so I devoted all my energies to the task of winning the daughter's good graces. In three years she
had grown into a perfect beauty: she knew it, and by
her blushes as she spoke to me I knew she was thinking
of what had passed between us in the presence of my
housekeeper. I was anxious to find out whether she

would acknowledge the fact, or deny it altogether. If she had done so I should have despised her. When I had seen her before, the blossom of her beauty was still in the bud, now it had opened out in all its splendour.

"Charming Sara," I said, "you have so enchanted me that I cannot help asking you a couple of questions, which if you value my peace of mind you will answer. Do you remember what happened at Berne?"

"Yes."

"And do you repent of what you did?"

"No."

No man of any delicacy could ask the third question, which may be understood. I felt sure that Sara would make me happy—nay, that she was even longing for the moment, and gave reins to my passions, determined to convince her that I was deserving of her love.

The waiter came to enquire if we had any orders, and I begged Madame M—— F—— to allow me to offer her some oysters. After the usual polite refusals she gave in, and I profited by her acceptance to order all the delicacies of the season, including a hare (a great delicacy in London), champagne, choice liqueurs, larks, ortolans, truffles, sweetmeats—everything, in fact, that money could buy, and I was not at all surprised when the bill proved to amount to ten guineas. But I was very much surprised when M. M—— F——, who had eaten like a Turk and drunk like a Swiss, said calmly that it was too dear.

I begged him politely not to trouble himself about the cost; and by way of proving that I did not share his opinion, I gave the waiter half-a-guinea; the worthy man looked as if he wished that such customers came more often. The Swiss, who had been pale and gloomy enough a short while before, was rubicund and affable. Sara glanced at me and squeezed my hand; I had conquered.

When the play was over, M—— F—— asked me if I would allow him to call on me. I embraced him in reply. His servant came in, and said that he could not find a coach; and I, feeling rather surprised that he had not brought his carriage, offered him the use of mine, telling my man to get me a sedan-chair.

"I accept your kind offer," said he, "on the condition that you allow me to occupy the chair."

I consented to this arrangement, and took the mother and the two daughters with me in the carriage.

On the way, Madame M—— F—— was very polite, gently blaming her husband for the rudeness of which I had to complain. I said that I would avenge myself by paying an assiduous court to him in the future; but she pierced me to the heart by saying that they were on the point of departing. "We wanted to go on the day after next," she said, "and to-morrow we shall have to leave our present rooms to their new occupants. A matter of business which my husband was not able to conclude will oblige us to stay for another week, and to-morrow we shall have the double task of moving and finding new apartments."

"Then you have not yet got new rooms?"

"No, but my husband says he is certain to find some to-morrow morning."

"Furnished, I suppose, for as you intend to leave you will be selling your furniture."

"Yes, and we shall have to pay the expenses of carriage to the buyer."

On hearing that M. M—— F—— was sure of finding lodgings, I was precluded from offering to accommo-

date them in my own house, as the lady might think that
I only made the offer because I was sure it would not be
accepted.

When we got to the door of their house we alighted,
and the mother begged me to come in. She and her
husband slept on the second floor, and the two girls on
the third. Everything was upside down, and as Madame M—— F—— had something to say to the landlady
she asked me to go up with her daughters. It was cold,
and the room we entered had no fire in it. The sister
went into the room adjoining and I stayed with Sara,
and all of a sudden I clasped her to my breast, and feeling that her desires were as ardent as mine I fell with
her on to a sofa where we mingled our beings in all
the delights of voluptuous ardours. But this happiness
was short lived; scarcely was the work achieved when we
heard a footstep on the stair. It was the father.

If M—— F—— had had any eyes he must have found
us out, for my face bore the marks of agitation, the
nature of which it was easy to divine. We exchanged
a few brief compliments; I shook his hand and disappeared. I was in such a state of excitement when I got
home that I made up my mind to leave England and to
follow Sara to Switzerland. In the night I formed my
plans, and resolved to offer the family my house during
the time they stayed in England, and if necessary to
force them to accept my offer.

In the morning I hastened to call on M—— F——,
and found him on his doorstep.

"I am going to try and get a couple of rooms," said
he.

"They are already found," I replied. "My house is at
your service, and you must give me the preference. Let
us come upstairs."

"Everybody is in bed."

"Never mind," said I, and we proceeded to go upstairs.

Madame M—— F—— apologized for being in bed. Her husband told her that I wanted to let them some rooms, but I laughed and said I desired they would accept my hospitality as that of a friend. After some polite denials my offer was accepted, and it was agreed that the whole family should take up their quarters with me in the evening.

I went home, and was giving the necessary orders when I was told that two young ladies wished to see me. I went down in person, and I was agreeably surprised to see Sara and her sister. I asked them to come in, and Sara told me that the landlady would not let their belonging out of the house before her father paid a debt of forty guineas, although a city merchant had assured her it should be settled in a week. The long and short of it was that Sara's father had sent me a bill and begged me to discount it.

I took the bill and gave her a bank note for fifty pounds in exchange, telling her that she could give me the change another time. She thanked me with great simplicity and went her way, leaving me delighted with the confidence she had placed in me.

The fact of M. M—— F——'s wanting forty guineas did not make me divine that he was in some straits, for I looked at everything through rose-coloured glasses, and was only too happy to be of service to him.

I made a slight dinner in order to have a better appetite for supper, and spent the afternoon in writing letters. In the evening M. M—— F——'s man came with three great trunks and innumerable card-board boxes, telling me that the family would soon follow; but

I awaited them in vain till nine o'clock. I began to get alarmed and went to the house, where I found them all in a state of consternation. Two ill-looking fellows who were in the room enlightened me; and assuming a jovial and unconcerned air, I said,——

"I'll wager, now, that this is the work of some fierce creditor."

"You are right," answered the father, "but I am sure of discharging the debt in five or six days, and that's why I put off my departure."

"Then you were arrested after you had sent on your trunks."

"Just after."

"And what have you done?"

"I have sent for bail."

"Why did you not send to me?"

"Thank you, I am grateful for your kindness, but you are a foreigner, and sureties have to be householders."

"But you ought to have told me what had happened, for I have got you an excellent supper, and I am dying of hunger."

It was possible that this debt might exceed my means, so I did not dare to offer to pay it. I took Sara aside, and on hearing that all his trouble was on account of a debt of a hundred and fifty pounds, I asked the bailiff whether we could go away if the debt was paid.

"Certainly," said he, shewing me the bill of exchange.

I took out three bank notes of fifty pounds each, and gave them to the man, and taking the bill I said to the poor Swiss,——

"You shall pay me the money before you leave England."

The whole family wept with joy, and after embracing

them all I summoned them to come and sup with me and forget the troubles of life.

We drove off to my house and had a merry supper, though the worthy mother could not quite forget her sadness. After supper I took them to the rooms which had been prepared for them, and with which they were delighted, and so I wished them good night, telling them that they should be well entertained till their departure, and that I hoped to follow them into Switzerland.

When I awoke the next day I was in a happy frame of of mind. On examining my desires I found that they had grown too strong to be overcome, but I did not wish to overcome them. I loved Sara, and I felt so certain of possessing her that I put all desires out of my mind; desires are born only of doubt, and doubt torments the soul. Sara was mine; she had given herself to me out of pure passion, without any shadow of self-interest.

I went to the father's room, and found him engaged in opening his trunks. His wife looked sad, so I asked her if she were not well. She replied that her health was perfect, but that the thought of the sea voyage troubled her sorely. The father begged me to excuse him at breakfast as he had business to attend to. The two young ladies came down, and after we had breakfast I asked the mother why they were unpacking their trunks so short a time before starting. She smiled and said that one trunk would be ample for all their possessions, as they had resolved to sell all superfluities. As I had seen some beautiful dresses, fine linen, and exquisite lace, I could not refrain from saying that it would be a great pity to sell cheaply what would have to be replaced dearly.

"You are right," she said, "but, nevertheless, there is

no pleasure so great as the consciousness of having paid one's debts."

"You must not sell anything," I replied, in a lively manner, "for as I am going to Switzerland with you I can pay your debts, and you shall repay me when you can."

At these words astonishment was depicted on her face.

"I did not think you were speaking seriously," said she.

"Perfectly seriously, and here is the object of my vows."

With these words I seized Sara's hand and covered it with kisses.

Sara blushed, said nothing, and the mother looked kindly at us; but after a moment's silence she spoke at some length, and with the utmost candour and wisdom. She gave me circumstantial information as to the position of the family and her husband's restricted means, saying that under the circumstances he could not have avoided running into debt, but that he had done wrong to bring them all with him to London.

"If he had been by himself," she said, "he could have lived here comfortably enough with only one servant, but with a family to provide for the two thousand crowns per annum provided by the Government are quite insufficient. My old father has succeeded in persuading the State to discharge my husband's debts, but to make up the extra expense they will not employ a *Chargé-d'affaires;* a banker with the title of agent will collect the interest on their English securities."

She ended by saying that she thought Sara was fortunate to have pleased me, but that she was not sure whether her husband would consent to the marriage.

The word "marriage" made Sara blush, and I was

pleased, though it was evident there would be difficulties in the way.

M—— F—— came back and told his wife that two clothes dealers would come to purchase their superfluous clothes in the afternoon; but after explaining my ideas I had not much trouble in convincing him that it would be better not to sell them, and that he could become my debtor to the amount of two hundred pounds, on which he could pay interest till he was able to return me my capital. The agreement was written out the same day, but I did not mention the marriage question, as his wife had told me she would discuss it with him in private.

On the third day he came down by himself to talk with me.

"My wife," he began, "has told me of your intentions, and I take it as a great honour, I assure you; but I cannot give you my Sara, as she is promised to M. de W——, and family reasons prevent me from going back from my word. Besides my old father, a strict Calvinist, would object to the difference in religion. He would never believe that his dear little grandchild would be happy with a Roman Catholic."

As a matter of fact I was not at all displeased at what he said. I was certainly very fond of Sara, but the word "marriage" had a disagreeable sound to me. I answered that circumstances might change in time, and that in the meanwhile I should be quite content if he would allow me to be the friend of the family and to take upon myself all the responsibility of the journey. He promised everything, and assured me that he was delighted at his daughter having won my affection.

After this explanation I gave Sara as warm marks of my love as decency would allow in the presence of her father and mother, and I could see that all the girl thought of was love.

The fifth day I went up to her room, and finding her in bed all the fires of passion flamed up in my breast, for since my first visit to their house I had not been alone with her. I threw myself upon her, covering her with kisses, and she shewed herself affectionate but reserved. In vain I endeavoured to succeed; she opposed a gentle resistance to my efforts, and though she caressed me, she would not let me attain my end.

"Why, divine Sara," said I, "do you oppose my loving ecstasy?"

"Dearest, I entreat of you not to ask for any more than I am willing to give."

"Then you no longer love me?"

"Cruel man, I adore you!"

"Then why do you treat me to a refusal, after having once surrendered unreservedly?"

"I have given myself to you, and we have both been happy, and I think that should be enough for us."

"There must be some reason for this change. If you love me, dearest Sara, this renunciation must be hard for you to bear."

"I confess it, but nevertheless I feel it is my duty. I have made up my mind to subdue my passion from no weak motive, but from a sense of what I owe to myself. I am under obligations to you, and if I were to repay the debt I have contracted with my body I should be degraded in my own eyes. When we enjoyed each other before only love was between us—there was no question of debit and credit. My heart is now the thrall of what I owe you, and to these debts it will not give what it gave so readily to love."

"This is a strange philosophy, Sara; believe me it is fallacious, and the enemy of your happiness as well as mine. These sophisms lead you astray and wound me to the heart. Give me some credit for delicacy of feeling, and believe me you owe me nothing."

"You must confess that if you had not loved me you would have done nothing for my father."

"Certainly I will confess nothing of the kind; I would readily do as much, and maybe more, out of regard for your worthy mother. It is quite possible, indeed, that in doing this small service for your father I had no thoughts of you at all."

"It might be so; but I do not believe it was so. Forgive me, dearest, but I cannot make up my mind to pay my debts in the way you wish."

"It seems to me that if you are grateful to me your love ought to be still more ardent."

"It cannot be more ardent than it is already."

"Do you know how grievously you make me suffer?"

"Alas! I suffer too; but do not reproach me; let us love each other still."

This dialogue is not the hundredth part of what actually passed between us till dinner-time. The mother came in, and finding me seated at the foot of the daughter's bed, laughed, and asked me why I kept her in bed. I answered with perfect coolness that we had been so interested in our conversation that we had not noticed the flight of time.

I went to dress, and as I thought over the extraordinary change which had taken place in Sara I resolved that it should not last for long.

We dined together gaily, and Sara and I behaved in all respects like two lovers. In the evening I took them to the Italian Opera, coming home to an excellent supper.

The next morning I passed in the city, having accounts to settle with my bankers. I got some letters of exchange on Geneva, and said farewell to the worthy Mr. Bosanquet. In the afternoon I got a coach for Madame M—— F—— to pay some farewells calls, and I went to say good-bye to my daughter at school. The dear little girl burst into tears, saying that she would be lost without me, and begging me not to forget her. I was deeply moved. Sophie begged me to go and see her mother before I left England, and I decided on doing so.

At supper we talked over our journey, and M. M—— F—— agreed with me that it would be better to go by Dunkirk than Ostend. He had very little more business to attend to. His debts were paid, and he said he thought he would have a matter of fifty guineas in his pocket at the journey's end, after paying a third share of all the travelling expenses. I had to agree to this, though I made up my mind at the same time not to let him see any of the accounts. I hoped to win Sara, in one way or another, when we got to Berne.

The next day, after breakfast, I took her hand in presence of her mother, and asked her if she would give me her heart if I could obtain her father's consent at Berne.

"Your mother," I added, "has promised me that hers shall not be wanting."

At this the mother got up, and saying that we had no doubt a good deal to talk over, she and her eldest daughter went out to pay some calls.

As soon as we were alone Sara said that she could not understand how I could have the smallest doubt as to whether her consent would be given.

"I have shewn you how well I love you," said she, tenderly; "and I am sure I should be very happy as your wife. You may be sure that your wishes will be mine, and that, however far you lead me, Switzerland shall claim no thought of mine."

I pressed the amorous Sara to my bosom in a transport of delight, which was shared by her; but as she saw me grow more ardent she begged me to be moderate. Clasping me in her arms she adjured me not to ask her for that which she was determined not to grant till she was mine by lawful wedlock.

"You will drive me to despair! Have you reflected that this resistance may cost me my life? Can you love, and yet entertain this fatal prejudice? And yet I am sure you love me, and pleasure too."

"Yes, dearest one, I do love you, and amorous pleasure with you; but you must respect my delicacy."

My eyes were wet with tears, and she was so affected that she fell fainting to the ground. I lifted her up and gently laid her on the bed. Her pallor alarmed me. I brought smelling-salts, I rubbed her forehead with Savoy-water, and she soon opened her eyes, and seemed delighted to find me calm again.

The thought of taking advantage of her helplessness would have horrified me. She sat up on the bed, and said,——

"You have just given a true proof of the sincerity of your affection."

"Did you think, sweetheart, that I was vile enough to abuse your weakness? Could I enjoy a pleasure in which you had no share?"

"I did not think you would do such a thing, but I should not have resisted, though it is possible that I should not have loved you afterwards."

"Sara, though you do not know, you charm my soul out of my body."

After this I sat down sadly on the bed, and abandoned myself to the most melancholy reflections, from which Sara did not endeavour to rouse me.

Her mother came in and asked why she was on the bed, but not at all suspiciously. Sara told her the truth.

M. M—— F—— came in soon after, and we dined together, but silently. What I had heard from the girl's lips had completely overwhelmed me. I saw I had nothing to hope for, and that it was time for me to look to myself. Six weeks before, God had delivered me from my bondage to an infamous woman, and now I was in danger of becoming the slave of an angel. Such were my reflections whilst Sara was fainting, but it was necessary for me to consider the matter at my leisure.

There was a sale of valuable articles in the city, the means taken for disposing of them being a lottery. Sara had read the announcement, and I asked her with her mother and sister to come with me and take part in it. I had not much trouble in obtaining their consent, and we found ourselves in distinguished company, among the persons present being the Countess of Harrington, Lady Stanhope, and Emilie and her daughters. Emilie had a strange case before the courts. She had given information to the police that her husband had been robbed of six thousand pounds, though everyone said that she herself was the thief.

Madame M—— F—— did not take a ticket, but she allowed me to take tickets for her daughters, who were in high glee, since for ten or twelve guineas they got articles worth sixty.

Every day I was more taken with Sara; but feeling

sure that I should only obtain slight favours from her, I thought it was time to come to an explanation. So after supper I said that as it was not certain that Sara could become my wife I had determined not to accompany them to Berne. The father told me I was very wise, and that I could still correspond with his daughter, Sara said nothing, but I could see she was much grieved.

I passed a dreadful night; such an experience was altogether new to me. I weighed Sara's reasons, and they seemed to me to be merely frivolous, which drove me to conclude that my caresses had displeased her.

For the last three days I found myself more than once alone with her; but I was studiously moderate, and she caressed me in a manner that would have made my bliss if I had not already obtained the one great favour. It was at this time I learnt the truth of the maxim that if abstinence is sometimes the spur of love, it has also the contrary effect. Sara had brought my feeling to a pitch of gentle friendship, while an infamous prostitute like the Charpillon, who knew how to renew hope and yet grant nothing, ended by inspiring me with contempt, and finally with hatred.

The family sailed for Ostend, and I accompanied them to the mouth of the Thames. I gave Sara a letter for Madame de W——. This was the name of the learned Hedvig whom she did not know. They afterwards became sisters-in-law, as Sara married a brother of M. de W——, and was happy with him.

Even now I am glad to hear tidings of my old friends and their doings, but the interest I take in such matters is not to be compared to my interest in some obscure story of ancient history. For our contemporaries, the companions, of our youthful follies, we have a kind of

contempt, somewhat similar to that which we entertain for ourselves. Four years ago I wrote to Madame G—— at Hamburg, and my letter began:
"After a silence of twenty-one years . . ."

She did not deign to reply, and I was by no means displeased. We cared no longer for one another, and it is quite natural that it should be so.

When I tell my reader who Madame G—— is, he will be amused. Two years ago I set out for Hamburg, but my good genius made me turn back to Dux; what had I to do at Hamburg?

After my guests were gone I went to the Italian Opera at Covent Garden, and met Goudar, who asked me if I would come to the Sartori's concert. He told me I should see a beautiful young English woman there who spoke Italian. As I had just lost Sara I did not much care about making new acquaintances, but still I was curious to see the young marvel. I indulged my curiosity, and I am glad to say that instead of being amused I was wearied, though the young English woman was pretty enough. A young Livonian, who called himself Baron of Stenau, seemed extremely interested in her. After supper she offered us tickets for the next concert, and I took one for myself and one for Goudar, giving her two guineas, but the Livonian baron took fifty tickets, and gave her a bank note for fifty guineas. I saw by this that he wanted to take the place by storm, and I liked his way of doing it. I supposed him to be rich, without caring to enquire into his means. He made advances to me and we became friends, and the reader will see in due time what a fatal acquaintance he was.

One day as I was walking with Goudar in Hyde Park he left me to speak to two ladies who seemed pretty.

He was not long absent, and said, when he rejoined me,——

"A Hanoverian lady, a widow and the mother of five daughters, came to England two months ago with her whole family. She lives close by, and is occupied in soliciting compensation from the Government for any injury that was done her by the passage of the Duke of Cumberland's army. The mother herself is sick and and never leaves her bed; she sends her two eldest daughters to petition the Government, and they are the two young ladies you have just seen. They have not met with any success. The eldest daughter is twenty-two, and the youngest fourteen; they are all pretty and can speak English, French, and German equally well, and are always glad to see visitors. I had been to visit them myself, but as I gave them nothing I do not care to go there alone a second time. If you like, however, I can introduce you."

"You irritate my curiosity. Come along, but if the one that pleases me is not complaisant she shall have nothing."

"They will not even allow one to take them by the hand."

"They are Charpillons, I suppose."

"It looks like it. But you won't see any men there."

We were shewn into a large room where I noticed three pretty girls and an evil-looking man. I began with the usual compliments, to which the girls replied politely, but with an air of great sadness.

Goudar spoke to the man, and then came to me shrugging his shoulders, and saying,——

"We have come at a sad time. That man is a bailiff who has come to take the mother to prison if she can't pay her landlord the twenty guineas' rent she owes him, and they haven't got a farthing. When the mother has been sent to prison the landlord will no doubt turn the girls out of doors."

"They can live with their mother for nothing."

"Not at all. If they have got the money they can have their meals in prison, but no one is allowed to live in a prison except the prisoners."

I asked one of them where her sisters were.

"They have gone out to look for money, for the landlord won't accept any surety, and we have nothing to sell."

"All this is very sad; what does your mother say?"

"She only weeps, and yet, though she is ill and cannot leave her bed, they are going to take her to prison. By way of consolation the landlord says he will have her carried."

"It is very hard. But your looks please me, mademoiselle, and if you will be kind I may be able to extricate you from the difficulty."

"I do not know what you mean by 'kind.'"

"Your mother will understand; go and ask her."

"Sir, you do not know us; we are honest girls, and ladies of position besides."

With these words the young woman turned her back on me, and began to weep again. The two others, who were quite as pretty, stood straight up and said not a word. Goudar whispered to me in Italian that unless we did something for them we should cut but a sorry figure there; and I was cruel enough to go away without saying a word.

CHAPTER XV

The Hanoverians

A S WE were leaving the house we met the two eldest sisters, who came home looking very sad. I was struck by their beauty, and extremely surprised to hear myself greeted by one of them, who said,——

"It is M. the Chevalier de Seingalt."

"Himself, mademoiselle, and sorely grieved at your misfortune."

"Be kind enough to come in again for a moment."

"I am sorry to say that I have an important engagement."

"I will not keep you for longer than a quarter of an hour."

I could not refuse so small a favour, and she employed the time in telling me how unfortunate they had been in Hanover, how they had come to London to obtain compensation, of their failure, their debts, the cruelty of the landlord, their mother's illness, the prison that awaited her, the likelihood of their being cast into the street, and the cruelty of all their acquaintances.

"We have nothing to sell, and all our resources consist of two shillings, which we shall have to spend on bread, on which we live."

"Who are your friends? How can they abandon you at such a time?"

She mentioned several names—among others, Lord Baltimore, Marquis Carracioli, the Neapolitan ambassador, and Lord Pembroke.

"I can't believe it," said I, "for I know the two last noblemen to be both rich and generous. There must be some good reason for their conduct, since you are beautiful; and for these gentlemen beauty is a bill to be honoured on sight."

"Yes, there is a reason. These rich noblemen abandon us with contempt. They refuse to take pity on us because we refuse to yield to their guilty passion."

"That is to say, they have taken a fancy to you, and as you will not have pity on them they refuse to have pity on you. Is it not so?"

"That is exactly the situation."

"Then I think they are in the right."

"In the right?"

"Yes, I am quite of their opinion. We leave you to enjoy your sense of virtue, and we spend our money in procuring those favours which you refuse us. Your misfortune really is your prettiness, if you were ugly you would get twenty guineas fast enough. I would give you the money myself, and the action would be put down to benevolence; whereas, as the case stands, if I were to give you anything it would be thought that I was actuated by the hope of favours to come, and I should be laughed at, and deservedly, as a dupe."

I felt that this was the proper way to speak to the girl, whose eloquence in pleading her cause was simply wonderful.

She did not reply to my oration, and I asked her how she came to know me.

"I saw you at Richmond with the Charpillon."

"She cost me two thousand guineas, and I got nothing for my money; but I have profited by the lesson, and in future I shall never pay in advance."

Just then her mother called her, and, begging me to

wait a moment, she went into her room, and returned almost directly with the request that I would come and speak to the invalid.

I found her sitting up in her bed; she looked about forty-five, and still preserved traces of her former beauty; her countenance bore the imprint of sadness, but had no marks of sickness whatsoever. Her brilliant and expressive eyes, her intellectual face, and a suggestion of craft about her, all bade me be on my guard, and a sort of false likeness to the Charpillon's mother made me still more cautious, and fortified me in my resolution to give no heed to the appeals of pity.

"Madam," I began, "what can I do for you?"

"Sir," she replied, "I have heard the whole of your conversations with my daughters, and you must confess that you have not talked to them in a very fatherly manner."

"Quite so, but the only part which I desire to play with them is that of lover, and a fatherly style would not have been suitable to the part. If I had the happiness of being their father, the case would be altered. What I have said to your daughters is what I feel, and what I think most likely to bring about the end I have in view. I have not the slightest pretence to virtue, but I adore the fair sex, and now you and they know the road to my purse. If they wish to preserve their virtue, why let them; nobody will trouble them, and they, on their side, must not expect anything from men. Good-bye, madam; you may reckon on my never addressing your daughters again."

"Wait a moment, sir. My husband was the Count of ——, and you see that my daughters are of respectable birth."

"Have you not pity for our situation?"

"I pity you extremely, and I would relieve you in an instant if your daughters were ugly, but as it is they are pretty, and that alters the case."

"What an argument!"

"It is a very strong one with me, and I think I am the best judge of arguments which apply to myself. You want twenty guineas; well, you shall have them after one of your five countesses has spent a joyous night with me."

"What language to a woman of my station! Nobody has ever dared to speak to me in such a way before."

"Pardon me, but what use is rank without a half-penny? Allow me to retire.

"To-day we have only bread to eat."

"Well, certainly that is rather hard on countesses."

"You are laughing at the title, apparently."

"Yes, I am; but I don't want to offend you. If you like, I will stop to dinner, and pay for all, yourself included."

"You are an eccentric individual. My girls are sad, for I am going to prison. You will find their company wearisome."

"That is my affair."

"You had much better give them the money you would spend on the dinner."

"No, madam. I must have at least the pleasures of sight and sound for my money. I will stay your arrest till to-morrow, and afterwards Providence may possibly intervene on your behalf."

"The landlord will not wait."

"Leave me to deal with him."

I told Goudar to go and see what the man would take to send the bailiff away for twenty-four hours. He returned with the message that he must have a guinea and bail for the twenty guineas, in case the lodgers might take to flight before the next day.

My wine merchant lived close by. I told Goudar to wait for me, and the matter was soon settled and the bailiff sent away, and I told the five girls that they might take their ease for twenty-four hours more.

I informed Goudar of the steps I had taken, and told him to go out and get a good dinner for eight people. He went on his errand, and I summoned the girls to their mother's bedside, and delighted them all by telling them that for the next twenty-four hours they were to make good cheer. They could not get over their surprise at the suddenness of the change I had worked in the house.

"But this is all I can do for you," said I to the mother. "Your daughters are charming, and I have obtained a day's respite for you all without asking for anything in return; I shall dine, sup, and pass the night with them without asking so much as a single kiss, but if your ideas have not changed by to-morrow you will be in exactly the same position as you were a few minutes ago, and I shall not trouble you any more with my attentions."

"What do you mean my 'changing my ideas'?"

"I need not tell you, for you know perfectly well what I mean."

"My daughters shall never become prostitutes."

"I will proclaim their spotless chastity all over London —but I shall spend my guineas elsewhere."

"You are a cruel man."

"I confess I can be very cruel, but it is only when I don't meet with kindness."

Goudar came back and we returned to the ladies' room, as the mother did not like to shew herself to my friend, telling me that I was the only man she had per-

mitted to see her in bed during the whole time she had
been in London.

Our English dinner was excellent in its way, but my
chief pleasure was to see the voracity with which the
girls devoured the meal. One would have thought they
were savages devouring raw meat after a long fast. I
had got a case of excellent wine and I made each of
them drink a bottle, but not being accustomed to such an
indulgence they became quite drunk. The mother had
devoured the whole of the plentiful helpings I had sent
in to her, and she had emptied a bottle of Burgundy,
which she carried very well.

In spite of their intoxication, the girls were perfectly
safe; I kept my word, and Goudar did not take the
slightest liberty. We had a pleasant supper, and after
a bowl of punch I left them feeling in love with the
whole bevy, and very uncertain whether I should be able
to shew as brave a front the next day.

As we were going away Goudar said that I was con-
ducting the affair admirably, but if I made a single slip I
should be undone.

I saw the good sense of his advice, and determined to
shew that I was as sharp as he.

The next day, feeling anxious to hear the result of
the council which the mother had doubtless held with
the daughters, I called at their house at ten o'clock. The
two eldest sisters were out, endeavouring to beat up some
more friends, and the three youngest rushed up to me
as if they had been spaniels and I their master, but they
would not even allow me to kiss them. I told them they
made a mistake, and knocked at the mother's door. She
told me to come in, and thanked me for the happy day
I had given them.

"Am I to withdraw my bail, countess?"

"You can do what you like, but I do not think you capable of such an action."

"You are mistaken. You have doubtless made a deep study of the human heart; but you either know little of the human mind, or else you think you have a larger share than any other person. All your daughters have inspired me with love, but were it a matter of life and death I would not do a single thing for them or you before you have done me the only favour that is in your power. I leave you to your reflections, and more especially to your virtues."

She begged me to stay, but I did not even listen to her. I passed by the three charmers, and after telling my wine merchant to withdraw his security I went in a furious mood to call on Lord Pembroke. As soon as I mentioned the Hanoverians he burst out laughing, and said these false innocents must be made to fulfil their occupation in a proper manner.

"They came whining to me yesterday," he proceeded, "and I not only would not give them anything, but I laughed them to scorn. They have got about twelve guineas out of me on false pretences; they are as cunning sluts as the Charpillon."

I told him what I had done the day before, and what I intended to offer: twenty guineas for the first, and as much for each of the others, but nothing to be paid in advance.

"I had the same idea myself, but I cried off, and I don't think you'll succeed, as Lord Baltimore offered them forty apiece; that is two hundred guineas in all, and the bargain has fallen through because they want the money to be paid in advance. They paid him a visit yesterday, but found him pitiless, for he has been taken in several times by them."

"We shall see what will happen when the mother is under lock and key; I'll bet we shall have them cheaply."

I came home for dinner, and Goudar, who had just been at their house, reported that the bailiff would only wait till four o'clock, that the two eldest daughters had come back empty-handed, and that they had been obliged to sell one of their dresses to buy a morsel of bread.

I felt certain that they would have recourse to me again, and I was right. We were at dessert when they put in an appearance. I made them sit down, and the eldest sister exhausted her eloquence to persuade me to give them another three days' grace.

"You will find me insensible," said I, "unless you are willing to adopt my plan. If you wish to hear it, kindly follow me into the next room."

She did so, leaving her sister with Goudar, and making her sit down on a sofa beside me, I shewed her twenty guineas, saying,——

"These are yours; but you know on what terms?"

She rejected my offer with disdain, and thinking she might wish to salve her virtue by being attacked, I set to work; but finding her resistance serious I let her alone, and begged her to leave my house immediately. She called to her sister, and they both went out.

In the evening, as I was going to the play, I called on my wine merchant to hear the news. He told me that the mother had been taken to prison, and that the youngest daughter had gone with her; but he did not know what had become of the four others.

I went home feeling quite sad, and almost reproaching myself for not having taken compassion on them; however, just as I was sitting down to supper they appeared before me like four Magdalens. The eldest, who was the orator of the company, told me that their mother was in prison, and that they would have to pass the night in the street if I did not take pity on them.

"You shall have rooms, beds, and good fires," said I, "but first let me see you eat."

Delight appeared on every countenance, and I had numerous dishes brought for them. They ate eagerly but sadly, and only drank water.

"Your melancholy and your abstinence displeases me," said I, to the eldest girl; "go upstairs and you will find everything necessary for your comfort, but take care to be gone at seven in the morning and not to let me see your faces again."

They went up to the second floor without a word.

An hour afterwards, just as I was going to bed, the eldest girl came into my room and said she wished to have a private interview with me. I told my negro to withdraw, and asked her to explain herself.

"What will you do for us," said she, "if I consent to share your couch?"

"I will give you twenty guineas, and I will lodge and board you as long as you give me satisfaction."

Without saying a word she began to undress, and got into bed. She was submissive and nothing more, and did not give me so much as a kiss. At the end of a quarter of an hour I was disgusted with her and got up, and giving her a bank note for twenty guineas I told her to put on her clothes and go back to her room.

"You must all leave my house to-morrow," I said, "for I am ill pleased with you. Instead of giving yourself up for love you have prostituted yourself. I blush for you."

She obeyed mutely, and I went to sleep in an ill humour.

At about seven o'clock in the morning I was awakened by a hand shaking me gently. I opened my eyes, and I was surprised to see the second daughter.

"What do you want?" I said, coldly.

"I want you to take pity on us, and shelter us in your house for a few days longer. I will be very grateful. My sister has told me all, you are displeased with her, but you must forgive her, for her heart is not her own. She is in love with an Italian who is in prison for debt."

"And I suppose you are in love with someone else?"

"No, I am not."

"Could you love me?"

She lowered her eyes, and pressed my hand gently.

I drew her towards me, and embraced her, and as I felt her kisses answer mine, I said,——

"You have conquered."

"My name is Victoire."

"I like it, and I will prove the omen a true one."

Victoire, who was tender and passionate, made me spend two delicious hours, which compensated me for my bad quarter of an hour of the night before.

When our exploits were over, I said,——

"Dearest Victoire, I am wholly thine. Let your mother be brought here as soon as she is free. Here are twenty guineas for you."

She did not expect anything, and the agreeable surprise made her in an ecstasy; she could not speak, but her heart was full of happiness. I too was happy, and I believed that a great part of my happiness was caused by the knowledge that I had done a good deed. We are queer creatures all of us, whether we are bad or good. From that moment I gave my servants orders to lay the table for eight persons every day, and told them that

I was only at home to Goudar. I spent money madly, and felt that I was within a measurable distance of poverty.

At noon the mother came in a sedan-chair, and went to bed directly. I went to see her, and did not evince any surprise when she began to thank me for my noble generosity. She wanted me to suppose that she thought I had given her daughters forty guineas for nothing, and I let her enjoy her hypocrisy.

In the evening I took them to Covent Garden, where the *castrato* Tenducci surprised me by introducing me to his wife, of whom he had two children. He laughed at people who said that a *castrato* could not procreate. Nature had made him a monster that he might remain a man; he was born *triorchis,* and as only two of the seminal glands had been destroyed the remaining one was sufficient to endow him with virility.

When I got back to my small seraglio I supped merrily with the five nymphs, and spent a delicious night with Victoire, who was overjoyed at having made my conquest. She told me that her sister's lover was a Neapolitan, calling himself Marquis de Petina, and that they were to get married as soon as he was out of prison. It seemed he was expecting remittances, and the mother would be delighted to see her daughter a marchioness.

"How much does the marquis owe?"

"Twenty guineas."

"And the Neapolitan ambassador allows him to languish in prison for such a beggarly sum? I can't believe it."

"The ambassador won't have anything to do with him, because he left Naples without the leave of the Government."

"Tell your sister that if the ambassador assures me that her lover's name is really the Marquis de Petina, I will get him out of prison immediately."

I went out to ask my daughter, and another boarder of whom I was very fond, to dinner, and on my way called on the Marquis of Caraccioli, an agreeable man, whose acquaintance I had made at Turin. I found the famous Chevalier d'Eon at his house, and I had no need of a private interview to make my inquiries about Petina.

"The young man is really what he professes to me," said the ambassador, "but I will neither receive him nor give him any money till I hear from my Government that he has received leave to travel."

That was enough for me, and I stayed there for an hour listening to d'Eon's amusing story.

Eon had deserted the embassy on account of ten thousand francs which the department of foreign affairs at Versailles had refused to allow him, though the money was his by right. He had placed himself under the protection of the English laws, and after securing two thousand subscribers at a guinea apiece, he had sent to press a huge volume in quarto containing all the letters he had received from the French Government for the last five or six years.

About the same time a London banker had deposited the sum of twenty thousand guineas at the Bank of England, being ready to wager that sum that Eon was a woman. The bet was taken by a number of persons who had formed themselves into a kind of company for the purpose, and the only way to decide it was that Eon should be examined in the presence of witnesses. The chevalier was offered half the wager, but he laughed them to scorn. He said that such an examination would dishonour him, were he man or woman. Caraccioli said that it could only dishonour him if he were a woman, but I could not agree with this opinion. At the end of a year the bet was declared off; but in the course of three years he received his pardon from the king, and appeared at Court in woman's dress, wearing the cross of St. Louis.

Louis XV. had always been aware of the chevalier's sex, but Cardinal Fleuri had taught him that it became kings to be impenetrable, and Louis remained so all his life.

When I got home I gave the eldest Hanoverian twenty guineas, telling her to fetch her marquis out of prison, and bring him to dine with us, as I wanted to know him. I thought she would have died with joy.

The third sister, having taken counsel with Victoire, and doubtless with her mother also, determined to earn twenty guineas for herself, and she had not much trouble in doing so. She it was on whom Lord Pembroke had cast the eye of desire.

These five girls were like five dishes placed before a gourmand, who enjoys them one after the other. To my fancy the last was always the best. The third sister's name was Augusta.

Next Sunday I had a large number of guests. There were my daughter and her friend, Madame Cornelis, and her son. Sophie was kissed and caressed by the Hanoverians, while I bestowed a hundred kisses on Miss Nancy Steyne, who was only thirteen, but whose young beauty worked sad havoc with my senses. My affection was supposed to be fatherly in its character, but, alas! it was of a much more fleshly kind. This Miss Nancy, who seemed to me almost divine, was the daughter of a rich merchant. I said that I wanted to make her father's acquaintance, and she replied that her father proposed coming to call on me that very day. I was

delighted to hear of the coincidence, and gave orders
that he should be shewn in as soon as he came.

The poor marquis was the only sad figure in the
company. He was young and well-made, but thin and
repulsively ugly. He thanked me for my kindness,
saying that I had done a wise thing, as he felt sure the
time would come when he would repay me a hundred-
fold.

I had given my daughter six guineas to buy a pelisse,
and she took me to my bedroom to shew it me. Her
mother followed her to congratulate me on my seraglio.

At dinner gaiety reigned supreme. I sat between my
daughter and Miss Nancy Steyne, and felt happy. Mr.
Steyne came in as we were at the oysters. He kissed his
daughter with that tender affection which is more char-
acteristic, I think, of English parents than those of any
other nation.

Mr. Steyne had dined, but he nevertheless ate a hundred scolloped oysters, in the preparation of which my
cook was wonderfully expert; he also honoured the
champagne with equal attention.

We spent three hours at the table and then proceeded
to the third floor, where Sophie accompanied her
mother's singing on the piano, and young Cornelis displayed his flute-playing talents. Mr. Steyne swore that
he had never been present at such a pleasant party in
his life, adding that pleasure was forbidden fruit in
England on Sundays and holidays. This convinced
me that Steyne was an intelligent man, though his
French was execrable. He left at seven, after giving
a beautiful ring to my daughter, whom he escorted back
to school with Miss Nancy.

The Marquis Petina foolishly observed to me that he
did not know where to find a bed. I understood what

he wanted, but I told him he would easily find one with a little money. Taking his sweetheart aside I gave her a guinea for him, begging her to tell him not to visit me again till he was invited.

When all the guests were gone, I led the five sisters to the mother's room. She was wonderfully well, eating, drinking, and sleeping to admiration, and never doing anything, not even reading or writing. She enjoyed the *dolce far niente* in all the force of the term. However, she told me she was always thinking of her family, and of the laws which it imposed on her.

I could scarcely help laughing, but I only said that if these laws were the same as those which her charming daughters followed, I thought them wiser than Solon's.

I drew Augusta on to my knee, and said,——

"My lady, allow me to kiss your delightful daughter."

Instead of giving me a direct answer, the old hypocrite began a long sermon on the lawfulness of the parental kiss. All the time Augusta was lavishing on me secret but delicious endearments.

O tempora! O mores!

The next day I was standing at my window, when the Marquis Caraccioli, who was passing by, greeted me, and asked me if he could come in. I bade him welcome, and summoning the eldest sister told the ambassador that this young lady was going to marry the Marquis Petina as soon as his remittances arrived.

He addressed himself to her, and spoke as follows:

"Mademoiselle, it is true that your lover is really a marquis, but he is very poor and will never have any money; and if he goes back to Naples he will be imprisoned, and if he is released from the State prison his creditors will put him in the Vittoria."

However this salutary warning had no effect.

After the ambassador had taken his leave I was dressing to take a ride when Augusta told me that, if I liked, Hippolyta her sister would come with me, as she could ride beautifully.

"That's amusing," said I, "make her come down."

Hippolyta came down and begged me to let her ride with me, saying that she would do me credit.

"Certainly;" said I, "but have you a man's riding suit or a woman's costume?"

"No."

"Then we must put off the excursion till to-morrow."

I spent the day in seeing that a suit was made for her, and I felt quite amorous when Pegu, the tailor, measured her for the breeches. Everything was done in time and we had a charming ride, for she managed her horse with wonderful skill.

After an excellent supper, to which wine had not been lacking, the happy Hippolyta accompanied Victoire into my room and helped her to undress. When she kissed her sister I asked if she would not give me a kiss too, and after some jesting Augusta changed the joke into earnest by bidding her come to bed beside me, without taking the trouble to ask my leave, so sure did she feel of my consent. The night was well spent, and I had no reason to complain of want of material, but Augusta wisely let the newcomer have the lion's share of my attentions.

Next day we rode out again in the afternoon, followed by my negro, who was a skilful horseman himself. In Richmond Park Hippolyta's dexterity astonished me; she drew all eyes on her. In the evening we came home well pleased with our day's ride, and had a good supper.

As the meal proceeded I noticed that Gabrielle, the

youngest of all, looked sad and a little sulky. I asked
her the reason, and with a little pout that became her
childish face admirably, she replied,——

"Because I can ride on horseback as well as my
sister."

"Very good," said I, "then you shall ride the day
after to-morrow." This put her into a good temper
again.

Speaking of Hippolyta's skill, I asked her where she
had learnt to ride. She simply burst out laughing. I
asked her why she laughed, and she said,——

"Why, because I never learnt anywhere; my only
masters were courage and some natural skill."

"And has your sister learnt?"

"No," said Gabrielle, "but I can ride just as well."

I could scarcely believe it, for Hippolyta had seemed
to float on her horse, and her riding shewed the utmost
skill and experience. Hoping that her sister would vie
with her, I said that I would take them out together,
and the very idea made them both jump with joy.

Gabrielle was only fifteen, and her shape, though not
fully developed, was well marked, and promised a perfect beauty by the time she was in her maturity. Full
of grace and simplicity, she said she would like to come
with me to my room, and I readily accepted her offer,
not caring whether the scheme had been concerted between her and her other sisters.

As soon as we were alone, she told me that she had
never had a lover, and she allowed me to assure myself
of the fact with the same child-like simplicity. Gabrielle
was like all the others; I would have chosen her if I had
been obliged to make the choice. She made me feel
sorry for her sake, to hear that the mother had made
up her mind to leave. In the morning I gave her her fee

of twenty guineas and a handsome ring as a mark of
my peculiar friendship, and we spent the day in getting ready our habits for the ride of the day following.

Gabrielle got on horseback as if she had had two
years in the riding school. We went along the streets
at a walking pace, but as soon as we were in the open
country we broke into a furious gallop, and kept it up
till we got to Barnet, where we stopped to breakfast.
We had done the journey in twenty-five minutes, although the distance is nearly ten miles. This may
seem incredible, but the English horses are wonderfully
swift, and we were all of us well mounted. My two
nymphs looked ravishing. I adored them, and I adored
myself for making them so happy.

Just as we were remounting, who should arrive but
Lord Pembroke. He was on his way to St. Alban's.
He stopped his horse, and admired the graceful riding
of my two companions; and not recognizing them immediately, he begged leave to pay his court to them.
How I laughed to myself! At last he recognized them,
and congratulated me on my conquest, asking if I loved
Hippolyta. I guessed his meaning, and said I only
loved Gabrielle.

"Very good," said he; "may I come and see you?"

"Certainly," I replied.

After a friendly hand-shake we set out once more,
and were soon back in London.

Gabrielle was done up and went to bed directly; she
slept on till the next morning without my disturbing
her peaceful sleep, and when she awoke and found herself in my arms, she began to philosophise.

"How easy it is," said she, "to be happy when one
is rich, and how sad it is to see happiness out of one's
reach for lack of a little money. Yesterday I was the

happiest of beings, and why should I not be as happy all my days? I would gladly agree that my life should be short provided that it should be a happy one."

I, too, philosophised, but my reflections were sombre. I saw my resources all but exhausted, and I began to meditate a journey to Lisbon. If my fortune had been inexhaustible, the Hanoverians might have held me in their silken fetters to the end of my days. It seemed to me as if I loved them more like a father than a lover, and the fact that I slept with them only added to the tenderness of the tie. I looked into Gabrielle's eyes, and there I saw but love. How could such a love exist in her unless she were naturally virtuous, and yet devoid of those prejudices which are instilled into us in our early years.

The next day Pembroke called and asked me to give him a dinner. Augusta delighted him. He made proposals to her which excited her laughter as he did not want to pay till after the event, and she would not admit this condition. However, he gave her a bank note for ten guineas before he left, and she accepted it with much grace. The day after he wrote her a letter, of which I shall speak presently.

A few minutes after the nobleman had gone the mother sent for me to come to her, and after paying an eloquent tribute to my virtues, my generosity, and my unceasing kindness towards her family, she made the following proposal:

"As I feel sure that you have all the love of a father for my daughters, I wish you to become their father in reality! I offer you my hand and heart; become my husband, you will be their father, their lord and mine. What do you say to this?"

I bit my lips hard and had great difficulty in restraining my inclination to laughter. Nevertheless, the amazement, the contempt, and the indignation which this unparalleled piece of impudence aroused in me soon brought me to myself. I perceived that this consummate hypocrite had counted on an abrupt refusal, and had only made this ridiculous offer with the idea of convincing me that she was under the impression that I had left her daughters as I had found them, and that the money I had spent on them was merely a sign of my tender and fatherly affection. Of course she knew perfectly well how the land lay, but she thought to justify herself by taking this step. She was aware that I could only look upon such a proposal as an insult, but she did not care for that.

I resolved to keep on the mask, and replied that her proposition was undoubtedly a very great honour for me, but it was also a very important question, and so I begged her to allow me some time for consideration.

When I got back to my room I found there the mistress of the wretched Marquis Petina, who told me that her happiness depended on a certificate from the Neapolitan ambassador that her lover was really the person he professed to be. With this document he would be able to claim a sum of two hundred guineas, and then they could both go to Naples, and he would marry her there. "He will easily obtain the royal pardon," said she. "You, and you alone, can help us in the matter, and I commend myself to your kindness."

I promised to do all I could for her. In fact, I called on the ambassador, who made no difficulty about giving the required certificate. For the moment my chilly conquest was perfectly happy, but though I saw she was very grateful to me I did not ask her to prove her gratitude.

CHAPTER XVI

Augusta Becomes Lord Pembroke's Titular Mistress—
The King of Corsica's Son—M. du Claude, or the
Jesuit Lavalette—Departure of the Hanoverians—I
Balance My Accounts—The Baron Stenau—The Eng-
lish Girl, and What She Gave Me—Daturi—My
Flight from London—Comte St. Germain—Wesel

L ORD PEMBROKE wrote to Augusta offering her
fifty guineas a month for three years, with lodging,
board, servants, and carriage at St. Albans, without reckoning what she might expect from his grateful affection
if it were returned.

Augusta translated the letter for me, and asked for
my advice.

"I can't give you any counsel," said I, "in a matter
which only concerns your own heart and your own interests."

She went up to her mother, who would come to no
conclusion without first consulting me, because, as she
said, I was the wisest and most virtuous of men. I am
afraid the reader will differ from her here, but I comfort myself by the thought that I, too, think like the
reader. At last it was agreed that Augusta should accept the offer if Lord Pembroke would find a surety
in the person of some reputable London merchant, for
with her beauty and numerous graces she was sure to
become Lady Pembroke before long. Indeed, the
mother said she was perfectly certain of it, as otherwise

she could not have given her consent, as her daughters were countesses, and too good to be any man's mistresses.

The consequence was that Augusta wrote my lord a letter, and in three days it was all settled. The merchant duly signed the contract, at the foot of which I had the honour of inscribing my name as a witness, and then I took the merchant to the mother, and he witnessed her cession of her daughter. She would not see Pembroke, but she kissed her daughter, and held a private colloquy with her.

The day on which Augusta left my house was signalized by an event which I must set down.

The day after I had given the Marquis Petina's future bride the required certificate, I had taken out Gabrielle and Hippolyta for a ride. When I got home I found waiting for me a person calling himself Sir Frederick, who was said to be the son of Theodore, King of Corsica, who had died in London. This gentleman said he wished to speak to me in private, and when we were alone he said he was aware of my acquaintance with the Marquis Petina, and being on the eve of discounting a bill of two hundred guineas for him he wished to be informed whether it was likely that he could meet the bill when it fell due.

"It is important that I should be informed on that point," he added, "for the persons who are going to discount the bill want me to put my signature to it."

"Sir," I replied, "I certainly am acquainted with the marquis, but I know nothing about his fortune. However, the Neapolitan ambassador assured me that he was the Marquis Petina."

"If the persons who have the matter in hand should drop it, would you discount the bill? You shall have it cheap."

"I never meddle with these speculations. Good day, Sir Frederick."

The next day Goudar came and said that a M. du Claude wanted to speak to me.

"Who is M. du Claude?"

"The famous Jesuit Lavalette, who was concerned in the great bankruptcy case which ruined the Society in France. He fled to England under a false name. I advise you to listen to him, for he must have plenty of money."

"A Jesuit and a bankrupt; that does not sound very well."

"Well, I have met him in good houses, and knowing that I was acquainted with you he addressed himself to me. After all, you run no risk in listening to what he has to say."

"Well, well, you can take me to him; it will be easier to avoid any entanglement than if he came to see me."

Goudar went to Lavalette to prepare the way, and in the afternoon he took me to see him. I was well enough pleased to see the man, whose rascality had destroyed the infamous work of many years. He welcomed me with great politeness, and as soon as we were alone he shewed me a bill of Petina's, saying,——

"The young man wants me to discount it, and says you can give me the necessary information."

I gave the reverend father the same answer as I had given the King of Corsica's son, and left him angry with this Marquis of Misery who had given me so much needless trouble. I was minded to have done with him, and resolved to let him know through his mistress that I would not be his reference, but I could not find an opportunity that day.

The next day I took my two nymphs for a ride, and

asked Pembroke to dinner. In vain we waited for
Petina's mistress; she was nowhere to be found. At
nine o'clock I got a letter from her, with a German
letter enclosed for her mother. She said that feeling
certain that her mother would not give her consent to
her marriage, she had eloped with her lover, who had
got together enough money to go to Naples, and when
they reached that town he would marry her. She begged
me to console her mother and make her listen to reason,
as she had not gone off with an adventurer but with a
man of rank, her equal. My lips curled into a smile
of pity and contempt, which made the three sisters curious. I shewed them the letter I had just received, and
asked them to come with me to their mother.

"Not to-night," said Victoire, "this terrible news
would keep her awake."

I took her advice and we supped together, sadly
enough.

I thought the poor wretch was ruined for life, and I
reproached myself with being the cause of her misfortune; for if I had not released the marquis from prison
this could never have happened. The Marquis Caraccioli had been right in saying that I had done a good
deed, but a foolish one. I consoled myself in the arms
of my dear Gabrielle.

I had a painful scene with the mother the next morning. She cursed her daughter and her seducer, and even
blamed me. She wept and stormed alternately.

It is never of any use to try and convince people in
distress that they are wrong, for one may only do harm,
while if they are left to themselves they soon feel that
they have been unjust, and are grateful to the person who
let them exhaust their grief without any contradiction.

After this event I spent a happy fortnight in the society of Gabrielle, whom Hippolyta and Victoire looked on as my wife. She made my happiness and I made hers in all sorts of ways, but especially by my fidelity; for I treated her sisters as if they had been my sisters, shewing no recollection of the favours I had obtained from them, and never taking the slightest liberty, for I knew that friendship between women will hardly brook amorous rivalry. I had bought them dresses and linen in abundance, they were well lodged and well fed, I took them to the theatre and to the country, and the consequence was they all adored me, and seemed to think that this manner of living would go on for ever. Nevertheless, I was every day nearer and nearer to moral and physical bankruptcy. I had no more money, and I had sold all my diamonds and precious stones. I still possessed my snuff-boxes, my watches, and numerous trifles, which I loved and had not the heart to sell; and, indeed, I should not have got the fifth part of what I gave for them. For a whole month I had not paid my cook, or my wine merchant, but I liked to feel that they trusted me. All I thought of was Gabrielle's love, and of this I assured myself by a thousand delicacies and attentions.

This was my condition when one day Victoire came to me with sadness on her face, and said that her mother had made up her mind to return to Hanover, as she had lost all hope of getting anything from the English Court.

"When does she intend to leave?"

"In three or four days."

"And is she going without telling me, as if she were leaving an inn after paying her bill?"

"On the contrary, she wishes to have a private talk with you."

I paid her a visit, and she began by reproaching me tenderly for not coming to see her more often. She said that as I had refused her hand she would not run the risk of incurring censure or slander of any kind. "I thank you from my heart," she added, "for all the kindness you have shewn my girls, and I am going to take the three I have left away, lest I lose them as I have lost the two eldest. If you like, you may come too and stay with us as long as you like in my pretty country house near the capital."

Of course I had to thank her and reply that my engagements did not allow me to accept her kind offer.

Three days after, Victoire told me, as I was getting up, that they were going on board ship at three o'clock. Hippolyta and Gabrielle made me come for a ride, according to a promise I had given them the night before. The poor things amused themselves, while I grieved bitterly, as was my habit when I had to separate from anyone that I loved.

When we came home I lay down on my bed, not taking any dinner, and seeing nothing of the three sisters till they had made everything ready for the journey. I got up directly before they left, so as not to see the mother in my own room, and I saw her in hers just as she was about to be taken down into my carriage, which was in readiness at the door. The impudent creature expected me to give her some money for the journey, but perceiving that I was not likely to bleed, she observed, with involuntary sincerity, that her purse contained the sum of a hundred and fifty guineas, which I had given to her daughters; and these daughters of hers were present, and sobbed bitterly.

When they were gone I closed my doors to everyone, and spent three days in the melancholy occupation of making up my accounts. In the month I had spent with the Hanoverians I had dissipated the whole of the sum resulting from the sale of the precious stones, and I found that I was in debt to the amount of four hundred guineas. I resolved to go to Lisbon by sea, and sold my diamond cross, six or seven gold snuff-boxes (after removing the portraits), all my watches except one, and two great trunks full of clothes. I then discharged my debts and found I was eighty guineas to the good, this being what remained of the fine fortune I had squandered away like a fool or a philosopher, or, perhaps, a little like both. I left my fine house where I had lived so pleasantly, and took a little room at a guinea a week. I still kept my negro, as I had every reason to believe him to be a faithful servant.

After taking these measures I wrote to M. de Bragadin, begging him to send me two hundred sequins.

Thus having made up my mind to leave London without owing a penny to anyone, and under obligations to no man's purse, I waited for the bill of exchange from Venice. When it came I resolved to bid farewell to all my friends and to try my fortune in Lisbon, but such was not the fate which the fickle goddess had assigned to me.

A fortnight after the departure of the Hanoverians (it was the end of February in the year 1764), my evil genius made me go to the "Canon Tavern," where I usually dined in a room by myself. The table was laid and I was just going to sit down, when Baron Stenau came in and begged me to have my dinner brought into the next room, where he and his mistress were dining.

"I thank you," said I, "for the solitary man grows weary of his company."

I saw the English woman I had met at Sartori's, the same to whom the baron had been so generous. She spoke Italian, and was attractive in many ways, so I was well pleased to find myself opposite to her, and we had a pleasant dinner.

After a fortnight's abstinence it was not surprising that she inspired me with desires, but I concealed them nevertheless, for her lover seemed to respect her. I only allowed myself to tell the baron that I thought him the happiest of men.

Towards the close of the dinner the girl noticed three dice on the mantel and took them up, saying,——

"Let us have a wager of a guinea, and spend it on oysters and champagne."

We could not refuse, and the baron having lost called the waiter and gave him his orders.

While we were eating the oysters she suggested that we should throw again to see which should pay for the dinner.

We did so and she lost.

I did not like my luck, and wishing to lose a couple of guineas I offered to throw against the baron. He accepted, and to my annoyance I won. He asked for his revenge and lost again.

"I don't want to win your money," said I, "and I will give you your revenge up to a hundred guineas."

He seemed grateful and we went on playing, and in less than half an hour he owed me a hundred guineas.

"Let us go on," said he.

"My dear baron, the luck's against you; you might lose a large sum of money. I really think we have had enough."

Without heeding my politeness, he swore against fortune and against the favour I seemed to be shewing him. Finally he got up, and taking his hat and cane, went out, saying,——

"I will pay you when I come back."

As soon as he had gone the girl said:

"I am sure you have been regarding me as your partner at play."

"If you have guessed that, you will also have guessed that I think you charming."

"Yes, I think I have."

"Are you angry with me?"

"Not in the least."

"You shall have the fifty guineas as soon as he has paid me."

"Very good, but the baron must know nothing about it."

"Of course not."

The bargain was scarcely struck before I began to shew her how much I loved her. I had every reason to congratulate myself on her complaisance, and I thought this meeting a welcome gleam of light when all looked dark around me. We had to make haste, however, as the door was only shut with a catch. I had barely time to ascertain her address and the hour at which she could see me, and whether I should have to be careful with her lover. She replied that the baron's fidelity was not of a character to make him very exacting. I put the address in my pocket, and promised to pass a night with her.

The baron came in again, and said,——

"I have been to a merchant to discount this bill of exchange, and though it is drawn on one of the best house in Cadiz, and made out by a good house in

London, he would not have anything to do with it."

I took the bill and saw some millions mentioned on it, which astonished me.

The baron said with a laugh that the currency was Portuguese milries, and that they amounted to five hundred pounds sterling.

"If the signatures are known," said I, "I don't understand why the man won't discount it. Why don't you take it to your banker?"

"I haven't got one. I came to England with a thousand gold pieces in my pocket, and I have spent them all. As I have not got any letters of credit I cannot pay you unless the bill is discounted. If you have got any friends on the Exchange, however, you could get it done."

"If the names prove good ones I will let you have the money to-morrow morning."

"Then I will make it payable to your order."

He put his name to it, and I promised to send him either the money or the bill before noon on the day following. He gave me his address and begged me to come and dine with him, and so we parted.

The next day I went to Bosanquet, who told me that Mr. Leigh was looking out for bills of exchange on Cadiz, and I accordingly waited on him. He exclaimed that such paper was worth more than gold to him, and gave me five hundred and twenty guineas, of course after I had endorsed it.

I called on the baron and gave him the money I had just received, and he thanked me and gave me back the hundred guineas. Afterwards we had dinner, and fell to talking of his mistress.

"Are you in love with her?" said I.

"No; I have plenty of others, and if you like her you can have her for ten guineas."

I liked this way of putting it, though I had not the slightest idea of cheating the girl out of the sum I had promised her. On leaving the baron I went to see her, and as soon as she heard that the baron had paid me she ordered a delicious supper, and made me spend a night that obliterated all my sorrows from my memory. In the morning, when I handed over the fifty guineas, she said that as a reward for the way in which I kept my promise I could sup with her whenever I liked to spend six guineas. I promised to come and see her often.

The next morning I received a letter through the post, written in bad Italian, and signed, *"Your obedient godson, Daturi."* This godson of mine was in prison for debt, and begged me to give him a few shillings to buy some food.

I had nothing particular to do, the appellation of *godson* made me curious, and so I went to the prison to see Daturi, of whose identity I had not the slightest idea. He was a fine young man of twenty; he did not know me, nor I him. I gave him his letter, and begging me to forgive him he drew a paper from his pocket and shewed me his certificate of baptism, on which I saw my own name inscribed beside his name and those of his father and mother, the parish of Venice, where he was born, and the church in which he was baptized; but still I racked my memory in vain; I could not recollect him.

"If you will listen to me," he said, "I can set you right; my mother has told me the story a hundred times."

"Go on," said I, "I will listen;" and as he told his story I remembered who he was.

This young man whom I had held at the font as the son of the actor Daturi was possibly my own son. He had come to London with a troupe of jugglers to play the illustrious part of clown, or *pagliazzo,* but having quarrelled with the company he had lost his place and had got into debt to the extent of ten pounds sterling, and for this debt he had been imprisoned. Without saying anything to him about my relations with his mother, I set him free on the spot, telling him to come to me every morning, as I would give him two shillings a day for his support.

A week after I had done this good work I felt that I had caught the fearful disease from which the god Mercury had already delivered me three times, though with great danger and peril of my life. I had spent three nights with the fatal English woman, and the misfortune was doubly inconvenient under the circumstances. I was on the eve of a long sea voyage, and though Venus may have risen from the waves of the sea, sea air is by no means favourable to those on whom she has cast her malign aspect. I knew what to do, and resolved to have my case taken in hand without delay.

I left my house, not with the intention of reproaching the English woman after the manner of fools, but rather of going to a good surgeon, with whom I could make an agreement to stay in his house till my cure was completed.

I had my trunks packed just as if I was going to leave London, excepting my linen, which I sent to my washerwoman who lived at a distance of six miles from town, and drove a great trade.

The very day I meant to change my lodging a letter was handed to me. It was from Mr. Leigh, and ran as follows:

"The bill of exchange I discounted for you is a forgery, so please to send me at your earliest convenience the five hundred and twenty guineas; and if the man who has cheated you will not reimburse the money, have him arrested. For Heaven's sake do not force me to have you arrested to-morrow, and whatever you do make haste, for this may prove a hanging matter."

Fortunately I was by myself when I received the letter. I fell upon my bed, and in a moment I was covered with a cold sweat, while I trembled like a leaf. I saw the gallows before me, for nobody would lend me the money, and they would not wait for my remittance from Venice to reach me.

To my shuddering fit succeeded a burning fever. I loaded my pistols, and went out with the determination of blowing out Baron Stenau's brains, or putting him under arrest if he did not give me the money. I reached his house, and was informed that he had sailed for Lisbon four days ago.

This Baron Stenau was a Livonian, and four months after these events he was hanged at Lisbon. I only anticipate this little event in his life because I might possibly forget it when I come to my sojourn at Riga.

As soon as I heard he was gone I saw there was no remedy, and that I must save myself. I had only ten or twelve guineas left, and this sum was insufficient. I went to Trèves, a Venetian Jew to whom I had a letter from Count Algarotti, the Venetian banker. I did not think of going to Bosanquet, or Sanhel, or Salvador, who might possibly have got wind of my trouble, while Trèves had no dealings with these great bankers, and discounted a bill for a hundred sequins readily enough.

With the money in my pocket I made my way to my lodging, while deadly fear dogged every step. Leigh had given me twenty-four hours' breathing time, and I did not think him capable of breaking his word, still it would not do to trust to it. I did not want to lose my linen nor three fine suits of clothes which my tailor was keeping for me, and yet I had need of the greatest promptitude.

I called in Jarbe and asked him whether he would prefer to take twenty guineas and his dismissal, or to continue in my service. I explained that he would have to wait in London for a week, and join me at the place from which I wrote to him.

"Sir," said he, "I should like to remain in your service, and I will rejoin you wherever you please. When are you leaving?"

"In an hour's time; but say not a word, or it will cost me my life."

"Why can't you take me with you?"

"Because I want you to bring my linen which is at the wash, and my clothes which the tailor is making. I will give you sufficient money for the journey."

"I don't want anything. You shall pay me what I have spent when I rejoin you. Wait a moment."

He went out and came back again directly, and holding out sixty guineas, said,——

"Take this, sir, I entreat you, my credit is good for as much more in case of need."

"I thank you, my good fellow, but I will not take your money, but be sure I will not forget your fidelity."

My tailor lived close by and I called on him, and seeing that my clothes were not yet made up I told him that I should like to sell them, and also the gold lace that was to be used in the trimming. He instantly gave me thirty guineas which meant a gain to him of twenty-five per cent. I paid the week's rent of my lodging, and after bidding farewell to my negro I set out with Daturi. We slept at Rochester, as my strength would carry me no farther. I was in convulsions, and had a sort of delirium. Daturi was the means of saving my life.

I had ordered post-horses to continue our journey, and Daturi of his own authority sent them back and went for a doctor, who pronounced me to be in danger of an apoplectic fit and ordered a copious blood-letting, which restored my calm. Six hours later he pronounced me fit to travel. I got to Dover early in the morning, and had only half an hour to stop, as the captain of the packet said that the tide would not allow of any delay. The worthy sailor little knew how well his views suited mine. I used this half hour in writing to Jarbe, telling him to rejoin me at Calais, and Mrs. Mercier, my land-lady, to whom I had addressed the letter, wrote to tell me that she had given it him with her own hands. However, Jarbe did not come. We shall hear more of this negro in the course of two years.

The fever and the virus that was in my blood put me in danger of my life, and on the third day I was *in extremis*. A fourth blood-letting exhausted my strength, and left me in a state of coma which lasted for twenty-four hours. This was succeeded by a crisis which restored me to life again, but it was only by dint of the most careful treatment that I found myself able to continue my journey a fortnight after my arrival in France.

Weak in health, grieved at having been the innocent cause of the worthy Mr. Leigh's losing a large sum of money, humiliated by my flight from London, indignant with Jarbe, and angry at being obliged to abandon my Portuguese project, I got into a post-chaise with Daturi, not knowing where to turn or where to go, or whether I had many more weeks to live.

I had written to Venice asking M. de Bragadin to send the sum I have mentioned to Brussels instead of London.

When I got to Dunkirk, the day after I left Paris, the first person I saw was the merchant S——, the husband of that Thérèse whom my readers may remember, the niece of Tiretta's mistress, with whom I had been in love seven years ago. The worthy man recognized me, and seeing his astonishment at the change in my appearance I told him I was recovering from a long illness, and then asked after his wife.

"She is wonderfully well," he answered, "and I hope we shall have the pleasure of seeing you to dinner to-morrow."

I said I wanted to be off at day-break, but he would not hear of it, and protested he would be quite hurt if I went away without seeing his wife and his three children. At last I appeased him by saying that we would sup together.

My readers will remember that I had been on the point of marrying Thérèse, and this circumstance made me ashamed of presenting myself to her in such a sorry plight.

In a quarter of an hour the husband arrived with his wife and three children, the eldest of whom looked about six. After the usual greetings and tiresome enquiries after my health, Thérèse sent back the two younger children, rightly thinking that the eldest would be the only one in whom I should take any interest. He was a charming boy; and as he was exactly like his mother, the worthy merchant had no doubts as to the parentage of the child.

I laughed to myself at finding my offspring thus scattered all over Europe. At supper Thérèse gave me news of Tiretta. He had entered the Dutch East India Company's service, but having been concerned in a revolt at Batavia, he had only escaped the gallows by flight. I had my own thoughts as to the similarity between his destiny and mine, but I did not reveal them. After all it is an easy enough matter for an adventurous man, who does not look where he is going, to get hanged for a mere trifle.

The next day, when I got to Tournay, I saw some grooms walking fine horses up and down, and I asked to whom they belonged.

"To the Comte de St. Germain, the adept, who has been here a month, and never goes out. Everybody who passes through the place wants to see him; but he is invisible."

This was enough to give me the same desire, so I wrote him a letter, expressing my wish to speak to him, and asking him to name an hour. His reply, which I have preserved, ran as follows:

"The gravity of my occupation compels me to exclude everyone, but you are an exception. Come whenever you like, you will be shewn in. You need not mention my name nor your own. I do not ask you to share my repast, for my food is not suitable to others—to you least of all, if your appetite is what it used to be."

At nine o'clock I paid my call, and found he had grown a beard two inches long. He had a score of retorts before him, full of liquids in various stages of digestion. He told me he was experimenting with colours for his own amusement, and that he had established a hat factory for Count Cobenzl, the Austrian ambassador at Brussels. He added that the count had only given him a hundred and fifty thousand florins, which were insufficient. Then we spoke of Madame d'Urfé.

"She poisoned herself," said he, "by taking too strong a dose of the Universal Medicine, and her will shews that she thought herself to be with child. If she had come to me, I could have really made her so, though it is a difficult process, and science has not advanced far enough for us to be able to guarantee the sex of the child."

When he heard the nature of my disease, he wanted me to stay three days at Tournay for him to give me fifteen pills, which would effectually cure me, and restore me to perfect health. Then he shewed me his *magistrum*, which he called *athoeter*. It was a white liquid contained in a well-stoppered phial. He told me that this liquid was the universal spirit of nature, and that if the wax on the stopper was pricked ever so lightly, the whole of the contents would disappear. I begged him to make the experiment. He gave me the phial and a pin, and I pricked the wax, and lo! the phial was empty.

"It is very fine," said I, "but what good is all this?"

"I cannot tell you; that is my secret."

He wanted to astonish me before I went, and asked me if I had any money about me. I took out several pieces and put them on the table. He got up, and without saying what he was going to do he took a burning coal and put it on a metal plate, and placed a twelve-sols piece with a small black grain on the coal. He then blew it, and in two minutes it seemed on fire.

"Wait a moment," said the alchemist, "let it get cool;" and it cooled almost directly.

"Take it; it is yours," said he.

I took up the piece of money and found it had become gold. I felt perfectly certain that he had smuggled my silver piece away, and had substituted a gold piece coated with silver for it. I did not care to tell him as much, but to let him see that I was not taken in, I said,——

"It is really very wonderful, but another time you should warn me what you are going to do, so that the operation might be attentively watched, and the piece of money noted before being placed on the burning coal."

"Those that are capable of entertaining doubts of my art," said the rogue, "are not worthy to speak to me."

This was in his usual style of arrogance, to which I was accustomed. This was the last time I saw this celebrated and learned impostor; he died at Schlesing six or seven years after. The piece of money he gave me was pure gold, and two months after Field-marshal Keith took such a fancy to it that I gave it him.

I left Tournay the next morning, and stopped at Brussels to await the answer of the letter which I had written to M. de Bragadin. Five days after I got the letter with a bill of exchange for two hundred ducats.

I thought of staying in Brussels to get cured, but Daturi told me that he had heard from a rope-dancer that his father and mother and the whole family were at Brunswick, and he persuaded me to go there, assuring me that I should be carefully looked after.

He had not much difficulty in getting me to go to Brunswick, as I was curious to see again the mother of my godson, so I started the same day. At Ruremonde

I was so ill that I had to stop for thirty-six hours. At Wesel I wished to get rid of my post-chaise, for the horses of the country are not used to going between shafts, but what was my surprise to meet General Bekw—— there.

After the usual compliments had passed, and the general had condoled with me on my weak state of health, he said he should like to buy my chaise and exchange it for a commodious carriage, in which I could travel all over Germany. The bargain was soon struck, and the general advised me to stay at Wesel where there was a clever young doctor from the University of Leyden, who would understand my case better than the Brunswick physicians.

Nothing is easier than to influence a sick man, especially if he be in search of fortune, and knows not where to look for the fickle goddess. General Bekw——, who was in garrison at Wesel, sent for Dr. Pipers, and was present at my confession and even at the examination.

I will not revolt my readers by describing the disgusting state in which I was, suffice it to say that I shudder still when I think of it.

The young doctor, who was gentleness personified, begged me to come and stay with him, promising that his mother and sisters should take the greatest care of me, and that he would effect a radical cure in the course of six weeks if I would carry out all his directions. The general advised me strongly to stay with the doctor, and I agreed all the more readily as I wished to have some amusement at Brunswick and not to arrive there deprived of the use of all my limbs. I therefore gave in, but the doctor would not hear of any agreement. He told me that I could give him whatever I liked when

I went away, and he would certainly be satisfied. He took his leave to go and make my room ready, and told me to come in an hour's time. I went to his house in a sedan-chair, and held a handkerchief before my face, as I was ashamed that the young doctor's mother and sisters should see me in the state I was in.

As soon as I got to my room, Daturi undressed me and I went to bed.

CHAPTER XVII

My Cure—Daturi is Beaten by Some Soldiers—I Leave Wesel for Brunswick—Redegonde—Brunswick—The Hereditary Prince—The Jew—My Stay at Wolfenbuttel—The Library—Berlin—Calsabigi and the Berlin Lottery—Mdlle. Bélanger

AT SUPPER-TIME, the doctor, his mother, and one of his sisters came to see me. All of them bore the love of their kind written on their features; they assured me that I should have all possible care at their hands. When the ladies were gone the doctor explained his treatment. He said that he hoped to cure me by the exhibition of sudorifices and mercurial pills, but he warned me I must be very careful in my diet and must not apply myself in any way. I promised to abide by his directions, and he said that he would read me the newspaper himself twice a week to amuse me, and by way of a beginning he informed me that the famous Pompadour was dead.

Thus I was condemned to a state of perfect rest, but it was not the remedies or the abstinence I dreaded most; I feared the effects of ennui; I thought I should die of it. No doubt the doctor saw the danger as well as myself, for he asked me if I would mind his sister coming and working in my room occasionally with a few of her friends. I replied that, despite my shame of shewing myself to young ladies in such a condition, I accepted her offer with delight. The sister was very grateful for what she was pleased to call my kindness, for my room was the only one which looked in the street, and as everyone knows girls are very fond of inspecting the passers-by. Unfortunately this arrangement turned out ill for Daturi. The poor young man had only received the education of a mountebank, and it was tiresome for him to pass all his time in my company. When he saw that I had plenty of friends, he thought I could dispense with his society, and only thought of amusing himself. On the third day towards the evening he was carried home covered with bruises. He had been in the guard-room with the soldiers, and some quarrel having arisen he had got a severe beating. He was in a pitiable state; all over blood and with three teeth missing. He told me the story with tears, and begged me to take vengeance on his foes.

I sent my doctor to General Bekw——, who said that all he could do was to give the poor man a bed in the hospital. Baturi had no bones broken, and in a few days was quite well, so I sent him on to Brunswick with a passport from General Salomon. The loss of his teeth secured him from the conscription; this, at any rate, was a good thing.

The treatment of the young doctor was even more successful than he had anticipated, for in a month I was perfectly well again, though terribly thin. The worthy people of the house must have taken an idea of me not in the least like myself; I was thought to be the most patient of men, and the sister and her young lady friends must have considered me as modesty personified; but these virtues only resulted from my illness and my great depression. If you want to discover the character of a man, view him in health and freedom; a captive and in sickness he is no longer the same man.

I gave a beautiful dress to the sister, and twenty louis to the doctor, and both seemed to me extremely satisfied.

On the eve of my departure I received a letter from Madame du Rumain, who had heard I was in want from my friend Baletti, and sent me a bill of exchange on Amsterdam for six hundred florins. She said I could repay her at my convenience, but she died before I was able to discharge the debt.

Having made up my mind to go to Brunswick, I could not resist the temptation to pass through Hanover, for whenever I thought of Gabrielle I loved her still. I did not wish to stop any length of time, for I was poor and I had to be careful of my health. I only wished to pay her a flying visit on the estate which her mother had at Stocken, as she had told me. I may also say that curiosity was a motive for this visit.

I had decided to start at day-break in my new carriage, but the fates had ordained it otherwise.

The English general wrote me a note asking me to sup with him, telling me that some Italians would be present, and this decided me to stay on, but I had to promise the doctor to observe strict temperance.

My surprise may be imagined when I saw the Redegonde and her abominable mother. The mother did not recognize me at first, but Redegonde knew me directly, and said,——

"Good Heavens! how thin you have become!"

I complimented her on her beauty, and indeed she had improved wonderfully.

"I have just recovered from a dangerous illness," said I, "and I am starting for Brunswick at day-break tomorrow."

"So are we," she exclaimed, looking at her mother.

The general, delighted to find that we knew each other, said we could travel together.

"Hardly, I think," I replied, "unless the lady-mother has changed her principles since I knew her."

"I am always the same," she said, dryly enough; but I only replied with a glance of contempt.

The general held a bank at faro at a small table. There were several other ladies and some officers, and the stakes were small. He offered me a place, but I excused myself, saying that I never played while on a journey.

At the end of the deal the general returned to the charge, and said,——

"Really, chevalier, this maxim of yours is anti-social; you must play."

So saying he drew several English bank notes from his pocket-book, telling me they were the same I had given him in London six months ago.

"Take your revenge," he added; "there are four hundred pounds here."

"I don't want to lose as much as that," I replied, "but I will risk fifty pounds to amuse you."

With this I took out the bill of exchange that Madame du Rumain had sent me.

The general went on dealing, and at the third deal I found I was fifty guineas to the good, and with that I was satisfied. Directly afterwards supper was announced, and we went into the dining-room.

Redegonde, who had learnt French admirably, kept everybody amused. She had been engaged by the Duke of Brunswick as second singer, and she had come from Brussels. She bemoaned her journey in the uncomfortable post-chaise, and expressed a fear that she would be ill by the time she got to her journey's end.

"Why, there's the Chevalier Seingalt all alone in a most comfortable carriage," said the general.

Redegonde smiled.

"How many people will your carriage hold?"

"Only two."

"Then it's out of the question, for I never let my daughter travel alone with anybody."

A general burst of laughter, in which Redegonde joined, seemed to confuse the mother in some degree; but like a good daughter Redegonde explained that her mother was always afraid of her being assassinated.

The evening passed away in pleasant conversation, and the younger singer did not need much persuasion to seat herself at the piano, where she sang in a manner that won genuine applause.

When I wanted to go the general begged me to breakfast with him, saying that the post-chaise did not go till twelve, and that this act of politeness was due to my young fellow-countrywoman. Redegonde joined in, reproaching me with my behaviour at Turin and Florence, though she had nothing really to complain of. I gave in, and feeling that I wanted rest I went to bed.

The next morning, at nine o'clock, I took leave of the worthy doctor and his family and walked to the general's, giving orders that my carriage should be brought round as soon as it was ready.

In half an hour Redegonde and her mother arrived, and I was astonished to see them accompanied by the brother who had been my servant at Florence.

When breakfast was over my carriage stood at the door, and I made my bow to the general and all the company, who were standing in the hall to see me off. Redegonde came down the steps with me, and asked if my carriage was comfortable, and then got into it. I got in after her without the slightest premeditation, and the postillion, seeing the carriage full, gave a crack with his whip and we were off, Redegonde shrieking with laughter. I was on the point of telling him to stop, but seeing her enjoyment of the drive I held my tongue, only waiting for her to say, "I have had enough." But I waited in vain, and we had gone over half a league before she said a word.

"I have laughed, and laugh still," she said, "when I think of what my mother will say at this freak of mine. I had no intentions in getting into the carriage, and I am sure you cannot have told the postillion to drive on."

"You may be quite sure of that."

"All the same my mother will believe it to be a deeply-laid plan, and that strikes me as amusing."

"So it is; I am quite satisfied, certainly. Now you are here you had better come on with me to Brunswick; you will be more comfortable than in a villainous stage coach."

"I should be delighted, but that would be pushing matters too far. No, we will stop at the first stage and wait for the coach."

"You may do so if you please, but you will excuse my waiting."

"What! you would leave me all alone?"

"You know, dear Redegonde, that I have always loved you, and I am ready to take you with me to Brunswick; what more can I say?"

"If you love me you will wait with me and restore me to my mother, who must be in despair."

"In spite of my devotion I am afraid I cannot do so."

Instead of turning sulky the young madcap began to laugh again, and I determined she should come with me to Brunswick.

When we got to the end of the stage there were no horses ready. I arranged matters with the postillion, and after baiting the horses we set out once more. The roads were fearful, and we did not come to the second posting-stage till nightfall.

We might have slept there, but not wishing to be caught up by the coach and to lose my prize, I ordered fresh horses and we resumed our journey in spite of Redegonde's tears and supplications. We travelled all night and reached Lippstadt in the early morning, and in spite of the unseasonableness of the hour I ordered something to eat. Redegonde wanted a rest, as indeed did I, but she had to give way when I said caressingly that we could sleep at Minden. Instead of scolding me she began to smile, and I saw she guessed what she had to expect; in fact, when we got to Minden we had supper, and then went to bed together as man and wife, and stayed in bed for five hours. She was quite kind, and only made me entreat her for form's sake.

We got to Hanover and put up at an excellent inn where we had a choice meal, and where I found the waiter who was at the inn in Zurich when I waited on the ladies at table. Miss Chudleigh had dined there with the Duke of Kingston, and they had gone on to Berlin.

We had a beautiful French bed in which to spend the night, and in the morning we were awakened by the noise of the stage coach. Redegonde not wishing to be surprised in my arms rang the bell and told the waiter by no means to admit the lady who would come out of the coach and ask to be shewn in directly; but her precaution was vain, for, as the waiter went out, the mother and son came in, and we were taken *in flagrante delicto*.

I told them to wait outside, and getting up in my shirt I locked the door. The mother began to abuse me and her daughter, and threatened me with criminal proceedings if I did not give her up. Redegonde, however, calmed her by telling her the story, and she believed, or pretended to believe, it was all chance; but she said,——

"That's all very well; but you can't deny, you little slut, that you have been sleeping with him."

"Oh, there's no harm in that, for you know, dear mamma, nobody does anything asleep."

Without giving her the time to reply she threw her arms round her neck and promised to go on with her in the coach.

After things had been thus settled, I dressed myself, and gave them all a good breakfast, and went on my way to Brunswick, where I arrived a few hours before them.

Redegonde had deprived me of my curiosity to see Gabrielle; besides, in the condition I was in, my vanity would have suffered grievously. As soon as I had settled in a good inn I sent for Daturi, who came immediately, elegantly dressed, and very anxious to introduce to me a certain Signor Nicolini, theatrical manager. This Nicolini understood his craft perfectly, and was high in favour with the prince to whom his daughter Anna was mistress. He gave me a distinguished and a cordial greeting, and was very anxious that I should stay with him, but I was able to escape the constraint of such an arrangement without giving him any offense. I accepted his offer to take my meals at his table, which was furnished by an excellent cook and surrounded by a distinguished company. Here was no gathering of men of title, with the cold and haughty manners of the Court, all were talented, and such company to my mind was delightful.

I was not well, and I was not rich, or else I should have made a longer stay at Brunswick, which had its charms for me. But we will not anticipate, though as old age steals on a man he is never tired of dwelling again and again on the incidents of his past life, in spite of his desire to arrest the sands which run out so quickly.

The third day after my arrival at Brunswick, Redegonde knowing that I was dining at Nicolini's came there too. Everybody had found out, somehow or other, that we had travelled from Wesel to Hanover together, and they were at liberty to draw whatever conclusions they pleased.

Two days later the crown prince arrived from Potsdam on a visit to his future bride, the daughter of the reigning duke, whom he married the year after.

The Court entertained in the most magnificent manner, and the hereditary prince, now the reigning duke, honoured me with an invitation. I had met his highness at an assembly in Soho Square, the day after he had been made a London citizen.

It was twenty-two years since I had been in love with Daturi's mother. I was curious to see the ravages which time had worked on her, but I had reason to repent of my visit, for she had grown terribly ugly. She knew it herself, and a blush of shame appeared on those features which had once been fair.

The prince had an army of six thousand foot in good condition. This army was to be reviewed on a plain at a little distance from the town, and I went to see the spectacle, and was rewarded by having rain dripping

down my back the whole time. Among the numerous
spectators were many persons of fashion, ladies in handsome dresses, and a good sprinkling of foreigners. I
saw the Honourable Miss Chudleigh, who honoured me
by addressing me, and asked me, amongst other questions, how long I had left London. She was dressed
in Indian muslin, and beneath it she only wore a chemise
of fine cambric, and by the time the rain had made her
clothes cling to her body she looked more than naked,
but she did not evince any confusion. Most of the ladies
sheltered themselves from the rain under elegant tents
which had been erected.

The troops, who took no notice of the weather, executed their manœuvres, and fired their muskets in a
manner which seemed to satisfy good judges.

There was nothing further to attract me at Brunswick, and I thought of spending the summer at Berlin,
which I concluded would be more amusing than a small
provincial town. Wanting an overcoat I bought the
material from a Jew, who offered to discount bills of
exchange for me if I had any. I had the bill which
Madame du Rumain had sent me, and finding that it
would be convenient for me to get it discounted, I gave
it to the Israelite, who cashed it, deducting commission at the ordinary rate of two per cent. The letter
was payable to the order of the Chevalier de Seingalt,
and with that name I endorsed it.

I thought no more of the matter, but early the next
day the same Jew called on me, and told me that I must
either return him his money, or give sureties for the
amount till he had ascertained whether the bill was a
forgery or not.

I was offended at this piece of impertinence, and feel-

ing certain that the bill was a good one I told the fellow
that he might set his mind at rest and let me alone, as
I should not give him any sureties.

"I must either have the money or the surety," said
he, "and if you refuse I will have you arrested; your
character is well known."

This was too much for me, and raising my cane I
gave him a blow on the head which he must have felt
for many a long day. I then dressed and dined with
Nicolini, without thinking or speaking of this disagreeable incident.

The next day as I was taking a walk outside the
town walls, I met the prince on horseback, followed by
a single groom. I bowed to him as he passed, but he
came up to me and said,——

"You are leaving Brunswick, chevalier?"

"In two or three days, your highness."

"I heard this morning that a Jew has brought a complaint against you for beating him because he asked
you to give him security for a bill of exchange which
he was afraid of."

"My lord, I cannot answer for the effects of my indignation against a rascal who dared to come and insult
me in my own house, but I do know that if I had given
him security I should have impugned my own honour.
The impertinent scoundrel threatened to have me arrested, but I know that a just Government rules here,
and not arbitarary power."

"You are right; it would be unjust to have you arrested, but he is afraid for his ducats."

"He need not be afraid, my lord, for the bill is drawn
by a person of honour and of high station in society."

"I am delighted to hear it. The Jew said he would

never have discounted the bill if you had not mentioned my name."

"That's a lie! Your highness' name never passed my lips."

"He also says that you endorsed the bill with a false name."

"Then he lies again, for I signed myself Seingalt, and that name is mine."

"In short, it is a case of a Jew who has been beaten, and is afraid of being duped. I pity such an animal, and I must see what I can do to prevent his keeping you here till he learns the fate of the bill at Amsterdam. As I have not the slightest doubt as to the goodness of the bill, I will take it up myself, and this very morning: thus you will be able to leave when you like. Farewell, chevalier! I wish you a pleasant journey."

With this compliment the prince left me, without giving me time to answer him. I might have felt inclined to tell him that by taking up the bill he would give the Jew and everyone else to understand that it was a favour done to me, to the great hurt of my honour, and that consequently I should be obliged by his doing nothing of the kind. But though the prince was a man of generosity and magnanimity, he was deficient in that delicate quality which we call tact. This defect, common amongst princes, arises from their education, which places them above the politeness which is considered necessary in ordinary mortals.

He could not have treated me worse than he did, if he had been certain of my dishonesty, and wished me to understand that I was forgiven, and that he would bear all the consequences of my misdemeanour. With this idea in my head, I said to myself,——

"Perhaps, indeed, this is exactly what the prince does think. Is it the Jew or me that he pities? If the latter, I think I must give him a lesson, though I do not wish to cause him any humiliation."

Feeling deeply humiliated myself, and pondering on my position, I walked away, directing my attention especially to the duke's concluding words. I thought his wish for a pleasant journey supremely out of place, under the circumstances, in the mouth of one who enjoyed almost absolute power. It was equivalent to an order to leave the town, and I felt indignant at the thought.

I therefore resolved to vindicate my honour by neither going away nor remaining.

"If I stay," I said to myself, "the Jew will be adjudged to be in the right; and if I go the duke will think I have profited by his favour, and so to speak, by his present of fifty louis if the bill were protested. I will not let anyone enjoy a satisfaction which is no one due."

After these considerations, which I thought worthy of a wiser head than mine, I packed up my trunk, ordered horses, and after a good dinner and the payment of my bill I went to Wolfenbuttel with the idea of spending a week there. I was sure of finding amusement, for Wolfenbuttel contains the third largest library in Europe, and I had long been anxious to see it.

The learned librarian, whose politeness was all the better for being completely devoid of affection, told me that not only could I have whatever books I wished to see, but that I could take them to my lodging, not even excepting the manuscripts, which are the chief feature in that fine library.

I spent a week in the library, only leaving it to take

my meals and go to bed, and I count this week as one
of the happiest I have ever spent, for then I forgot
myself completely; and in the delight of study, the past,
the present, and the future were entirely blotted out.
Of some such sort, I think, must be the joys of the
redeemed; and now I see that only a few trifling little
circumstances and incidents were wanting to make me
a perfect sage. And here I must note a circumstance
which my readers may scarcely believe, but which, for
all that, is quite true—namely, that I have always preferred virtue to vice, and that when I sinned I did so
out of mere lightness of heart, for which, no doubt, I
shall be blamed by many persons. But, no matter—
a man has only to give an account of his actions to two
beings, to himself here and to God hereafter.

At Wolfenbuttel I gathered a good many hints on
the "Iliad" and "Odyssey," which will not be found
in any commentator, and of which the great Pope knew
nothing. Some of these considerations will be found
in my translation of the "Iliad," the rest are still in
manuscript, and will probably never see the light. However, I burn nothing, not even these Memoirs, though
I often think of doing so, but the time never comes.

At the end of the week I returned to the same inn
at Brunswick which I had occupied before, and let my
godson Daturi know of my arrival.

I was delighted to hear that no one suspected that
I had spent the fortnight within five leagues of Brunswick. Daturi told me that the general belief was that
I had returned the Jew his money and got the bill of
exchange back. Nevertheless I felt sure that the bill
had been honoured at Amsterdam, and that the duke
knew that I had been staying at Wolfenbuttel.

Daturi told me that Nicolini was expecting to see me

at dinner, and I was not astonished to hear of it, for I had not taken leave of anyone. I accordingly went, and the following incident, which served to justify me in the eyes of all men, took place:

We were at the roast when one of the prince's servants came in with the Jew I had beaten. The poor man came up humbly to me, and spoke as follows:

"I am ordered to come here, sir, to apologize for suspecting the authenticity of the bill of exchange you gave me. I have been punished by being fined the amount of my commission."

"I wish that had been your only punishment," said I.

He made me a profound bow, and went out, saying that I was only too good.

When I got back to the inn, I found a letter from Redegonde in which she reproached me tenderly for not having been once to see her all the time I had been at Brunswick, and begging me to breakfast with her in a little country house.

"I shall not be in my mother's company," she added, "but in that of a young lady of your acquaintance, whom, I am sure, you will be glad to see once more."

I liked Redegonde, and I had only neglected her at Brunswick because my means did not allow my making her a handsome present. I resolved to accept her invitation, my curiosity being rather stimulated by the account of the young lady.

I was exact at the time indicated, and I found Redegonde looking charming in a pretty room on the ground floor, and with her was a young artiste whom I had known as a child shortly before I had been put under the Leads. I pretended to be delighted to see her, but I was really quite taken up with Redegonde, and congratulated her upon her pretty house. She said she had taken it for six months, but did not sleep there.

After coffee had been served we were on the point of going out for a stroll, when who should come in but the prince. He smiled pleasantly when he saw us, and apologized to Redegonde for interrupting our little party.

The appearance of the prince enlightened me as to the position of my delightful fellow countrywoman, and I understood why she had been so precise about the time at which I was to come. Redegonde had made the conquest of the worthy prince, who was always disposed to gallantry, but felt it his duty during the first year of his marriage with the King of England's sister to preserve some kind of incognito in his amours.

We spent an hour in walking up and down and talking of London and Berlin, but nothing was said of the Jew or the bill of exchange. He was delighted with my warm eulogium of his library at Wolfenbuttel, and laughed with all his heart when I said that unless it had been for the intellectual nourishment I enjoyed, the bad fare at the inn would certainly have reduced me to half my present size.

After bidding a graceful farewell to the nymph, the prince left us, and we heard him galloping away on his horse.

When I was alone with Redegonde, far from begging for new favours, I advised her to be faithful to the prince; but though appearances were certainly not deceitful in this case, she would not admit anything. This was in accordance with her part as young mistress, and I did not reproach her for her want of confidence.

I spent the rest of the day at the inn, and started the next morning at day-break.

When I got to Magdeburg, I took a letter of introduc-

tion from General Bekw—— to an officer. He shewed
me the fortress, and kept me for three days making me
taste all the pleasures of the table, women, and gaming.
However, I was very moderate, and managed to increase my savings in a small degree, contenting myself
with modest wagers.

From Magdeburg I went straight to Berlin, without
caring to stop at Potsdam, as the king was not there.
The fearful Prussian roads with their sandy soil made
me take three days to do eighteen Prussian miles.
Prussia is a country of which much could be made with
labour and capital, but I do not think it will ever become a really fine country.

I put up at the "Hotel de Paris," which was both
comfortable and economical. Madame Rufin who kept
it had entered into the spirit of her business without
losing her French politeness, and thus the inn had got
a reputation. As soon as I was in my room she came
to ask me if I were satisfied, and to make divers arrangements for my comfort. There was a table d'hôte,
and those who ate in their private rooms paid double.

"This arrangement," I said, "may suit you, but for
the present it will not suit me. I want to dine in my
own room, but I don't want to pay double; I will therefore pay as if I were in the public room, but if you like
you need only send me up half the number of dishes."

"I agree, on the condition that you sup with me; we
will not put it in the accounts, and you will only meet
friends at my little suppers."

I thought her proposal so curious a one that I had a
great inclination to laugh, but finding it at the same
time very advantageous I accepted frankly, and as if
we had long been friends.

On the first day I was tired, and did not sup with her

till the day following. Madame Rufin had a husband who attended to the cooking, and a son, but neither of them came to these suppers. The first time I went to one of them I met an elderly but agreeable and sensible gentleman. He lodged in a room adjoining mine, and called himself Baron Treidel; his sister had married the Duke of Courland, Jean Ernest Biron, or Birlen. The baron, who was extremely pleasant, became my friend, and remained so for the couple of months I spent in Berlin. I also met a Hamburg merchant, named Greve, and his wife, whom he had just married and had brought to Berlin that she might see the marvels of the Warrior-King's Court. She was as pleasant as her husband, and I paid her an assiduous court. A lively and high-spirited individual called Noel, who was the sole and beloved cook of his Prussian Majesty, was the fourth person. He only came rarely to the suppers on account of his duties in the king's kitchen. As I have said, his majesty had only this one cook, and Noel had only one scullion to help him.

M. Noel, the ambassador of the French Republic at the Hague, is, as I am assured, the son of this cook, who was an excellent man. And here I must say, in despite of my hatred for the French Revolutionary Government, that I am not at all ill pleased that a man of talents should be enabled to fill exalted offices, which under the old system of privilege were often occupied by fools.

If it had not been for the culinary skill of Noel the cook, the famous Atheist physician Lamétrie would not have died of indigestion, for the pie he succeeded in eating in his extremity was made by Noel.

Lamétrie often supped with Madame Rufin and I thought it disobliging of him to die so soon, for I should have liked to know him, as he was a learned man and full of mirth. He expired laughing, though it is said that death from indigestion is the most painful of all. Voltaire told me that he thought Lamétrie the most obstinate Atheist in the world, and I could easily believe it after reading his works. The King of Prussia himself pronounced his funeral oration, using the words, "It is not wonderful that he only believed in the existence of matter, for all the spirit in the world was enclosed in his own body." No one but a king would venture on such a sally in a funeral oration. However, Frederick the Great was a Deist and not an Atheist; but that is of little consequence, since he never allowed the belief in a God to influence his actions in the slightest degree. Some say that an Atheist who ponders over the possible existence of a God is better than a Deist who never thinks of the Deity, but I will not venture to decide this point.

The first visit I paid in Berlin was to Calsabigi, the younger brother of the Calsabigi with whom I had founded the lottery in Paris in 1757. He had left Paris and his wife too, and had set up a lottery in Brussels; but his extravagance was so great that he became a bankrupt in spite of the efforts of Count Cobenzl to keep him going. He fled from Brussels to Berlin, and was introduced to the King of Prussia. He was a plausible speaker, and persuaded the monarch to establish a lottery, to make him the manager, and to give him the title of Counsellor of State. He promised that the lottery should bring in an annual revenue of at least two hundred thousand crowns, and only asked a percentage of ten per cent. for himself.

The lottery had been going for two years, and had had a great success, as hitherto it had had no large losses; but the king, who knew that the luck might turn, was always in a fidget about it. With this idea he told Calsabigi that he must carry it on on his own responsibility and pay him a hundred thousand crowns per annum, that being the cost of his Italian Theatre.

I happened to call on Calsabigi on the very day on which the king intimated to him this decision. After talking over our old relationship and the vicissitudes we had both experienced, he told me what had happened; it seemed an unexpected blow to him. The next drawing, he said, would be at the king's risk; but the public would have to be informed that in future the lottery would be a private one. He wanted capital to the amount of two million crowns, for he foresaw that otherwise the lottery would collapse, as people would not risk their money without the certainty of being paid in the event of their winning. He said he would guarantee me an income of ten thousand crowns per annum if I succeeded in making the king change his mind, and by way of encouragement he recalled to my mind the effect of my persuasive powers at Paris seven years before.

" 'Tis a good omen," said he, "and without any superstition I believe that the good genius of the lottery has brought me to Berlin just now."

I laughed at his illusions, but I pitied him. I shewed him the impossibility of convincing an individual whose only argument was, "I am afraid, and I don't wish to be afraid any longer." He begged me to stay to dinner and introduced me to his wife. This was a double surprise for me, in the first place because I thought General La Motte, as his first wife was called, to be still living, and in the second place because I recognized in this second wife of his, Mdlle. Bélanger. I addressed the usual compliments to her and enquired after her mother. She replied with a profound sigh, and told me not to ask any questions about her family as she had only bad news to tell me.

I had known Madame Bélanger at Paris; she was a widow with one daughter, and seemed to be well off. Now I saw this daughter, pretty enough and well married, and yet in this doleful humour, and I felt embarrassed and yet curious.

After Calsabigi had placed me in a position to entertain a high opinion of the skill of his cook, he shewed me his horses and carriages, begging me to take a drive with his wife and come back to supper, which, as he said, was his best meal.

When we were in the carriage together, the necessity of talking about something led me to ask the lady by what happy chain of circumstances she found herself the wife of Calsabigi.

"His real wife is still alive, so I have not the misfortune of occupying that position, but everyone in Berlin thinks I am his lawful wife. Three years ago I was deprived of my mother and the means of livelihood at one stroke, for my mother had an annuity. None of my relations were rich enough to help me, and wishing to live virtuously above all things I subsisted for two years on the sale of my mother's furniture, boarding with a worthy woman who made her living by embroidery. I learnt her art, and only went out to mass on Sundays. I was a prey to melancholy, and when I had spent all I had I went to M. Brea, a Genoese, on whom I thought I could rely. I begged him to get me a place as a mere waiting-maid, thinking that I was tolerably competent for such a position. He promised

to do what he could for me, and five or six days afterwards he made me the following proposal:

"He read me a letter from Calsabigi, of whom I had
never heard, in which he charged him to send a virtuous
young lady to Berlin. She must be of good birth, good
education, and pleasant appearance, as when his aged
and infirm wife died he intended to marry her.

"As such a person would most probably be badly off,
Calsabigi begged M. Brea to give her fifty louis to buy
clothes and linen and fifty louis to journey to Berlin
with a maid. M. Brea was also authorized to promise
that the young lady should hold the position of Calsabigi's wife, and be presented in that character to all his
friends; that she should have a waiting-maid, a carriage,
an allowance of clothes, and a certain monthly amount
as pin-money to be spent as she chose. He promised,
if the arrangement was not found suitable, to set her
free at the end of a year, giving her a hundred louis,
and leaving her in possession of whatever money she
might have saved, and such clothes and jewels as he
might have given her; in fine, if the lady agreed to live
with him till he was able to marry her, Calsabigi promised to execute a deed of gift in her favour to the amount
of ten thousand crowns which the public would believe
to be her dowry, and if he died before being able to
marry her she would have a right to claim the aforesaid sum from his estate.

"With such fine promises did Brea persuade me to
leave my native country to come and dishonour myself
here, for though everybody treats me as if I were his
wife, it is probably known that I am only his mistress.
I have been here for six months, and I have never had
an instant's happiness."

"Has he not kept the conditions you have mentioned?"

"Conditions! Calsabigi's state of health will kill him long before his wife, and in that case I shall have nothing, for he is loaded with debt, and his creditors would have the first claim on the estate. Besides, I do not like him; and the reason is that he loves me too much. You can understand that; his devotion worries me."

"At all events, you can return to Paris in six months' time, or, in fact, do anything you like when the term stipulated has expired. You will get your hundred louis, and can lay in a pretty stock of linen."

"If I go to Paris I shall be dishonoured, and if I remain here I shall be dishonoured. In fact, I am very unhappy, and Brea is the cause of my woe. Nevertheless, I can't blame him, as he could not have been aware that his friend's property only consisted of debts. And now the king has withdrawn his countenance, the lottery will fail, and Calsabigi will inevitably become a bankrupt."

She had studiously refrained from exaggeration, and I could not help confessing that she was to be pitied. I advised her to try and sell the deed of gift for ten thousand crowns, as it was not likely he would raise any objection.

"I have thought it over," said she, "but to do that I have need of a friend; of course, I do not expect to dispose of it save at a great loss."

I promised to see what I could do for her.

There were four of us at supper. The fourth person was a young man who had helped in the Paris and Brussels Lotteries, and had followed Calsabigi to Berlin. He was evidently in love with Mdlle. Bélanger, but I did not think his love was crowned with success.

At dessert Calsabigi begged me to give him my opin-

ion of a scheme he had drafted, the aim of which was
to bring in a sum of two million crowns, so that the
credit of the lottery might remain secure.

The lady left us to talk business at our ease. She
was between twenty-four and twenty-five, and without
having much wit she possessed a great knowledge of the
usages of society, which is better than wit in a woman;
in fine, she had all that a man could well desire. The
sentiments I felt for her were confined to those of friendship and esteem after the confidence she had placed
in me.

Calsabigi's project was brief, but clear and well imagined. He invited capitalists not to speculate in the lottery, but to guarantee it for a certain sum. In the case
of the lottery's losing, each guarantor would have to
share in paying according to the sum named, and in like
manner they would share in the profits.

I promised to give him my opinion in writing by the
next day, and I substituted the following plan for his:

1. A capital of a million, would, I judged, be ample.

2. This million should be divided into a hundred shares
of ten thousand crowns each.

3. Each share must be taken up before a notary, who
would answer for the shareholder's solvency.

4. All dividends to be paid the third day after the
drawing.

5. In case of loss the shareholder to renew his share.

6. A cashier, chosen by a majority of four-fifths of
the shareholders, to have the control of all moneys.

7. Winning tickets to be paid the day after the drawing.

8. On the eve of a drawing the shareholders' cashier
to have an account of receipts from the lottery cashier,
and the former to lock the safe with three keys, one of

which to remain in his hands, one in the hands of the lottery cashier, and one in the hands of the manager of the lottery.

9. Only the simple drawing, the *ambe* and the *terne* to be retained; the *quarterne* and the *quine* to be abolished.

10. On the three combinations a shilling to be the minimum, and a crown the maximum stake; the offices to be closed twenty-four hours before the drawing.

11. Ten per cent. to go to Calsabigi, the manager; all expenses of farming to be paid by him.

12. Calsabigi to be entitled to the possession of two shares, without a guarantee being required.

I saw by Calsabigi's face that the plan did not please him, but I told him that he would not get shareholders save on these terms, or on terms even less favourable to himself.

He had degraded the lottery to the level of biribi; his luxury and extravagance caused him to be distrusted; it was known that he was head over ears in debt; and the king could not banish the fear that he would be cheated in spite of the keenness of his comptroller-general.

The last drawing under the king's sanction made everyone in good spirits, for the lottery lost twenty thousand crowns. The king sent the money immediately by a privy councillor, but it was said, when he heard the result of the drawing, that he burst out laughing, observing,——

"I knew it would be so, and I am only too happy to have got quit of it so cheaply."

I thought it my duty to go and sup with the director to console him, and I found him in a state of great depression. He could not help thinking that his unhappy drawing would make the task of getting shareholders more difficult than ever. Hitherto the lottery had always been a gainer, but its late loss could not have come at a worse time.

Nevertheless, he did not lose heart, and the next morning the public were informed by printed bills that the office would remain closed till a sufficient number of guarantors were found.

CHAPTER XVIII

Lord Keith—My Appointment to Meet the King in the Garden of Sans-Souci—My Conversation with Frederick the Great—Madame Denis—The Pomeranian Cadets—Lambert—I Go to Mitau—My Welcome at the Court, and My Administrative Journey

THE fifth day after my arrival at Berlin I presented myself to the lord-marshal, who since the death of his brother had been styled Lord Keith. I had seen him in London after his return from Scotland, where he had been reinstated in the family estates, which had been confiscated for Jacobitism. Frederick the Great was supposed to have brought this about. Lord Keith lived at Berlin, resting on his laurels, and enjoying the blessings of peace.

With his old simplicity of manner he told me he was glad to see me again, and asked if I proposed making any stay at Berlin. I replied that I would willingly do so if the king would give me a suitable office. I asked him if he would speak a word in my favour; but he replied that the king liked to judge men's characters for himself, and would often discover merit where no one had suspected its presence, and *vice versâ*.

He advised me to intimate to the king in writing that I desired to have the honour of an interview. "When you speak to him," the good old man added, "you may say that you know me, and the king will doubtless address me on the subject, and you may be sure what I say shall not be to your disadvantage."

"But, my lord, how can I write to a monarch of whom I know nothing, and who knows nothing of me? I should not have thought of such a step."

"I daresay, but don't you wish to speak to him?"

"Certainly."

"That is enough. Your letter will make him aware of your desire and nothing more."

"But will he reply?"

"Undoubtedly; he replies to everybody. He will tell you when and where he will see you. His Majesty is now at Sans-Souci. I am curious to know the nature of your interview with the monarch who, as you can see, is not afraid of being imposed on."

When I got home I wrote a plain but respectful letter to the king, asking where and at what time I could introduce myself to him.

In two days I received a letter signed "Frederick," in which the receipt of my letter was acknowledged, and I was told that I should find his majesty in the garden of Sans-Souci at four o'clock.

As may be imagined I was punctual to my appointment. I was at Sans-Souci at three, clad in a simple black dress. When I got into the court-yard there was not so much as a sentinel to stop me, so I went on mounted a stair, and opened a door in front of me. I found myself in a picture-gallery, and the curator came up to me and offered to shew me over it.

"I have not come to admire these masterpieces," I replied, "but to see the king, who informed me in writing that I should find him in the garden."

"He is now at a concert playing the flute; he does so every day after dinner. Did he name any time?"

"Yes, four o'clock, but he will have forgotten that."

"The king never forgets anything; he will keep the appointment, and you will do well to go into the garden and await him."

I had been in the garden for some minutes when I saw him appear, followed by his reader and a pretty spaniel. As soon as he saw me he accosted me, taking off his old hat, and pronouncing my name. Then he asked in a terrible voice what I wanted of him. This greeting surprised me, and my voice stuck in my throat.

"Well, speak out. Are you not the person who wrote to me?"

"Yes, sire, but I have forgotten everything now. I thought that I should not be awed by the majesty of a king, but I was mistaken. My lord-marshal should have warned me."

"Then he knows you? Let us walk. What is it that you want? What do you think of my garden?"

His enquiries after my needs and of his garden were simultaneous. To any other person I should have answered that I did not know anything about gardening, but this would have been equivalent to refusing to answer the question; and no monarch, even if he be a philosopher, could endure that. I therefore replied that I thought the garden superb.

"But," he said, "the gardens of Versailles are much finer."

"Yes, sire, but that is chiefly on account of the fountains."

"True, but it is not my fault; there is no water here. I have spent more than three hundred thousand crowns to get water, but unsuccessfully."

"Three hundred thousand crowns, sire! If your majesty had spent them all at once, the fountains should be here."

"Oh, oh! I see you are acquainted with hydraulics."

I could not say that he was mistaken, for fear of offending him, so I simply bent my head, which might mean either yes or no. Thank God the king did not trouble to test my knowledge of the science of hydraulics, with which I was totally unacquainted.

He kept on the move all the time, and as he turned his head from one side to the other hurriedly asked me what forces Venice could put into the field in war time.

"Twenty men-of-war, sire, and a number of galleys."

"What are the land forces?"

"Seventy thousand men, sire; all of whom are subjects of the Republic, and assessing each village at one man."

"That is not true; no doubt you wish to amuse me by telling me these fables. Give me your opinions on taxation."

This was the first conversation I had ever had with a monarch. I made a rapid review of the situation, and found myself much in the same position as an actor of the improvised comedy of the Italians, who is greeted by the hisses of the gods if he stops short a moment. I therefore replied with all the airs of a doctor of finance that I could say something about the theory of taxation.

"That's what I want," he replied, "for the practice is no business of yours."

"There are three kinds of taxes, considered as to their effects. The first is ruinous, the second a necessary evil, and the third invariably beneficial."

"Good! Go on."

"The ruinous impost is the royal tax, the necessary is the military, and the beneficial is the popular."

As I had not given the subject any thought I was in a disagreeable position, for I was obliged to go on speaking, and yet not to talk nonsense.

"The royal tax, sire, is that which deplenishes the purses of the subject to fill the coffers of the king."

"And that kind of tax is always ruinous, you think."

"Always, sire; it prevents the circulation of money— the soul of commerce and the mainstay of the state."

"But if the tax be levied to keep up the strength of the army, you say it is a necessary evil."

"Yes, it is necessary and yet evil, for war is an evil."

"Quite so; and now about the popular tax."

"This is always a benefit, for the monarch takes with one hand and gives with the other; he improves towns and roads, founds schools, protects the sciences, cherishes the arts; in fine, he directs this tax towards improving the condition and increasing the happiness of his people."

"There is a good deal of truth in that. I suppose you know Calsabigi?"

"I ought to, your majesty, as he and I established the Genoa Lottery at Paris seven years ago."

"In what class would you put this taxation, for you will agree that it is taxation of a kind?"

"Certainly, sire, and not the least important. It is beneficial when the monarch spends his profits for the good of the people."

"But the monarch may lose?"

"Once in fifty."

"Is that conclusion the result of a mathematical calculation?"

"Yes, sire."

"Such calculations often prove deceptive."

"Not so, may it please your majesty, when God remains neutral."

"What has God got to do with it?"

"Well, sire, we will call it destiny or chance."

"Good! I may possibly be of your opinion as to the calculation, but I don't like your Genoese Lottery. It seems to me an elaborate swindle, and I would have nothing more to do with it, even if it were positively certain that I should never lose."

"Your majesty is right, for the confidence which makes the people risk their money in a lottery is perfectly fallacious."

This was the end of our strange dialogue, and stopping before a building he looked me over, and then, after a short silence, observed,——

"Do you know that you are a fine man?"

"Is it possible that, after the scientific conversation we have had, your majesty should select the least of the qualities which adorn your life guardsmen for remark?"

The king smiled kindly, and said,——

"As you know Marshal Keith, I will speak to him of you."

With that he took off his hat, and bade me farewell. I retired with a profound bow.

Three or four days after the marshal gave me the agreeable news that I had found favour in the king's eyes, and that his majesty thought of employing me.

I was curious to learn the nature of this employment, and being in no kind of hurry I resolved to await events in Berlin. The time passed pleasantly enough, for I was either with Calsabigi, Baron Treidel, or my landlady, and when these resources failed me, I used to walk in the park, musing over the events of my life.

Calsabigi had no difficulty in obtaining permission to continue the lottery on his own account, and he boldly announced that henceforward he would conduct the lottery on his own risk. His audacity was crowned with success, and he obtained a profit of a hundred thousand crowns. With this he paid most of his debts, and gave his mistress ten thousand crowns, she returning the document entitling her to that amount. After this lucky drawing it was easy to find guarantors, and the lottery went on successfully for two or three years.

Nevertheless Calsabigi ended by becoming bankrupt and died poor enough in Italy. He might be compared to the Danaides; the more he got the more he spent. His mistress eventually made a respectable marriage and returned to Paris, where she lived in comfort.

At the period of which I am speaking, the Duchess of Brunswick, the king's sister, came to pay him a visit. She was accompanied by her daughter who married the Crown Prince of Prussia in the following year. I saw the king in a suit of lustring trimmed with gold lace, and black silk stockings on his legs. He looked truly comic, and more like a theatrical heavy father than a great king. He came into the hall with his sister on his arm and attracted universal attention, for only very old men could remember seeing him without his uniform and top-boots.

I was not aware that the famous Madame Denis was at Berlin, and it was therefore an agreeable surprise to me to see her in the ballet one evening, dancing a *pas seul* in an exquisite manner. We were old friends, and I resolved to pay her a visit the next day.

I must tell the reader (supposing I ever have one), that when I was about twelve years old I went to the theatre with my mother and saw, not without much heart-beating, a girl of eight who danced a minuet in so ravishing a manner that the whole house applauded loudly. This young dancer, who was the pantaloon's daughter, charmed me to such a degree that I could not resist going to her dressing-room to compliment her on her performance. I wore the cassock in those days, and she was astonished when she heard her father order her to get up and kiss me. She kissed me, nevertheless, with much grace, and though I received the compliment with a good deal of awkwardness I was so delighted, that I could not help buying her a little ring from a toy merchant in the theatre. She kissed me again with great gratitude and enthusiasm.

The pleasantest part about this was that the sequin I had given for the ring belonged to Dr. Gozzi, and so when I went back to him I was in a pitiable state, for I had not only spent money which did not belong to me, but I had spent it for so small a favour as a kiss.

I knew that the next day I should have to give an account of the money he had entrusted to me, and not having the least idea as to what I should say, I had a bad night of it. The next morning everything came out, and my mother made up the sequin to the doctor. I laugh now when I think of this childish piece of gallantry, which was an omen of the extent to which my heart was to be swayed by the fair sex.

The toy-woman who had sold me the ring came the next day at dinner-time to our house, and after producing several rings and trinkets which were judged too dear, she began to praise my generosity, and said that I had not thought the ring I had given to pretty Jeannette too dear. This did my business; and I had to confess the whole, laying my fault to the account of love, and promising not to do such a thing again. But when I uttered the word love, everybody roared with laughter, and began to make cruel game of me. I wished myself a mile away, and registered an interior resolve never to confess my faults again. The reader knows how well I kept my promise.

The pantaloon's little daughter was my mother's god-daughter, and my thoughts were full of her. My mother, who loved me and saw my pain, asked me if I would like the little girl to be asked to supper. My grand-mother, however, opposed the idea, and I was obliged to her.

The day after this burlesque scene I returned to Padua, where Bettina soon made me forget the little ballet-girl. I saw her again at Charlottenbourg, and that was now seventeen years ago.

I longed to have a talk with her, and to see whether she would remember me, though I did not expect her to do so. I asked if her husband Denis was with her, and they told me that the king had banished him because he ill-treated her.

I called on her the day after the performance, and was politely received, but she said she did not think she had had the pleasure of seeing me before.

By degrees I told her of the events of her childhood, and how she enchanted all Venice by the grace with which she danced the minuet. She interrupted me by saying that at that time she was only six years old.

"You could not be more," I replied, "for I was only ten; and nevertheless, I fell in love with you, and never have I forgotten the kiss you gave me by your father's order in return for some trifling present I made you."

"Be quiet; you gave me a beautiful ring, and I kissed you of my own free will. You wore the cassock then. I have never forgotten you. But can it really be you?"

"It is indeed."

"I am delighted to see you again. But I could never have recognized you, and I suppose you would not have recognized me."

"No, I should not have known you, unless I had heard your name mentioned."

"One alters in twenty years, you know."

"Yes, one cannot expect to have the same face as at six."

"You can bear witness that I am not more than twenty-six, though some evil speakers give me ten years more."

"You should not take any notice of such calumnies, my dear. You are in the flower of your age, and made for the service of love. For my part, I congratulate myself on being able to tell you that you are the first woman that inspired me with a real passion."

We could not help becoming affectionate if we continued to keep up the conversation in this style, but experience had taught us that it was well to remain as we were for the present.

Madame Denis was still fresh and youthful looking, though she persisted in abbreviating her age by ten years. Of course she could not deceive me, and she must have known it, nevertheless, she liked me to bear outward testimony to her youthfulness. She would have detested me if I had attempted to prove to her what she knew perfectly well, but did not care to confess. No doubt she cared little for my thoughts on the subject, and she may have imagined that I owed her gratitude for diminishing her age, as it enabled me to diminish my own to make our tales agree. However, I did not trouble myself much about it, for it is almost a duty in an actress to disguise her age, as in spite of talent the public will not forgive a woman for having been born too soon.

I thought her behaviour augured well, and I hoped she

would not make me languish long. She shewed me her house, which was all elegance and good taste. I asked her if she had a lover, and she replied with a smile that all Berlin thought so, but that it was nevertheless deceived on the principal point, as the individual in question was more of a father than a lover.

"But you deserve to have a real lover; I cannot conceive how you can do without one."

"I assure you I don't trouble myself about it. I am subject to convulsions, which are the plague of my life. I want to try the Teplitz waters, which are said to be excellent for all nervous affections; but the king has refused his permission, which I, nevertheless, hope to obtain next year."

I felt ardently disposed, and I thought she was pleased with the restraint I put upon myself.

"Will you be annoyed," said I, "if I call upon you frequently?"

"If you don't mind I will call myself your niece, or your cousin, and then we can see each other."

"Do you know that that may possibly be true? I would not swear that you were not my sister."

This sally made us talk of the friendship that had subsisted between her father and my mother, and we allowed ourselves those caresses which are permitted to near relations; but feeling that things were going too far we ceased. As she bade me farewell, she asked me to dine with her the next day, and I accepted.

As I went back to my inn I reflected on the strange combinations which made my life one continuous chain of events, and I felt it my duty to give thanks to eternal Providence, for I felt that I had been born under a happy star.

The next day, when I went to dine with Madame

Denis, I found a numerous company assembled. The first person who greeted me with the warmth of an old friend was a young dancer named Aubri, whom I had known at Paris and at Venice. He was famous for having been the lover of one of the most exalted Venetian ladies, and at the same time her husband's pathic. It was said that this scandalous intimacy was of such a nature that Aubri used to sleep between the husband and wife. At the beginning of Lent the State Inquisitors sent him to Trieste. He introduced me to his wife, who danced like himself and was called *La Pantina*. He had married her at St. Petersburg, from which city he had just come, and they were going to spend the winter in Paris. The next person who advanced to greet me was a fat man, who held out his hand and said we had been friends twenty-five years ago, but that we were so young then that it would be no wonder if we did not know each other. "We knew each other at Padua, at Dr. Gozzi's," he added; "my name is Joseph da Loglio."

"I remember you," I replied, "in those days you were violoncello at the Russian chapel."

"Exactly; and now I am returning to my native land to leave it no more. I have the honour to introduce you to my wife, who was born at St. Petersburg, but is a daughter of Modonis the violinist, whose reputation is European. In a week I shall be at Dresden, where I hope to have the honour of seeing Madame Casanova, your mother."

I was delighted to find myself in such congenial society, but I could see that Madame Denis did not relish these recollections extending over a quarter of a century, and I turned the conversation to the events at St. Petersburg which had resulted in Catherine the Great ascending the throne. Da Loglio told us that he had taken a small part in this conspiracy, and had thought it prudent to get out of the way. "Fortunately," he added, "this was a contingency I had long provided against, and I am in a position to spend the rest of my days in comfort in Italy."

Madame Denis then observed:

"A week ago a Piedmontese, named Audar, was introduced to me. He had been a chief mover in the conspiracy, and the empress gave him a present of a hundred thousand roubles and an order to leave Russia immediately."

I heard afterwards that this Audar bought an estate in Piedmont on which he built a fine mansion. In two or three years it was struck by a thunder-bolt, and the unfortunate man was killed in the ruins of his own house. If this was a blow from an Almighty hand, it could not, at all events, have been directed by the genius of Russia, for if the unfortunate Peter III. had lived, he would have retarded Russian civilization by a hundred years.

The Empress Catherine rewarded all the foreigners who had assisted her in her plots most magnificently, and shewed herself grateful to the Russians who had helped her to mount the throne; while, like a crafty politician, she sent such nobles as she suspected to be averse to revolution out of the country.

It was Da Loglio and his pretty wife who determined me to betake myself to Russia in case the King of Prussia did not give me any employment. I was assured that I should make my fortune there, and Da Loglio promised to give me good instructions.

As soon as this worthy man left Berlin my intimacy with Madame Denis commenced. One night when I was supping with her she was seized with convulsions which lasted all the night. I did not leave her for a moment, and in the morning, feeling quite recovered, her gratitude finished what my love had begun twenty-six years before, and our amorous commerce lasted while I stayed at Berlin. We shall hear of her again at Florence six years later.

Some days after Madame Denis took me to Potsdam to shew me all the sights of the town. Our intimacy offended no one, for she was generally believed to be my niece, and the general who kept her either believed the report, or like a man of sense pretended to believe it.

Amongst other notable things I saw at Potsdam was the sight of the king commanding the first battalion of his grenadiers, all picked men, the flower of the Prussian army.

The room which we occupied at the inn faced a walk by which the king passed when he came from the castle. The shutters were all closed, and our landlady told us that on one occasion when a pretty dancer called La Reggiana was sleeping in the same room, the king had seen her *in puris naturalibus.* This was too much for his modesty, and he had ordered the shutters to be closed, and closed they had remained, though this event was four years old. The king had some cause to fear, for he had been severely treated by La Barbarina. In the king's bedroom we saw her portrait, that of La Cochois, sister to the actress who became Marchioness d'Argens, and that of Marie Theresa, with whom Frederick had been in love, or rather he had been in love with the idea of becoming emperor.

After we had admired the beauty and elegance of the castle, we could not help admiring the way in which the master of the castle was lodged. He had a mean room, and slept on a little bed with a screen around it. There was no dressing-gown and no slippers. The valet·

shewed us an old cap which the king put on when he had
a cold; it looked as if it must be very uncomfortable.
His majesty's bureau was a table covered with pens,
paper, half-burnt manuscripts, and an ink-pot; beside
it was a sofa. The valet told us that these manuscripts
contained the history of the last Prussian war, and the
king had been so annoyed by their accidentally getting
burnt that he had resolved to have no more to do with
the work. He probably changed his mind, for the book,
which is little esteemed, was published shortly after his
death.

Five or six weeks after my curious conversation with
the monarch, Marshal Keith told me that his majesty
had been pleased to create me a tutor to the new corps
of Pomeranian cadets which he was just establishing.
There were to be fifteen cadets and five tutors, so that
each should have the care of three pupils. The salary
was six hundred crowns and board found. The duty of
the tutors was to follow or accompany the cadets wherever they went, Court included. I had to be quick in
making up my mind, for the four others were already in-
stalled, and his majesty did not like to be kept waiting.
I asked Lord Keith where the college was, and I promised to give him a reply by the next day.

I had to summon all my powers of self-restraint to my
assistance when I heard this extravagant proposal as
coming from a man who was so discreet in most things,
but my astonishment was increased when I saw the abode
of these fifteen young noblemen of rich Pomerania. It
consisted of three or four great rooms almost devoid of
furniture, several whitewashed bedrooms, containing a
wretched bed, a deal table, and two deal chairs. The
young cadets, boys of twelve or thirteen, all looked dirty
and untidy, and were boxed up in a wretched uniform

which matched admirably their rude and rustic faces.
They were in company with their four governors, whom
I took for their servants, and who looked at me in a
stupefied manner, not daring to think that I was to be
their future colleague.

Just as I was going to bid an eternal farewell to this
abode of misery, one of the governors put his head out
of the window and exclaimed,——

"The king is riding up."

I could not avoid meeting him, and besides, I was glad
enough to see him again, especially in such a place.

His majesty came up with his friend Icilius, examined
everything, and saw me, but did not honour me with a
word. I was elegantly dressed, and wore my cross set
with brilliants. But I had to bite my lips so as not to
burst out laughing when Frederick the Great got in a
towering rage at a chamber utensil which stood beside
one of the beds, and which did not appear to be in a
very cleanly condition.

"Whose bed is this?" cried the monarch.

"Mine, sire," answered a trembling cadet.

"Good! but it is not you I am angry with; where is
your governor?"

The fortunate governor presented himself, and the
monarch, after honouring him with the title of *blockhead*, proceeded to scold him roundly. However, he
ended by saying that there was a servant, and that the
governor ought to see that he did his work properly.

This disgusting scene was enough for me, and I hastened to call on Marshal Keith to announce my determination. The old soldier laughed at the description I
gave him of the academy, and said I was quite right to
despise such an office; but that I ought, nevertheless, to
go and thank the king before I left Berlin. I said I did

not feel inclined for another interview with such a man, and he agreed to present my thanks and excuses in my stead.

I made up my mind to go to Russia, and began my preparations in good earnest. Baron Treidel supported my resolve by offering to give me a letter of introduction to his sister, the Duchess of Courland. I wrote to M. de Bragadin to give me a letter for a banker at St. Petersburg, and to remit me through him every month a sum which would keep me in comfort.

I could not travel without a servant, and chance kindly provided me with one. I was sitting with Madame Rufin, when a young Lorrainer came in; like Bias, he bore all his fortune with him, but, in his case, it was carried under his arm. He introduced himself thus:

"Madam, my name is Lambert, I come from Lorraine, and I wish to lodge here."

"Very good, sir, but you must pay for your board and lodging every day."

"That, madam, is out of the question, for I have not got a farthing, but I shall have some money when I discover who I am."

"I am afraid I cannot put you up on those conditions, sir."

He was going away with a mortified air, when my heart was touched, and I called him back.

"Stay," said I, "I will pay for you to-day."

Happiness beamed over his face.

"What have you got in that little bundle?" said I.

"Two shirts, a score of mathematical books, and some other trifles."

I took him to my room, and finding him tolerably well educated, I asked him how he came to be in such a state of destitution.

"I come from Strasburg," he replied, "and a cadet of a regiment stationed there having given me a blow in a coffee-house I paid him a visit the next day in his own room and stabbed him there.

"After this I went home, made up my bundle, and left the town. I walked all the way and lived soberly, so that my money lasted till this morning. To-morrow I shall write to my mother, who lives at Luneville, and I am sure she will send me some money."

"And what do you think of doing?"

"I want to become a military engineer, but if needs must I am ready to enlist as a private soldier."

"I can give you board and lodging till you hear from your mother."

"Heaven has sent you in my way," said he, kissing my hand gratefully.

I did not suspect him of deceiving me, though he stumbled somewhat in his narrative. However my curiosity led me to write to M. Schauenbourg, who was then at Strasburg, to enquire if the tale were true.

The next day I happened to meet an officer of engineers, who told me that young men of education were so plentiful that they did not receive them into the service unless they were willing to serve as common soldiers. I was sorry for the young man to be reduced so low as that. I began to spend some time with him every day in mathematical calculations, and I conceived the idea of taking him with me to St. Petersburg, and broached the subject to him.

"It would be a piece of good fortune for me," he replied, "and to shew my gratitude I will gladly wait on you as a servant during the journey."

He spoke French badly, but as he was a Lorrainer I was not astonished at that. Nevertheless I was surprised to find that he did not know a word of Latin, and that his spelling was of the wildest description. He saw me laughing, but did not seem in the least ashamed. Indeed he said that he had only gone to school to learn mathematics, and that he was very glad that he had escaped the infliction of learning grammar. Indeed, on every subject besides mathematics, he was profoundly ignorant. He had no manners whatever; in fact, he was a mere peasant.

Ten or twelve days later I received a letter from M. de Schauenbourg, saying that the name of Lambert was unknown in Strasburg, and that no cadet had been killed or wounded.

When I shewed Lambert this letter he said that as he wished to enter the army he thought it would be of service to him to shew that he was brave, adding that as this lie had not been told with the idea of imposing on me I should forgive it.

"Poverty," said he, "is a rascally teacher, that gives a man some bad lessons. I am not a liar by disposition, but I have nevertheless told you a lie on another and a more important matter. I don't expect any money whatever from my poor mother, who rather needs that I should send money to her. So forgive me, and be sure I shall be a faithful servant to you."

I was always ready to forgive other men's peccadilloes, and not without cause. I liked Lambert's line of argument, and told him that we would set out in five or six days.

Baron Bodisson, a Venetian who wanted to sell the king a picture by Andrea del Sarto, asked me to come with him to Potsdam and the desire of seeing the monarch once again made me accept the invitation. When I reached Potsdam I went to see the parade at which

Frederick was nearly always to be found. When he saw
me he came up and asked me in a familiar manner when
I was going to start for St. Petersburg.

"In five or six days, if your majesty has no objection."

"I wish you a pleasant journey; but what do you hope
to do in that land?"

"What I hoped to do in this land, namely, to please
the sovereign."

"Have you got an introduction to the empress?"

"No, but I have an introduction to a banker."

"Ah! that's much better. If you pass through Prussia on your return I shall be delighted to hear of your
adventures in Russia."

"Farewell, sire."

Such was the second interview I had with this great
king, whom I never saw again.

After I had taken leave of all my friends I applied to
Baron Treidel, who gave me a letter for M. de Kaiserling, lord-chancellor at Mitau, and another letter for his
sister, the Duchess of Courland, and I spent the last
night with the charming Madame Denis. She bought my
post-chaise, and I started with two hundred ducats in
my purse. This would have been ample for the whole
journey if I had not been so foolish as to reduce it by
half at a party of pleasure with some young merchants
at Dantzic. I was thus unable to stay a few days at
Koenigsberg, though I had a letter to Field-Marshal von
Lewald, who was the governor of the place. I could only
stay one day to dine with this pleasant old soldier, who
gave me a letter for his friend General Woiakoff, the
Governor of Riga.

I found I was rich enough to arrive at Mitau in state,
and I therefore took a carriage and six, and reached my
destination in three days. At the inn where I put up

I found a Florentine artiste named Bregonei, who over-whelmed me with caresses, telling me that I had loved her when I was a boy and wore the cassock. I saw her six years later at Florence, where she was living with Madame Denis.

The day after my departure from Memel, I was accosted in the open country by a man whom I recognized as a Jew. He informed me that I was on Polish territory, and that I must pay duty on whatever merchandise I had with me.

"I am no merchant," said I, "and you will get nothing out of me."

"I have the right to examine your effects," replied the Israelite, "and I mean to make use of it."

"You are a madman," I exclaimed, and I ordered the postillion to whip him off.

But the Jew ran and seized the fore horses by the bridle and stopped us, and the postillion, instead of whipping him, waited with Teutonic calm for me to come and send the Jew away. I was in a furious rage, and leaping out with my cane in one hand and a pistol in the other I soon put the Jew to flight after applying about a dozen good sound blows to his back. I noticed that during the combat my fellow-traveller, my Archimedes-in-ordinary, who had been asleep all the way, did not offer to stir. I reproached him for his cowardice; but he told me that he did not want the Jew to say that we had set on him two to one.

I arrived at Mitau two days after this burlesque adventure and got down at the inn facing the castle. I had only three ducats left.

The next morning I called on M. de Kaiserling, who read the Baron de Treidel's letter, and introduced me to his wife, and left me with her to take the baron's letter to his sister.

Madame de Kaiserling ordered a cup of chocolate to be brought me by a beautiful young Polish girl, who stood before me with lowered eyes as if she wished to give me the opportunity of examining her at ease. As I looked at her a whim came into my head, and, as the reader is aware, I have never resisted any of my whims. However, this was a curious one. As I have said, I had only three ducats left, but after I had emptied the cup of chocolate I put it back on the plate and the three ducats with it.

The chancellor came back and told me that the duchess could not see me just then, but that she invited me to a supper and ball she was giving that evening. I accepted the supper and refused the ball, on the pretext that I had only summer clothes and a black suit. It was in the beginning of October, and the cold was already commencing to make itself felt. The chancellor returned to the Court, and I to my inn.

Half an hour later a chamberlain came to bring me her highness's compliments, and to inform me that the ball would be a masked one, and that I could appear in domino.

"You can easily get one from the Jews," he added. He further informed me that the ball was to have been a full-dress one, but that the duchess had sent word to all the guests that it would be masked, as a stranger who was to be present had sent on his trunks.

"I am sorry to have caused so much trouble," said I.

"Not at all," he replied, "the masked ball will be much more relished by the people."

He mentioned the time it was to begin, and left me.

No doubt the reader will think that I found myself in an awkward predicament, and I will be honest and confess I was far from being at my ease. However, my good luck came to my assistance.

As Prussian money (which is the worst in Germany) is not current in Russia, a Jew came and asked me if I had any friedrichs d'or, offering to exchange them against ducats without putting me to any loss.

"I have only ducats," I replied, "and therefore I cannot profit by your offer."

"I know it sir, and you give them away very cheaply."

Not understanding what he meant, I simply gazed at him, and he went on to say that he would be glad to let me have two hundred ducats if I would kindly give him a bill on St. Petersburg for roubles to that amount.

I was somewhat surprised at the fellow's trustfulness, but after pretending to think the matter over I said that I was not in want of ducats, but that I would take a hundred to oblige him. He counted out the money gratefully, and I gave him a bill on the banker, Demetrio Papanelopoulo, for whom Da Loglio had given me a letter. The Jew went his way, thanking me, and saying that he would send me some beautiful dominos to choose from. Just then I remembered that I wanted silk stockings, and I sent Lambert after the Jew to tell him to send some. When he came back he told me that the landlord had stopped him to say that I scattered my ducats broadcast, as the Jew had informed him that I had given three ducats to Madame de Kaiserling's maid.

This, then, was the key to the mystery, and it made me lose myself in wonder at the strangeness of the decrees of fortune. I should not have been able to get a single crown at Mitau if it had not been for the way in which I scattered my three remaining ducats. No doubt the astonished girl had published my generosity all over the town, and the Jew, intent on money-making, had hastened to offer his ducats to the rich nobleman who thought so little of his money.

I repaired to Court at the time appointed, and M. de Kaiserling immediately presented me to the duchess, and she to the duke, who was the celebrated Biron, or Birlen, the former favourite of Anna Ivanovna. He was six feet in height, and still preserved some traces of having been a fine man, but old age had laid its heavy hand on him. I had a long talk with him the day after the ball.

A quarter of an hour after my arrival, the ball began with a polonaise. I was a stranger with introductions, so the duchess asked me to open the ball with her. I did not know the dance, but I managed to acquit myself honourably in it, as the steps are simple and lend themselves to the fancy of the dancer.

After the polonaise we danced minuets, and a somewhat elderly lady asked me if I could dance the "King Conqueror," so I proceeded to execute it with her. It had gone out of fashion since the time of the Regency, but my companion may have shone in it in those days. All the younger ladies stood round and watched us with admiration.

After a square dance, in which I had as partner Mdlle. de Manteufel, the prettiest of the duchess's maids of honour, her highness told me that supper was ready. I came up to her and offered my arm, and presently found myself seated beside her at a table laid for twelve where I was the only gentleman. However, the reader need not envy me; the ladies were all elderly dowagers, who had long lost the power of turning men's heads. The duchess took the greatest care of my comforts, and at the end of the repast gave me with her own hands a glass of liqueur, which I took for Tokay and praised accordingly, but it turned out to be only old English ale. I took her back to the ball when we rose from table. The young chamberlain who had invited me told me the names of all the ladies present, but I had no time to pay my court to any of them.

The next day I dined with M. de Kaiserling, and handed Lambert over to a Jew to be clothed properly.

The day after I dined with the duke with a party consisting only of men. The old prince made me do most of the talking, and towards the end of the dinner the conversation fell upon the resources of the country which was rich in minerals and semi-minerals. I took it into my head to say that these resources ought to be developed, and that they would become precious if that were done. To justify this remark I had to speak upon the matter as if I had made it my principal study. An old chamberlain, who had the control of the mines, after allowing me to exhaust my enthusiasm, began to discuss the question himself, made divers objections, but seemed to approve of many of my remarks.

If I had reflected when I began to speak in this manner that I should have to act up to my words, I should certainly have said much less; but as it was, the duke fancied that I knew much more than I cared to say. The result was that, when the company had risen from the table, he asked me if I could spare him a fortnight on my way to St. Petersburg. I said I should be glad to oblige him, and he took me to his closet and said that the chamberlain who had spoken to me would conduct me over all the mines and manufactories in his duchies, and that he would be much obliged if I would write down any observations that struck me. I agreed to his proposal, and said I would start the next day.

The duke was delighted with my compliance, and gave the chamberlain the necessary orders, and it was agreed that he should call for me at day-break with a carriage and six.

When I got home I made my preparations, and told Lambert to be ready to accompany me with his case of instruments. I then informed him of the object of the journey, and he promised to assist me to the best of his ability, though he knew nothing about mines, and still less of the science of administration.

We started at day-break, with a servant on the box, and two others preceding us on horseback, armed to the teeth. We changed horses every two or three hours, and the chamberlain having brought plenty of wine we refreshed ourselves now and again.

The tour lasted a fortnight, and we stopped at five iron and copper manufactories. I found it was not necessary to have much technical knowledge to make notes on what I saw; all I required was a little sound argument, especially in the matter of economy, which was the duke's main object. In one place I advised reforms, and in another I counselled the employment of more hands as likely to benefit the revenue. In one mine where thirty convicts were employed I ordered the construction of a short canal, by which three wheels could be turned and twenty men saved. Under my direction Lambert drew the plans, and made the measurements with perfect accuracy. By means of other canals I proposed to drain whole valleys, with a view to obtain the sulphur with which the soil was permeated.

I returned to Mitau quite delighted at having made myself useful, and at having discovered in myself a talent which I had never suspected.

I spent the following day in making a fair copy of my

report and in having the plans done on a larger scale.

The day after I took the whole to the duke, who seemed well pleased; and as I was taking leave of him at the same time he said he would have me drive to Riga in one of his carriages, and he gave me a letter for his son, Prince Charles, who was in garrison there.

The worthy old man told me to say plainly whether I should prefer a jewel or a sum of money of equivalent value.

"From a philosopher like your highness," I replied, "I am not afraid to take money, for it may be more useful to me than jewels."

Without more ado he gave me a draft for four hundred albertsthalers, which I got cashed immediately, the albertsthaler being worth half a ducat. I bade farewell to the duchess, and dined a second time with M. de Kaiserling.

The next day the young chamberlain came to bring me the duke's letter, to wish me a pleasant journey, and to tell me that the Court carriage was at my door. I set out well pleased with the assistance the stuttering Lambert had given me, and by noon I was at Riga. The first thing I did was to deliver my letter of introduction to Prince Charles.

CHAPTER XIX

*My Stay at Riga—Campioni—St. Héleine—D'Aragon—
Arrival of the Empress—I Leave Riga and Go to St.
Petersburg—I See Society—I Buy Zaira*

PRINCE CHARLES DE BIRON, the younger son of
the Duke of Courland, Major-General in the Russian service, Knight of the Order of St. Alexander
Newski, gave me a distinguished reception after reading
his father's letter. He was thirty-six years of age, pleas-
ant-looking without being handsome, and polite and
well-mannered, and he spoke French extremely well. In
a few sentences he let me know what he could do for me
if I intended to spend some time at Riga. His table,
his friends, his pleasures, his horses, his advice, and his
purse, all these were at my service, and he offered them
with the frankness of the soldier and the geniality of
the prince.

"I cannot offer you a lodging," he said, "because I
have hardly enough room for myself, but I will see that
you get a comfortable apartment somewhere."

The apartment was soon found, and I was taken to it
by one of the prince's aides-de-camp. I was scarcely established when the prince came to see me, and made me
dine with him just as I was. It was an unceremonious
dinner, and I was pleased to meet Campioni, of whom I
have spoken several times in these Memoirs. He was a
dancer, but very superior to his fellows, and fit for the
best company polite, witty, intelligent, and a libertine

in a gentlemanly way. He was devoid of prejudices, and fond of women, good cheer, and heavy play, and knew how to keep an even mind both in good and evil fortune. We were mutually pleased to see each other again.

Another guest, a certain Baron de St. Héleine from Savoy, had a pretty but very insignificant wife. The baron, a fat man, was a gamester, a gourmand, and a lover of wine; add that he was a past master in the art of getting into debt and lulling his creditors into a state of false security, and you have all his capacities, for in all other respects he was a fool in the fullest sense of the word. An aide-de-camp and the prince's mistress also dined with us. This mistress, who was pale, thin, and dreamy-looking, but also pretty, might be twenty years old. She hardly ate anything, saying that she was ill and did not like anything on the table. Discontent shewed itself on her every feature. The prince endeavoured, but all in vain, to make her eat and drink, she refused everything disdainfully. The prince laughed good-humouredly at her in such a manner as not to wound her feelings.

We spent two hours pleasantly enough at table, and after coffee had been served, the prince, who had business, shook me by the hand and left me with Campioni, telling me always to regard his table as my last resource.

This old friend and fellow-countryman took me to his house to introduce me to his wife and family. I did not know that he had married a second time. I found the so-called wife to be an Englishwoman, thin, but full of intelligence. She had a daughter of eleven, who might easily have been taken for fifteen; she, too, was marvellously intelligent, and danced, sang, and played on the piano and gave such glances that shewed that nature had been swifter than her years. She made

a conquest of me, and her father congratulated me to my
delight, but her mother offended her dreadfully by calling her baby.

I went for a walk with Campioni, who gave me a
good deal of information, beginning with himself.

"I have lived for ten years," he said, "with that
woman. Betty, whom you admired so much, is not
my daughter, the others are my children by my Englishwoman. I have left St. Petersburg for two years, and I
live here well enough, and have pupils who do me credit.
I play with the prince, sometimes winning and sometimes
losing, but I never win enough to enable me to satisfy
a wretched creditor I left at St. Petersburg, who perse-
cutes me on account of a bill of exchange. He may put
me in prison any day, and I am always expecting him
to do so."

"Is the bill for a large sum?"

"Five hundred roubles."

"That is only two thousand francs."

"Yes, but unfortunately I have not got it."

"You ought to annul the debt by paying small sums on
account."

"The rascal won't let me."

"Then what do you propose doing?"

"Win a heavy sum, if I can, and escape into Poland.

"The Baron de St. Héleine will run away, too if he can,
for he only lives on credit. The prince is very useful to
us, as we are able to play at his house; but if we get
into difficulty he could not extricate us, as he is heavily
in debt himself. He always loses at play. His mistress
is expensive, and gives him a great deal of trouble by her
ill-humour."

"Why is she so sour?"

"She wants him to keep his word, for he promised to

get her married at the end of two years; and on the strength of this promise she let him give her two children. The two years have passed by and the children are there, and she will no longer allow him to have anything to do with her for fear of having a third child."

"Can't the prince find her a husband?"

"He did find her a lieutenant, but she won't hear of anybody under the rank of major."

The prince gave a state dinner to General Woyakoff (for whom I had a letter), Baroness Korf, Madame Ittinoff, and to a young lady who was going to marry Baron Budberg, whom I had known at Florence, Turin, and Augsburg, and whom I may possibly have forgotten to mention.

All these friends made me spend three weeks very pleasantly, and I was especially pleased with old General Woyakoff. This worthy man had been at Venice fifty years before, when the Russians were still called Muscovites, and the founder of St. Petersburg was still alive. He had grown old like an oak, without changing his horizons. He thought the world was just the same as it had been when he was young, and was eloquent in his praise of the Venetian Government, imagining it to be still the same as he had left it.

At Riga an English merchant named Collins told me that the so-called Baron de Stenau, who had given me the forged bill of exchange, had been hanged in Portugal. This "baron" was a poor clerk, and the son of a small tradesman, and had left his desk in search of adventure, and thus he had ended. May God have mercy upon his soul!

One evening a Russian, on his way from Poland, where he had been executing some commission for the Russian Court, called on the prince, played, and lost twenty thousand roubles on his word of honour. Campioni was the dealer. The Russian gave bills of exchange in payment of his debts; but as soon as he got to St. Petersburg he dishonoured his own bills, and declared them worthless, not caring for his honour or good faith. The result of this piece of knavery was not only that his creditors were defrauded, but gaming was henceforth strictly forbidden in the officers' quarters.

This Russian was the same that betrayed the secrets of Elizabeth Petrovna, when she was at war with Prussia. He communicated to Peter, the empress's nephew and heir-presumptive, all the orders she sent to her generals, and Peter in his turn passed on the information to the Prussian king whom he worshipped.

On the death of Elizabeth, Peter put this traitor at the head of the department for commerce, and the fellow actually made known, with the Czar's sanction, the service for which he had received such a reward, and thus, instead of looking upon his conduct as disgraceful, he gloried over it. Peter could not have been aware of the fact that, though it is sometimes necessary to reward treachery, the traitor himself is always abhorred and despised.

I have remarked that it was Campioni who dealt, but he dealt for the prince who held the bank. I had certain claims, but as I remarked that I expected nothing and would gladly sell my expectations for a hundred roubles, the prince took me at my word and gave me the amount immediately. Thus I was the only person who made any money by our night's play.

Catherine II., wishing to shew herself to her new subjects, over whom she was in reality supreme, though she had put the ghost of a king in the person of Stanislas Poniatowski, her former favourite, on the throne of

Poland, came to Riga, and it was then I saw this great sovereign for the first time. I was a witness of the kindness and affability with which she treated the Livonian nobility, and of the way in which she kissed the young ladies, who had come to kiss her hand, upon the mouth. She was surrounded by the Orloffs and by other nobles who had assisted in placing her on the throne. For the comfort and pleasure of her loyal subjects the empress graciously expressed her intention of holding a bank at faro of ten thousand roubles.

Instantly the table and the cards were brought forward, and the piles of gold placed in order. She took the cards, pretended to shuffle them, and gave them to the first comer to cut. She had the pleasure of seeing her bank broken at the first deal, and indeed this result was to be expected, as anybody not an absolute idiot could see how the cards were going. The next day the empress set out for Mitau, where triumphal arches were erected in her honour. They were made of wood, as stone is scarce in Poland, and indeed there would not have been time to build stone arches.

The day after her arrival great alarm prevailed, for news came that a revolution was ready to burst out at St. Petersburg, and some even said that it had begun. The rebels wished to have forth from his prison the hapless Ivan Ivanovitz, who had been proclaimed emperor in his cradle, and dethroned by Elizabeth Petrovna. Two officers to whom the guardianship of the prince had been confided had killed the poor innocent monarch when they saw that they would be overpowered.

The assassination of the innocent prince created such a sensation that the wary Panin, fearing for the results, sent courier after courier to the empress urging her to return to St. Petersburg and shew herself to the people.

Catherine was thus obliged to leave Mitau twenty-four hours after she had entered it, and after hastening back to the capital she arrived only to find that the excitement had entirely subsided. For politic reasons the assassins of the wretched Ivan were rewarded, and the bold man who had endeavoured to rise by her fall was beheaded.

The report ran that Catherine had concerted the whole affair with the assassins, but this was speedily set down as a calumny. The czarina was strong-minded, but neither cruel nor perfidious. When I saw her at Riga she was thirty-five, and had reigned two years. She was not precisely handsome, but nevertheless her appearance was pleasing, her expression kindly, and there was about her an air of calm and tranquillity which never left her.

At about the same time a friend of Baron de St. Héleine arrived from St. Petersburg on his way to Warsaw. His name was Marquis Dragon, but he called himself d'Aragon. He came from Naples, was a great gamester, a skilled swordsman, and was always ready to extract himself from a difficulty by a duel. He had left St. Petersburg because the Orloffs had persuaded the empress to prohibit games of chance. It was thought strange that the prohibition should come from the Orloffs, as gaming had been their principal means of gaining a livelihood before they entered on the more dangerous and certainly not more honourable profession of conspiracy. However, this measure was really a sensible one. Having been gamesters themselves they knew that gamesters are mostly knaves, and always ready to enter into any intrigue or conspiracy provided it assures them some small gain; there could not have been better judges of gaming and its consequences than they were.

But though a gamester may be a rogue he may still have a good heart, and it is only just to say that this was

the case with the Orloffs. Alexis gained the slash which
adorns his face in a tavern, and the man who gave the
blow had just lost to him a large sum of money, and
considered his opponent's success to be rather the result
of dexterity than fortune. When Alexis became rich and
powerful, instead of revenging himself, he hastened to
make his enemy's fortune. This was nobly done.

Dragon, whose first principle was always to turn up
the best card, and whose second principle was never to
shirk a duel, had gone to St. Petersburg in 1759 with the
Baron de St. Héleine. Elizabeth was still on the throne,
but Peter, Duke of Holstein, the heir-presumptive, had
already begun to loom large on the horizon. Dragon
used to frequent the fencing school where the prince was
a frequent visitor, and there encountered all comers successfully. The duke got angry, and one day he took
up a foil and defied the Neapolitan marquis to a combat.
Dragon accepted and was thoroughly beaten, while the
duke went off in triumph, for he might say from henceforth that he was the best fencer in St. Petersburg.

When the prince had gone, Dragon could not withstand the temptation of saying that he had only let
himself be beaten for fear of offending his antagonist;
and this boast soon got to the grand-duke's ears. The
great man was terribly enraged, and swore he would
have him banished from St. Petersburg if he did not use
all his skill, and at the same time he sent an order to
Dragon to be at the fencing school the next day.

The impatient duke was the first to arrive, and
d'Aragon was not long in coming. The prince began
reproaching him for what he had said the day before,
but the Neapolitan, far from denying the fact, expressed
himself that he had felt himself obliged to shew his re-

spect for his prince by letting him rap him about for upwards of two hours.

"Very good," said the duke, "but now it is your turn; and if you don't do your best I will drive you from St. Petersburg."

"My lord, your highness shall be obeyed. I shall not allow you to touch me once, but I hope you will deign to take me under your protection."

The two champions passed the whole morning with the foils, and the duke was hit a hundred times without being able to touch his antagonist. At last, convinced of Dragon's superiority, he threw down his foil and shook him by the hand, and made him his fencer-in-ordinary, with the rank of major in his regiment of Holsteiners.

Shortly after, D'Aragon having won the good graces of the duke obtained leave to hold a bank at faro in his court, and in three or four years he amassed a fortune of a hundred thousand roubles, which he took with him to the Court of King Stanislas, where games of all sorts were allowed. When he passed through Riga, St. Héleine introduced him to Prince Charles, who begged him to call on him the next day, and to shew his skill with the foils against himself and some of his friends. I had the honour to be of the number; and thoroughly well he beat us, for his skill was that of a demon. I was vain enough to become angry at being hit at every pass, and told him that I should not be afraid to meet him at a game of sharps. He was calmer, and replied by taking my hand, and saying,——

"With the naked sword I fence in quite another style, and you are quite right not to fear anyone, for you fence very well."

D'Aragon set out for Warsaw the next day, but he unfortunately found the place occupied by more cunning Greeks than himself. In six months they had relieved him of his hundred thousand roubles, but such is the lot of gamesters; no craft can be more wretched than theirs.

A week before I left Riga (where I stayed two months) Campioni fled by favour of the good Prince Charles, and in a few days the Baron de St. Héleine followed him without taking leave of a noble army of creditors. He only wrote a letter to the Englishman Collins, to whom he owed a thousand crowns, telling him that like an honest man he had left his debts where he had contracted them. We shall hear more of these three persons in the course of two years.

Campioni left me his travelling carriage, which obliged me to use six horses on my journey to St. Petersburg. I was sorry to leave Betty, and I kept up an epistolary correspondence with her mother throughout the whole of my stay at St. Petersburg.

I left Riga with the thermometer indicating fifteen degrees of frost, but though I travelled day and night, not leaving the carriage for the sixty hours for which my journey lasted, I did not feel the cold in the least. I had taken care to pay all the stages in advance, and Marshal Braun, Governor of Livonia, had given me the proper passport. On the box seat was a French servant who had begged me to allow him to wait on me for the journey in return for a seat beside the coachman. He kept his word and served me well, and though he was but ill clad he bore the horrible cold for two days and three nights without appearing to feel it. It is only a Frenchman who can bear such trials; a Russian in similar attire would have been frozen to death in twenty-four hours, despite plentiful doses of corn brandy.

I lost sight of this individual when I arrived at St. Petersburg, but I met him again three months after, richly dressed, and occupying a seat beside mine at the table of M. de Czernitscheff. He was the *uchitel* of the young count, who sat beside him. But I shall have occasion to speak more at length of the office of *uchitel*, or tutor, in Russia.

As for Lambert, who was beside me in the carriage, he did nothing but eat, drink, and sleep the whole way; seldom speaking, for he stammered, and could only talk about mathematical problems, on which I was not always in the humour to converse. He was never amusing, never had any sensible observation to make on the varied scenes through which we passed; in short, he was a fool, and wearisome to all save himself.

I was only stopped once, and that was at Nawa, where the authorities demanded a passport, which I did not possess. I told the governor that as I was a Venetian, and only travelled for pleasure, I did not conceive a passport would be necessary, my Republic not being at war with any other power, and Russia having no embassy at Venice.

"Nevertheless," I added, "if your excellency wills it I will turn back; but I shall complain to Marshal Braun, who gave me the passport for posting, knowing that I had not the political passport."

After rubbing his forehead for a minute, the governor gave me a pass, which I still possess, and which brought me into St. Petersburg, without my having to allow the custom-house officers to inspect my trunks.

Between Koporie and St. Petersburg there is only a wretched hut for the accommodation of travellers. The country is a wilderness, and the inhabitants do not even speak Russian. The district is called Ingria, and I believe the jargon spoken has no affinity with any other language. The principal occupation of the peasants is robbery, and the traveller does well not to leave any of his effects alone for a moment.

I got to St. Petersburg just as the first rays of the sun began to gild the horizon. It was in the winter solstice, and the sun rose at the extremity of an immense plain at twenty-four minutes past nine, so I am able to state that the longest night in Russia consists of eighteen hours and three quarters.

I got down in a fine street called the Millione. I found a couple of empty rooms, which the people of the house furnished with two beds, four chairs, and two small tables, and rented to me very cheaply. Seeing the enormous stoves, I concluded they must consume a vast amount of wood, but I was mistaken. Russia is the land of stoves as Venice is that of cisterns. I have inspected the interior of these stoves in summer-time as minutely as if I wished to find out the secret of making them; they are twelve feet high by six broad, and are capable of warming a vast room. They are only re-fuelled once in twenty-four hours, for as soon as the wood is reduced to the state of charcoal a valve is shut in the upper part of the stove.

It is only in the houses of noblemen that the stoves are refuelled twice a day, because servants are strictly forbidden to close the valve, and for a very good reason.

If a gentleman chance to come home and order his servants to warm his room before he goes to bed, and if the servant is careless enough to close the valve before the wood is reduced to charcoal, then the master sleeps his last sleep, being suffocated in three or four hours. When the door is opened in the morning he is found dead, and the poor devil of a servant is immediately hanged, whatever he may say. This sounds severe, and even cruel; but it is a necessary regulation, or else a servant would be able to get rid of his master on the smallest provocation.

After I had made an agreement for my board and lodging, both of which were very cheap (now St. Petersburg, is as dear as London), I brought some pieces of furniture which were necessaries for me, but which were not as yet much in use in Russia, such as a commode, a bureau, &c.

German is the language principally spoken in St. Petersburg, and I did not speak German much better then than I do now, so I had a good deal of difficulty in making myself understood, and usually excited my auditors to laughter.

After dinner my landlord told me that the Court was giving a masked ball to five thousand persons to last sixty hours. He gave me a ticket, and told me I only needed to shew it at the entrance of the imperial palace.

I decided to use the ticket, for I felt that I should like to be present at so numerous an assembly, and as I had my domino still by me a mask was all I wanted. I went to the palace in a sedan-chair, and found an immense crowd assembled, and dancing going on in several halls in each of which an orchestra was stationed. There were long counters loaded with eatables and drinkables at which those who were hungry or thirsty ate or drank as much as they liked. Gaiety and freedom reigned everywhere, and the light of a thousand wax candles illuminated the hall. Everything was wonderful, and all the more so from its contrast with the cold and darkness that were without. All at once I heard a masquer beside me say to another,——

"There's the czarina."

We soon saw Gregory Orloff, for his orders were to follow the empress at a distance.

I followed the masquer, and I was soon persuaded that it was really the empress, for everybody was repeating it, though no one openly recognized her. Those who really did not know her jostled her in the crowd, and I imagined that she would be delighted at being treated thus, as it was a proof of the success of her disguise. Several times I saw her speaking in Russian to one masquer and another. No doubt she exposed her vanity to some rude shocks, but she had also the inestimable advantage of hearing truths which her courtiers would certainly not tell her. The masquer who was pronounced to be Orloff followed her everywhere, and did not let her out of his sight for a moment. He could not be mistaken, as he was an exceptionally tall man and had a peculiar carriage of the head.

I arrested my progress in a hall where the French square dance was being performed, and suddenly there appeared a masquer disguised in the Venetian style. The costume was so complete that I at once set him down as a fellow-countryman, for very few strangers can imitate us so as to escape detection. As it happened, he came and stood next to me.

"One would think you were a Venetian," I said to him in French.

"So I am."

"Like myself."

"I am not jesting."

"No more am I."

"Then let us speak in Venetian."

"Do you begin, and I will reply."

We began our conversation, but when he came to the

word *Sabato,* Saturday, which is a *Sabo* in Venetian, I discovered that he was a real Venetian, but not from Venice itself. He said I was right, and that he judged from my accent that I came from Venice.

"Quite so," said I.

"I thought Bernadi was the only Venetian besides myself in St. Petersburg."

"You see you are mistaken."

"My name is Count Volpati di Treviso."

"Give me your address, and I will come and tell you who I am, for I cannot do so here."

"Here it is."

After leaving the count I continued my progress through this wonderful hall, and two or three hours after I was attracted by the voice of a female masquer speaking Parisian French in a high falsetto, such as is common at an opera ball.

I did not recognize the voice but I knew the style, and felt quite certain that the masquer must be one of my old friends, for she spoke with the intonations and phraseology which I had rendered popular in my chief places of resort at Paris.

I was curious to see who it could be, and not wishing to speak before I knew her, I had the patience to wait till she lifted her mask, and this occurred at the end of an hour. What was my surprise to see Madame Baret, the stocking-seller of the Rue St. Honoré. My love awoke from its long sleep, and coming up to her I said, in a falsetto voice,——

"I am your friend of the 'Hôtel d'Elbeuf.'"

She was puzzled, and looked the picture of bewilderment. I whispered in her ear, *"Gilbert Baret, Rue des Prouvères,"* and certain other facts which could only be known to herself and a fortunate lover.

She saw I knew her inmost secrets, and drawing me away she begged me to tell her who I was.

"I was your lover, and a fortunate one, too," I replied; "but before I tell you my name, with whom are you, and how are you?"

"Very well; but pray do not divulge what I tell you. I left Paris with M. d'Anglade, counsellor in the Court of Rouen. I lived happily enough for some time with him, and then left him to go with a theatrical manager, who brought me here as an actress under the name of de l'Anglade, and now I am kept by Count Rzewuski, the Polish ambassador. And now tell me who you are?"

Feeling sure of enjoying her again, I lifted my mask. She gave a cry of joy, and exclaimed,——

"My good angel has brought you to St. Petersburg."

"How do you mean?"

"Rzewuski is obliged to go back to Poland, and now I count on you to get me out of the country, for I can no longer continue in a station for which I was not intended, since I can neither sing nor act."

She gave me her address, and I left her delighted with my discovery. After having passed half an hour at the counter, eating and drinking of the best, I returned to the crowd and saw my fair stocking-seller talking to Count Volpati. He had seen her with me, and hastened to enquire my name of her. However, she was faithful to our mutual promise, and told him I was her husband, though the Venetian did not seem to give the least credence to this piece of information.

At last I was tired and left the ball, and went to bed intending to go to mass in the morning. I slept for some time and woke, but as it was still dark I turned on the other side and went to sleep again. At last I awoke again, and seeing the daylight stealing through my

double windows, I sent for a hairdresser, telling my
man to make haste as I wanted to hear mass on the
first Sunday after my arrival in St. Petersburg.

"But sir," said he, "the first Sunday was yesterday;
we are at Monday now."

"What! Monday?"

"Yes, sir."

I had spent twenty-seven hours in bed, and after
laughing at the mishap I felt as if I could easily believe
it, for my hunger was like that of a cannibal.

This is the only day which I really lost in my life;
but I do not weep like the Roman emperor, I laugh.
But this is not the only difference between Titus and
Casanova.

I called on Demetrio Papanelopulo, the Greek merchant, who was to pay me a hundred roubles a month.
I was also commended to him by M. da Loglio, and I
had an excellent reception. He begged me to come and
dine with him every day, paid me the roubles for the
month due, and assured me that he had honoured my
bill drawn at Mitau. He also found me a reliable servant, and a carriage at eighteen roubles, or six ducats
per month. Such cheapness has, alas! departed for
ever.

The next day, as I was dining with the worthy Greek
and young Bernardi, who was afterwards poisoned,
Count Volpati came in with the dessert, and told us
how he had met a Venetian at the ball who had promised
to come and see him.

"The Venetian would have kept his promise," said I,
"if he had not had a long sleep of twenty-seven hours.
I am the Venetian, and am delighted to continue our
acquaintance."

The count was about to leave, and his departure had

already been announced in the *St. Petersburg Gazette*. The Russian custom is not to give a traveller his passports till a fortnight has elapsed after the appearance of his name in the paper. This regulation is for the advantage of tradesmen, while it makes foreigners think twice before they contract any debts.

The next day I took a letter of introduction to M. Pietro Ivanovitch Melissino, colonel and afterwards general of artillery. The letter was written by Madame da Loglio, who was very intimate with Melissino. I was most politely welcomed, and after presenting me to his pleasant wife, he asked me once for all to sup with him every night. The house was managed in the French style, and both play and supper were conducted without any ceremony. I met there Melissino's elder brother, the procurator of the Holy Synod and husband of the Princess Dolgorouki. Faro went on, and the company was composed of trustworthy persons who neither boasted of their gains nor bewailed their losses to anyone, and so there was no fear of the Government discovering this infrigement of the law against gaming. The bank was held by Baron Lefort, son of the celebrated admiral of Peter the Great. Lefort was an example of the inconstancy of fortune; he was then in disgrace on account of a lottery which he had held at Moscow to celebrate the coronation of the empress, who had furnished him with the necessary funds. The lottery had been broken and the fact was attributed to the baron's supposed dishonesty.

I played for small stakes and won a few roubles. I made friends with Baron Lefort at supper, and he afterwards told me of the vicissitudes he had experienced.

As I was praising the noble calmness with which a certain prince had lost a thousand roubles to him, he laughed and said that the fine gamester I had mentioned played upon credit but never paid.

"How about his honour?"

"It is not affected by the non-payment of gaming debts. It is an understood thing in Russia that one who plays on credit and loses may pay or not pay as he wishes, and the winner only makes himself ridiculous by reminding the loser of his debt."

"Then the holder of the bank has the right to refuse to accept bets which are not backed by ready money."

"Certainly; and nobody has a right to be offended with him for doing so. Gaming is in a very bad state in Russia. I know young men of the highest rank whose chief boast is that they know how to conquer fortune; that is, to cheat. One of the Matuschkins goes so far as to challenge all foreign cheats to master him. He has just received permission to travel for three years, and it is an open secret that he wishes to travel that he may exercise his skill. He intends returning to Russia laden with the spoils of the dupes he has made."

A young officer of the guards named Zinowieff, a relation of the Orloffs, whom I had met at Melissino's, introduced me to Macartney, the English ambassador, a young man of parts and fond of pleasure. He had fallen in love with a young lady of the Chitroff family, and maid of honour to the empress, and finding his affection reciprocated a baby was the result. The empress disapproved strongly of this piece of English freedom, and had the ambassador recalled, though she forgave her maid of honour. This forgiveness was attributed to the young lady's skill in dancing. I knew the brother of this lady, a fine and intelligent young officer. I had the good fortune to be admitted to the Court, and there I had the pleasure of seeing Mdlle. Chitroff dancing, and also Mdlle.

Sievers, now Princesss ——, whom I saw again at Dresden four years ago with her daughter, an extremely genteel young princess. I was enchanted with Mdlle. Sievers, and felt quite in love with her; but as we were never introduced I had no opportunity of declaring my passion. Putini, the *castrato*, was high in her favour, as indeed he deserved to be, both for his talents and the beauties of his person.

The worthy Papanelopulo introduced me to Alsuwieff, one of the ministers, a man of wit and letters, and only one of the kind whom I met in Russia. He had been an industrious student at the University of Upsala, and loved wine, women, and good cheer. He asked me to dine with Locatelli at Catherinhoff, one of the imperial mansions, which the empress had assigned to the old theatrical manager for the remainder of his days. He was astonished to see me, and I was more astonished still to find that he had turned taverner, for he gave an excellent dinner every day to all who cared to pay a rouble, exclusive of wine. M. d'Alsuwieff introduced me to his colleague in the ministry, Teploff, whose vice was that he loved boys, and his virtue that he had strangled Peter III.

Madame Mécour, the dancer, introduced me to her lover, Ghelaghin, also a minister. He had spent twenty years of his life in Siberia.

A letter from Da Loglio got me a warm welcome from the *castrato* Luini, a delightful man, who kept a splendid table. He was the lover of Colonna, the singer, but their affection seemed to me a torment, for they could scarce live together in peace for a single day. At Luini's house I met another *castrato*, Millico, a great friend of the chief huntsman, Narischkin, who also became one of my friends. This Narischkin, a pleasant and a well-informed man, was the husband of the famous Maria Paulovna.

It was at the chief huntsman's splendid table that I met Calogeso Plato, now archbishop of Novgorod, and then chaplain to the empress. This monk was a Russian, and a master of ruses, understood Greek, and spoke Latin and French, and was what would be called a fine man. It was no wonder that he rose to such a height, as in Russia the nobility never lower themselves by accepting church dignities.

Da Loglio had given me a letter for the Princess Daschkoff, and I took it to her country house, at the distance of three versts from St. Petersburg. She had been exiled from the capital, because, having assisted Catherine to ascend the throne, she claimed to share it with her.

I found the princess mourning for the loss of her husband. She welcomed me kindly, and promised to speak to M. Panin on my behalf; and three days later she wrote to me that I could call on that nobleman as soon as I liked. This was a specimen of the empress's magnanimity; she had disgraced the princess, but she allowed her favourite minister to pay his court to her every evening. I have heard, on good authority, that Panin was not the princess's lover, but her father. She is now the President of the Academy of Science, and I suppose the *literati* must look upon her as another Minerva, or else they would be ashamed to have a woman at their head. For completeness' sake the Russians should get a woman to command their armies, but Joan d'Arcs are scarce.

Melissino and I were present at an extraordinary ceremony on the Day of the Epiphany, namely the blessing of the Neva, then covered with five feet of ice.

After the benediction of the waters children were baptized by being plunged into a large hole which had been made in the ice. On the day on which I was present the priest happened to let one of the children slip through his hands.

"*Drugoi!*" he cried.

That is, "*Give me another.*" But my surprise may be imagined when I saw that the father and mother of the child were in an ecstasy of joy; they were certain that the babe had been carried straight to heaven. Happy ignorance!

I had a letter from the Florentine Madame Bregonci for her friend the Venetian Roccolini, who had left Venice to go and sing at the St. Petersburg Theatre, though she did not know a note of music, and had never appeared on the stage. The empress laughed at her, and said she feared there was no opening in St. Petersburg for her peculiar talents, but the Roccolini, who was known as La Vicenza, was not the woman to lose heart for so small a check. She became an intimate friend of a French-woman named Proté, the wife of a merchant who lived with the chief huntsman. She was at the same time his mistress and the confidante of his wife Maria Petrovna, who did not like her husband, and was very much obliged to the Frenchwoman for delivering her from the conjugal importunities.

This Proté was one of the handsomest women I have ever seen, and undoubtedly the handsomest in St. Petersburg at that time. She was in the flower of her age. She had at once a wonderful taste for gallantry and for all the mysteries of the toilette. In dress she surpassed everyone, and as she was witty and amusing she captivated all hearts. Such was the woman whose friend and procuress La Vicenza had become. She received the applications of those who were in love with Madame Proté, and passed them on, while, whether a lover's suit was accepted or not, the procuress got something out of him.

I recognized Signora Roccolini as soon as I saw her, but as twenty years had elapsed since our last meeting she did not wonder at my appearing not to know her, and made no efforts to refresh my memory. Her brother was called Montellato, and he it was who tried to assassinate me one night in St. Mark's Square, as I was leaving the Ridotto. The plot that would have cost me my life, if I had not made my escape from the window, was laid in the Roccolini's house.

She welcomed me as a fellow-countryman in a strange land, told me of her struggles, and added that now she had an easy life of it, and associated with the pleasantest ladies in St. Petersburg.

"I am astonished that you have not met the fair Madame Proté at the chief huntsman's, for she is the darling of his heart. Come and take coffee with me to-morrow, and you shall see a wonder."

I kept the appointment, and I found the lady even more beautiful than the Venetian's praises of her had led me to expect. I was dazzled by her beauty, but not being a rich man I felt that I must set my wits to work if I wanted to enjoy her. I asked her name, though I knew it quite well, and she replied, *"Proté."*

"I am glad to hear it, madam," said I, "for you thereby promise to be mine."

"How so?" said she, with a charming smile. I explained the pun, and made her laugh. I told her amusing stories, and let her know the effect that her beauty had produced on me, and that I hoped time would soften her heart to me. The acquaintance was made, and thenceforth I never went to Narischkin's without calling on her, either before or after dinner.

The Polish ambassador returned about that time, and I had to forego my enjoyment of the fair Anglade, who accepted a very advantegeous proposal which was made her by Count Brawn. This charming Frenchwoman died of the small-pox a few months later, and there can be no doubt that her death was a blessing, as she would have fallen into misery and poverty after her beauty had once decayed.

I desired to succeed with Madame Proté, and with that idea I asked her to dinner at Locatelli's with Luini, Colonna, Zinowieff, Signora Vicenza, and a violinist, her lover. We had an excellent dinner washed down with plenty of wine, and the spirits of the company were wound up to the pitch I desired. After the repast each gentleman went apart with his lady, and I was on the point of success when an untoward accident interrupted us. We were summoned to see the proofs of Luini's prowess; he had gone out shooting with his dogs and guns.

As I was walking away from Catherinhoff with Zinowieff I noticed a young country-woman whose beauty astonished me. I pointed her out to the young officer, and we made for her; but she fled away with great activity to a little cottage, where we followed her. We went in and saw the father, mother, and some children, and in a corner the timid form of the fair maiden.

Zinowieff (who, by the way, was for twenty years Russian ambassador at Madrid) had a long conversation in Russian with the father. I did not understand what was said, but I guessed it referred to the girl because, when her father called her, she advanced submissively, and stood modestly before us.

The conversation over, Zinowieff went out, and I followed him after giving the master of the house a rouble.

Zinowieff told me what had passed, saying that he had asked the father if he would let him have the daughter as a maid-servant, and the father had replied that it should be so with all his heart, but that he must have a hundred roubles for her, as she was still a virgin. "So you see," added Zinowieff, "the matter is quite simple."

"How simple?"

"Why, yes; only a hundred roubles."

"And supposing me to be inclined to give that sum?"

"Then she would be your servant, and you could do anything you liked with her, except kill her."

"And supposing she is not willing?"

"That never happens, but if it did you could have beaten her."

"Well, if she is satisfied and I enjoy her, can I still continue to keep her?"

"You will be her master, I tell you, and can have her arrested if she attempts to escape, unless she can return the hundred roubles you gave for her."

"What must I give her per month?"

"Nothing, except enough to eat and drink. You must also let her go to the baths on Saturday and to the church on Sunday."

"Can I make her come with me when I leave St. Petersburg?"

"No, unless you obtain permission and find a surety, for though the girl would be your slave she would still be a slave to the empress."

"Very good; then will you arrange this matter for me? I will give the hundred roubles, and I promise you I will not treat her as a slave. But I hope you will care for my interests, as I do not wish to be duped."

"I promise you you shall not be duped; I will see to everything. Would you like her now?"

"No, to-morrow."

"Very good; then to-morrow it shall be."

We returned to St. Petersburg in a phaeton, and the next day at nine o'clock I called on Zinowieff, who said he was delighted to do me this small service. On the way he said that if I liked he could get me a perfect seraglio of pretty girls in a few days.

"No," said I, "one is enough." And I gave him the hundred roubles.

We arrived at the cottage, where we found the father, mother, and daughter. Zinowieff explained his business crudely enough, after the custom of the country, and the father thanked St. Nicholas for the good luck he had sent him. He spoke to his daughter, who looked at me and softly uttered the necessary *yes*.

Zinowieff then told me that I ought to ascertain that matters were intact, as I was going to pay for a virgin. I was afraid of offending her, and would have nothing to do with it; but Zinowieff said the girl would be mortified if I did not examine her, and that she would be delighted if I place her in a position to prove before her father and mother that her conduct had always been virtuous. I therefore made the examination as modestly as I could, and I found her to be intact. To tell the truth, I should not have said anything if things had been otherwise.

Zinowieff then gave the hundred roubles to the father, who handed them to his daughter, and she only took them to return them to her mother. My servant and coachman were then called in to witness as arrangement of which they knew nothing.

I called her Zaira, and she got into the carriage and returned with me to St. Petersburg in her coarse clothes, without a chemise of any kind. After I had dropped Zinowieff at his lodging I went home, and for four days I was engaged in collecting and arranging my slave's toilet, not resting till I had dressed her modestly in the French style. In less than three months she had learnt enough Italian to tell me what she wanted and to understand me. She soon loved me, and afterwards she got jealous. But we shall hear more of her in the following chapter.

CHAPTER XX

Crèvecœur—Bomback—Journey to Moscow—My Adventures At St. Petersburg

THE day on which I took Zaira I sent Lambert away, for I did not know what to do with him. He got drunk every day, and when in his cups he was unbearable. Nobody would have anything to say to him except as a common soldier, and that is not an enviable position in Russia. I got him a passport for Berlin, and gave him enough money for the journey. I heard afterwards that he entered the Austrian service.

In May, Zaira had become so beautiful that when I went to Moscow I dared not leave her behind me, so I took her in place of a servant. It was delicious to me to hear her chattering in the Venetian dialect I had taught her. On a Saturday I would go with her to the bath where thirty of forty naked men and women were bathing together without the slightest constraint. This absence of shame must arise, I should imagine, from native innocence; but I wondered that none looked at Zaira, who seemed to me the original of the statue of Psyche I had seen at the Villa Borghese at Rome. She was only fourteen, so her breast was not yet developed, and she bore about her few traces of puberty. Her skin was as white as snow, and her ebon tresses covered the whole of her body, save in a few places where the dazzling whiteness of her skin shone through. Her eyebrows were perfectly shaped, and her eyes, though they might have

518

been larger, could not have been more brilliant or more expressive. If it had not been for her furious jealousy and her blind confidence in fortune-telling by cards, which she consulted every day, Zaira would have been a paragon among women, and I should never have left her.

A young and distinguished-looking Frenchman came to St. Petersburg with a young Parisian named La Rivière, who was tolerably pretty but quite devoid of education, unless it were that education common to all the girls who sell their charms in Paris. This young man came to me with a letter from Prince Charles of Courland, who said that if I could do anything for the young couple he would be grateful to me. They arrived just as I was breakfasting with Zaira.

"You must tell me," said I to the young Frenchman, "in what way I can be of use to you."

"By admitting us to your company, and introducing us to your friends."

"Well, I am a stranger here, and I will come and see you, and you can come and see me, and I shall be delighted; but I never dine at home. As to my friends, you must feel that, being a stranger, I could not introduce you and the lady. Is she your wife? People will ask me who you are, and what you are doing at St. Petersburg. What am I to say? I wonder Prince Charles did not send you to someone else."

"I am a gentleman of Lorraine, and Madame la Rivière is my mistress, and my object in coming to St. Petersburg is to amuse myself."

"Then I don't know to whom I could introduce you under the circumstances; but I should think you will be able to find plenty of amusement without knowing anyone. The theatres, the streets, and even the Court entertainments, are open to everyone. I suppose you have plenty of money?"

"That's exactly what I haven't got, and I don't expect any either."

"Well, I have not much more, but you really astonish me. How could you have been so foolish as to come here without money?"

"Well, my mistress said we could do with what money we got from day to day. She induced me to leave Paris without a farthing, and up to now it seems to me that she is right. We have managed to get on somehow."

"Then she has the purse?"

"My purse," said she, "is in the pockets of my friends."

"I understand, and I am sure you have no difficulty in finding the wherewithal to live. If I had such a purse, it should be opened for you, but I am not a rich man."

Bomback, a citizen of Hamburg, whom I had known in England whence he had fled on account of his debts, had come to St. Petersburg and entered the army. He was the son of a rich merchant and kept up a house, a carriage, and an army of servants; he was a lover of good cheer, women, and gambling, and contracted debts everywhere. He was an ugly man, but full of wit and energy. He happened to call on me just as I was addressing the strange traveller whose purse was in the pocket of her friends. I introduced the couple to him, telling the whole story, the item of the purse excepted. The adventure was just to Bomback's taste, and he began making advances to Madame la Rivière, who received them in a thoroughly professional spirit, and I was inwardly amused and felt that her axiom was a true one. Bomback asked them to dine with him the next day, and begged them to come and take an unceremonious dinner the same day with him at Crasnacaback. I was included in the invitation, and Zaira, not understanding French, asked me what we were talking about, and on my telling her expressed a desire to accompany me. I gave in to appease her, for I knew the wish proceeded from jealousy, and that if I did not consent I should be tormented by tears, ill-humour, reproaches, melancholy, etc. This had occurred several times before, and so violent had she been that I had been compelled to conform to the custom of the country and beat her. Strange to say, I could not have taken a better way to prove my love. Such is the character of the Russian women. After the blows had been given, by slow degrees she became affectionate again, and a love encounter sealed the reconciliation.

Bomback left us to make his preparations in high spirits, and while Zaira was dressing, Madame Rivière talked in such a manner as to make me almost think that I was absolutely deficient in knowledge of the world. The astonishing thing was that her lover did not seem in the least ashamed of the part he had to play. He might say that he was in love with the Messalina, but the excuse would not have been admissible.

The party was a merry one. Bomback talked to the adventuress, Zaira sat on my knee, and Crèvecœur ate and drank, laughed in season and out of season, and walked up and down. The crafty Madame Rivière incited Bomback to risk twenty-five roubles at quinze; he lost and paid pleasantly, and only got a kiss for his money. Zaira, who was delighted to be able to watch over me and my fidelity, jested pleasantly on the Frenchwoman and the complaisance of her lover. This was altogether beyond her comprehension, and she could not understand how he could bear such deeds as were done before his face.

The next day I went to Bomback by myself, as I was sure of meeting young Russian officers, who would have annoyed me by making love to Zaira in their own language. I found the two travellers and the brothers Lunin, then lieutenants but now generals. The younger of them was as fair and pretty as any girl. He had been the beloved of the minister Teploff, and, like a lad of wit, he not only was not ashamed but openly boasted that it was his custom to secure the good-will of all men by his caresses.

He had imagined the rich citizen of Hamburg to be of the same tastes as Teploff, and he had not been mistaken; and so he degraded me by forming the same supposition. With this idea he seated himself next to me at table, and behaved himself in such a manner during dinner that I began to believe him to be a girl in man's clothes.

After dinner, as I was sitting at the fire, between him and the Frenchman, I imparted my suspicions to him; but jealous of the superiority of his sex, he displayed proof of it on the spot, and forthwith got hold of me and put himself in a position to make my happiness and his own as he called it. I confess, to my shame, that he might perhaps have succeeded, if Madame la Rivière, indignant at this encroachment of her peculiar province, had not made him desist.

Lunin the elder, Crèvecœur, and Bomback, who had been for a walk, returned at nightfall with two or three friends, and easily consoled the Frenchman for the poor entertainment the younger Lunin and myself had given him.

Bomback held a bank at faro, which only came to an end at eleven, when the money was all gone. We then supped, and the real orgy began, in which la Rivière bore the brunt in a manner that was simply astonishing. I and my friend Lunin were merely spectators, and poor Crèvecœur had gone to bed. We did not separate till day-break.

I got home, and, fortunately for myself, escaped the bottle which Zaira flung at my head, and which would infallibly have killed me if it had hit me. She threw herself on to the ground, and began to strike it with her forehead. I thought she had gone mad, and wondered whether I had better call for assistance; but she became quiet enough to call me assassin and traitor, with all the other abusive epithets that she could remember. To convict me of my crime she shewed me twenty-five cards, placed in order, and on them she displayed the various enormities of which I had been guilty.

I let her go on till her rage was somewhat exhausted, and then, having thrown her divining apparatus into the fire, I looked at her in pity and anger, and said that we must part the next day, as she had narrowly escaped killing me. I confessed that I had been with Bomback, and that there had been a girl in the house; but I denied all the other sins of which she accused me. I then went to sleep without taking the slightest notice of her, in spite of all she said and did to prove her repentance.

I woke after a few hours to find her sleeping soundly, and I began to consider how I could best rid myself of the girl, who would probably kill me if we continued living together. Whilst I was absorbed in these thoughts she awoke, and falling at my feet wept and professed her utter repentance, and promised never to touch another card as long as I kept her.

At last I could resist her entreaties no longer, so I took her in my arms and forgave her; and we did not part till she had received undeniable proofs of the return of my affection. I intended to start for Moscow in three days, and she was delighted when she heard she was to go.

Three circumstances had won me this young girl's furious affection. In the first place I often took her to see her family, with whom I always left a rouble; in the second I made her eat with me; and in the third I had beaten her three or four times when she had tried to prevent me going out.

In Russia beating is a matter of necessity, for words have no force whatever. A servant, mistress, or courtezan understands nothing but the lash. Words are altogether thrown away, but a few good strokes are entirely efficacious. The servant, whose soul is still more enslaved than his body, reasons somewhat as follows, after he has had a beating:

"My master has not sent me away, but beaten me; therefore he loves me, and I ought to be attached to him."

It is the same with the Russian soldier, and in fact with everybody. Honour stands for nothing, but with the knout and brandy one can get anything from them except heroical enthusiasm.

Papanelopulo laughed at me when I said that as I liked my Cossack I should endeavour to correct him with words only when he took too much brandy.

"If you do not beat him," he said, "he will end by beating you;" and he spoke the truth.

One day, when he was so drunk as to be unable to attend on me, I began to scold him, and threatened him with the stick if he did not mend his ways. As soon as he saw my cane lifted, he ran at me and got hold of it; and if I had not knocked him down immediately, he would doubtless have beaten me. I dismissed him on the spot. There is not a better servant in the world than a Russian. He works without ceasing, sleeps in front of the door of his master's bedroom to be always ready to fulfil his orders, never answering his reproaches, incapable of theft. But after drinking a little too much brandy he becomes a perfect monster; and drunkenness is the vice of the whole nation.

A coachman knows no other way of resisting the bitter cold to which he is exposed, than by drinking rye brandy. It sometimes happens that he drinks till he falls asleep, and then there is no awaking for him in this world. Unless one is very careful, it is easy to lose an ear, the nose, a cheek, or a lip by frost bites. One day as I was walking out on a bitterly cold day, a Russian noticed that one of my ears was frozen. He ran up to me and rubbed the affected part with a handful of snow till the circulation was restored. I asked him how he had noticed my state, and he said he had remarked the livid whiteness of my ear, and this, he said, was always a sign that the frost had taken it. What surprised me most of all is that sometimes the part grows again after it has dropped off. Prince Charles of Courland assured me that he had lost his nose in Siberia, and that it had grown again the next summer. I have been assured of the truth of this by several Russians.

About this time the empress made the architect **Rinaldi**, who had been fifty years in St. Petersburg, build her an enormous wooden amphitheatre so large as to cover the whole of the space in front of the palace. It would contain a hundred thousand spectators, and in it Catherine intended to give a vast tournament to all the knights of her empire. There were to be four parties of a hundred knights each, and all the cavaliers were to be clad in the national costume of the nations they represented. All the Russians were informed of this great festival, which was to be given at the expense of the sovereign, and the princes, counts, and barons were already arriving with their chargers from the most remote parts of the empire. Prince Charles of Courland wrote informing me of his intention to be present.

It had been ordained that the tournament should take place on the first fine day, and this precaution was a very wise one; for, excepting in the season of the hard frosts, a day without rain, or snow, or wind, is a marvel. In Italy, Spain, and France, one can reckon on fine weather, and bad weather is the exception, but it is quite the contrary in Russia. Ever since I have known this home of frost and the cold north wind, I laugh when I hear travelling Russians talking of the fine climate of their native country. However, it is a pardonable weakness, most of us prefer "mine" to "thine;" nobles affect to consider themselves of purer blood than the peasants from whom they sprang, and the Romans and other ancient nations pretended that they were the children of the gods, to draw a veil over their actual ancestors who were doubtless robbers. The truth is, that during the whole year 1756 there was not one fine day in Russia, or in Ingria at all events, and the mere proofs of this statement may be found in the fact that the tournament was not held in that year. It was postponed till the next, and the princes, counts, barons, and knights spent the winter in the capital, unless their purses forbade them to indulge in the luxuries of Court life. The dear Prince of Courland was in this case, to my great disappointment.

Having made all arrangements for my journey to Moscow, I got into my sleeping carriage with Zaira, having a servant behind who could speak both Russian and German. For twenty-four roubles the *chevochic* (hirer out of horses) engaged to carry me to Moscow in six days and seven nights with six horses. This struck me as being extremely cheap. The distance is seventy-two Russian stages, almost equivalent to five hundred Italian miles, or a hundred and sixty French leagues.

We set out just as a cannon shot from the citadel announced the close of day. It was towards the end of May, in which month there is literally no night at St. Petersburg. Without the report of the cannon no one would be able to tell when the day ended and the night began. One can read a letter at midnight, and the moonlight makes no appreciable difference. This continual day lasts for eight weeks, and during that time no one lights a candle. At Moscow it is different; a candle is always necessary at midnight if one wished to read.

We reached Novgorod in forty-eight hours, and here the *chevochic* allowed us a rest of five hours. I saw a circumstance there which surprised me very much, though one has no business to be surprised at anything if one travels much, and especially in a land of half savages. I asked the *chevochic* to drink, but he appeared to be in great melancholy. I enquired what was the matter, and he told Zaira that one of his horses had refused to eat, and that it was clear that if he could not eat he could not work. We followed him into the stable, and found the horse looking oppressed by care, its head lowered and motionless; it had evidently got no appetite. His master began a pathetic oration, looking tenderly at the animal, as if to arouse it to a sense of duty, and then taking its head, and kissing it lovingly, he put it into the manger, but to no purpose. Then the man began to weep bitterly, but in such a way that I had the greatest difficulty to prevent myself laughing, for I could see that he wept in the hope that his tears might soften the brute's heart. When he had wept some time he again put the horse's head into the manger, but again to no purpose. At this he got furious and swore to be avenged. He led the horse out of the stable, tied it to a post, and beat it with a thick stick for a quarter of an hour so violently that my heart bled for the poor animal. At last the *chevochic* was tired out, and taking the horse back to the stable he fastened up his head once more, and to my astonishment it began to devour its provender with the greatest appetite. At this the master jumped for joy, laughed, sang, and committed a thousand extravagancies, as if to shew the horse how happy it had made him. I was beside myself with astonishment, and concluded that such treatment would have succeeded nowhere but in Russia, where the stick seems to be the panacea or universal medicine.

They tell me, however, that the stick is gradually going out of fashion. Peter the Great used to beat his generals black and blue, and in his days a lieutenant had to receive with all submission the cuffs of his captain, who bent before the blows of his major, who did the same to his colonel, who received chastisement from his general. So I was informed by old General Woyakoff, who was a pupil of Peter the Great, and had often been beaten by the great emperor, the founder of St. Petersburg.

It seems to me that I have scarcely said anything about this great and famous capital, which in my opinion is built on somewhat precarious foundations. No one but Peter could have thus given the lie to Nature by building his immense palaces of marble and granite on mud and shifting sand. They tell me that the town is now in its manhood, to the honour of the great Catherine; but in the year 1765 it was still in its minority, and seemed to me only to have been built with the childish aim of seeing it fall into ruins. Streets were built with the certainty of having to repair them in six months' time. The whole place proclaimed itself to be the whim of a despot. If it is to be durable constant care will be required, for nature never gives up its rights and reasserts them when the constraint of man is withdrawn. My theory is that sooner or later the soil must give way and drag the vast city with it.

We reached Moscow in the time the *chevochic* had promised. As the same horses were used for the whole journey, it would have been impossible to travel more quickly. A Russian told me that the Empress Elizabeth had done the journey in fifty-two hours.

"You mean that she issued a ukase to the effect that she had done it," said a Russian of the old school; "and if she had liked she could have travelled more quickly still; it was only a question of the wording of the ukase."

Even when I was in Russia it was not allowable to doubt the infallibility of a ukase, and to do so was equivalent to high treason. One day I was crossing a canal at St. Petersburg by a small wooden bridge; Melissino Papanelopulo, and some other Russians were with me. I began to abuse the wooden bridge, which I characterized as both mean and dangerous. One of my companions said that on such a day it would be replaced by a fine stone bridge, as the empress had to pass there on some state occasion. The day named was three weeks off, and I said plainly that it was impossible. One of the Russians looked askance at me, and said there was no doubt about it, as a ukase had been published ordering that the bridge should be built. I was going to answer him, but Papanelopulo gave my hand a squeeze, and whispered *"Taci !"* (hush).

The bridge was not built, but I was not justified, for the empress published another ukase in which she declared it to be her gracious pleasure that the bridge should not be built till the following year. If anyone would see what a pure despotism is like, let him go to Russia.

The Russian sovereigns use the language of despotism on all occasions. One day I saw the empress, dressed in man's clothes, going out for a ride. Her master of the horse, Prince Repnin, held the bridle of the horse, which suddenly gave him a kick which broke his ankle-bone. The empress instantly ordained that the horse should be taken away, and that no one should mount it again under pain of death. All official positions in Russia have military rank assigned to them, and this sufficiently indicates the nature of the Government. The coachman-in-chief of her imperial highness holds the rank of colonel, as also does her chief cook. The *castrato* Luini was a lieutenant-colonel, and the painter Toretti only a captain, because he had only eight hundred roubles a year, while the coachman had three thousand. The sentinels at the doors of the palace have their muskets crossed, and ask those who wish to pass through what is their rank. When I was asked this question, I stopped short; but the quick-witted officer asked me how much I had a year, and on my replying, at a hazard, three thousand roubles, he gave me the rank of general, and I was allowed to pass. I saw the czarina for a moment; she stopped at the door and took off her gloves to give her hands to be kissed by the officer and the two sen-

tinels. By such means as this she had won the affection
of the corps, commanded by Gregorius Gregorovitch Orloff, on which her safety depended in case of revolution.

I made the following notes when I saw the empress
hearing mass in her chapel. The protopapa, or bishop,
received her at the door to give her the holy water, and
she kissed his episcopal ring, while the prelate, whose
beard was a couple of feet in length, lowered his head to
kiss the hands of his temporal sovereign and spiritual
head, for in Russia the he or she on the throne is the
spiritual as well as temporal head of the Church.

She did not evidence the least devotion during mass;
hypocrisy did not seem to be one of her vices. Now she
smiled at one of her suite, now at another, and occasionally she addressed the favourite, not because she had
anything to say to him, but to make him an object of
envy to the others.

One evening, as she was leaving the theatre where
Metastasio's *Olympiade* had been performed, I heard
her say,——

"The music of that opera has given the greatest pleasure to everyone, so of course I am delighted with it; but
it wearies me, nevertheless. Music is a fine thing, but
I cannot understand how anyone who is seriously occupied can love it passionately. I will have Buranello
here, and I wonder whether he will interest me in music,
but I am afraid nature did not constitute me to feel all
its charms."

She always argued in that way. In due time I will
set down her words to me when I returned from Moscow. When I arrived at that city I got down at a good
inn, where they gave me two rooms and a coach-house
for my carriage. After dinner I hired a small carriage
and a guide who could speak French. My carriage was

drawn by four horses, for Moscow is a vast city composed of four distinct towns, and many of the streets are rough and ill-paved. I had five or six letters of introduction, and I determined to take them all. I took Zaira with me, as she was as curious to see everything as a girl of fourteen naturally is. I do not remember what feast the Greek Church was keeping on that day, but I shall never forget the terrific bell-ringing with which my ears were assailed, for there are churches everywhere. The country people were engaged in sowing their grain, to reap it in September. They laughed at our southern custom of sowing eight months earlier, as unnecessary and even prejudicial to the crops, but I do not know where the right lies. Perhaps we may both be right, for there is no master to compare with experience.

I took all the introductions I had received from Narischkin, Prince Repnin, the worthy Pananelopulo, and Melissino's brother. The next morning the whole of the persons at whose houses I had left letters called on me. They all asked Zaira and myself to dinner, and I accepted the invitation of the first comer, M. Dimidoff, and promised to dine with the rest on the following days. Zaira, who had been tutored by me to some extent, was delighted to shew me that she was worthy of the position she occupied. She was exquisitely dressed, and won golden opinions everywhere, for our hosts did not care to enquire whether she were my daughter, my mistress, or my servant, for in this matter, as in many others, the Russians are excessively indulgent. Those who have not seen Moscow have not seen Russia, for the people of St. Petersburg are not really Russians at all. Their court manners are very different from their manners *au naturel,* and it may be said with truth that the true Russian is as a stranger in St. Petersburg. The citizens of

Moscow, and especially the rich ones, speak with pity of those, who for one reason or another, had expatriated themselves; and with them to expatriate one's self is to leave Moscow, which they consider as their native land. They look on St. Petersburg with an envious eye, and call it the ruin of Russia. I do not know whether this is a just view to take of the case, I merely repeat what I have heard.

In the course of a week I saw all the sights of Moscow —the manufacturers, the churches, the remains of the old days, the museums, the libraries, (of no interest to my mind), not forgetting the famous bell. I noticed that their bells are not allowed to swing like ours, but are motionless, being rung by a rope attached to the clapper.

I thought the Moscow women more handsome than those of St. Petersburg, and I attribute this to the great superiority of the air. They are gentle and accessible by nature; and to obtain the favour of a kiss on the lips, one need only make a show of kissing their hands.

There was good fare in plenty, but no delicacy in its composition or arrangement. Their table is always open to friends and acquaintances, and a friend may bring in five or six persons to dinner, and even at the end of the meals you will never hear a Russian say, "We have had dinner; you have come too late." Their souls are not black enough for them to pronounce such words as these. Notice is given to the cook, and the dinner begins over again. They have a delicious drink, the name of which I do not remember; but it is much superior to the sherbet of Constantinople. The numerous servants are not given water, but a light, nourishing, and agreeable fluid, which may be purchased very cheaply. They all hold St. Nicholas in the greatest reverence, only praying to God through the mediation of this saint, whose picture is always suspended in the principal room of the house. A person coming in makes first a bow to the image and then a bow to the master, and if perchance the image is absent, the Russian, after gazing all round, stands confused and motionless, not knowing what to do. As a general rule the Muscovites are the most superstitious Christians in the world. Their liturgy is in Greek, of which the people understand nothing, and the clergy, themselves extremely ignorant, gladly leave them completely in the dark on all matters connected with religion. I could never make them understand that the only reason for the Roman Christians making the sign of the Cross from left to right, while the Greeks make it from right to left, is that we say *spiritus sancti*, while they say *agion pneuma*.

"If you said *pneuma agion*," I used to say, "then you would cross yourself like us, and if we said *sancti spiritus* we should cross ourselves like you."

"The adjective," replied my interlocutor, "should always precede the substantive, for we should never utter the name of God without first giving Him some honourable epithet."

Such are nearly all the differences which divide the two churches, without reckoning the numerous idle tales which they have as well as ourselves, and which are by no means the least cherished articles of their faith.

We returned to St. Petersburg by the way we had come, but Zaira would have liked me never to leave Moscow. She had become so much in love with me by force of constant association that I could not think without a pang of the moment of separation. The day after our arrival in the capital I took her to her home, where she shewed her father all the little presents I had given her, and told him of the honour she had received as my daughter, which made the good man laugh heartily.

The first piece of news I heard was that a ukase had been issued, ordering the erection of a temple dedicated to God in the Moscöi opposite to the house where I resided. The empress had entrusted Rinaldi, the architect, with the erection. He asked her what emblem he should put above the portal, and she replied,——

"No emblem at all, only the name of God in large letters."

"I will put a triangle."

"No triangle at all; but only the name of God in whatever language you like, and nothing more."

The second piece of news was that Bomback had fled and had been captured at Mitau, where he believed himself in safety. M. de Simolia had arrested him. It was a grave case, for he had deserted; however, he was given his life, and sent into barracks at Kamstchatka. Crèvecœur and his mistress had departed, carrying some money with them, and a Florentine adventurer named Biliotti had fled with eighteen thousand roubles belonging to Papanelopulo, but a certain Bori, the worthy Greek's factotum, had caught him at Mitau and brought him back to St. Petersburg, where he was now in prison. Prince Charles of Courland arrived about this time, and I hastened to call upon him as soon as he advised me of his coming. He was lodging in a house belonging to Count Dimidoff, who owned large iron mines, and had made the whole house of iron, from attic to basement. The prince had brought his mistress with him, but she was still in an ill-humour, and he was beginning to get heartily sick of her. The man was to be pitied, for he could not get rid of her without finding her a husband, and this husband became more difficult to find every day. When the prince saw how happy I was with my Zaira, he could not help thinking how easily happiness may be won; but the fatal desire for luxury and empty show spoils all, and renders the very sweets of life as bitter as gall.

I was indeed considered happy, and I liked to appear so, but in my heart I was wretched. Ever since my imprisonment under The Leads, I had been subject to hæmorrhoids, which came on three or four times a year. At St. Petersburg I had a serious attack, and the daily pain and anxiety embittered my existence. A vegetarian doctor called Senapios, for whom I had sent, gave me the sad news that I had a blind or incomplete fistula in the rectum, and according to him nothing but the cruel bistoury would give me any relief, and indeed he said I had no time to lose. I had to agree, in spite of my dislike to the operation; but fortunately the clever surgeon whom the doctor summoned pronounced that if I would have patience nature itself would give me relief. I had much to endure, especially from the severe dieting to which I was subjected, but which doubtless did me good.

Colonel Melissino asked me to be present at a review which was to take place at three versts from St. Petersburg, and was to be succeeded by a dinner to twenty-four guests, given by General Orloff. I went with the prince, and saw a cannon fired twenty times in a minute, testing the performance with my watch.

My neighbour at dinner was the French ambassador. Wishing to drink deeply, after the Russian fashion, and thinking the Hungarian wine as innocent as champagne, he drank so bravely that at the end of dinner he had lost the use of his legs. Count Orloff made him drink still more, and then he fell asleep and was laid on a bed.

The gaiety of the meal gave me some idea of Russian wit. I did not understand the language, so M. Zinowieff translated the curious sallies to me while the applause they had raised was still resounding.

Melissino rose to his feet, holding a large goblet full of Hungarian wine in his hand. There was a general silence to listen to him. He drank the health of General Orloff in these words:

"May you die when you become rich."

The applause was general, for the allusion was to the unbounded generosity of Orloff. The general's reply struck me as better still, but it was equally rugged in character. He, too, took a full cup, and turning to Melissino, said,——

"May you never die till I slay you!"

The applause was furious, for he was their host and their general.

The Russian wit is of the energetic kind, devoid of grace; all they care about is directness and vigour.

Voltaire had just sent the empress his "Philosophy of History," which he had written for her and dedicated to her. A month after, an edition of three thousand copies came by sea, and was sold out in a week, for all the Russians who knew a little French were eager to possess a copy of the work. The leaders of the Voltaireans were two noblemen, named, respectively, Stroganoff and Schuvaloff. I have seen verses written by the former of these as good as Voltaire's own verses, and twenty years later I saw an ode by the latter of which Voltaire would not have been ashamed, but the subject was ill chosen; for it treated of the death of the great philosopher who had so studiously avoided using his pen on melancholy themes. In those days all Russians with any pretensions to literature read nothing but Voltaire, and when they had read all his writings they thought themselves as wise as their master. To me they seemed pigmies mimicking a giant. I told them that they ought to read all the books from which Voltaire had drawn his immense learning, and then, perhaps, they might become as wise as he. I remember the saying of a wise man at Rome: "Beware of the man of one book." I wonder whether the Russians are more profound now; but that is a question I cannot answer. At Dresden I knew Prince Biloselski, who was on his way back to Russia after having been ambassador at Turin. He was the author of an admirable work on metaphysics, and the analysis of the soul and reason.

Count Panin was the tutor of Paul Petrovitch, heir-presumptive to the throne. The young prince had a severe master, and dared not even applaud an air at the opera unless he first received permission to do so from his mentor.

When a courier brought the news of the sudden death of Francis I., Emperor of Germany and of the Holy Roman Empire, the czarina being at Czarsko-Zelo, the count minister-tutor was in the palace with his pupil, then eleven years old. The courier came at noon, and gave the dispatch into the hands of the minister, who was standing in the midst of a crowd of courtiers of whom I was one. The prince imperial was at his right hand. The minister read the dispatch in a low voice, and then said:

"This is news indeed. The Emperor of the Romans has died suddenly."

He then turned to Paul, and said to him,——

"Full court mourning, which your highness will observe for three months longer than the empress."

"Why so?" said Paul.

"Because, as Duke of Holstein, your highness has a right to attend the diet of the empire, a privilege," he added, turning to us, "which Peter the Great desired in vain."

I noted the attention with which the Grand Duke Paul listened to his mentor, and the care with which he concealed his joy at the news. I was immensely pleased with this way of giving instruction. I said as much to Prince Lobkowitz, who was standing by me, and he refined on my praises. This prince was popular with everyone. He was even preferred to his predecessor, Prince Esterhazy; and this was saying a great deal, for Esterhazy was adored in Russia. The gay and affable manner of Prince Lobkowitz made him the life and soul of all the parties at which he was present. He was a constant courtier of the Countess Braun, the reigning beauty, and everyone believed his love had been crowned with success, though no one could assert as much positively.

There was a great review held at a distance of twelve or fourteen versts from St. Petersburg, at which the empress and all her train of courtiers were present. The houses of the two or three adjoining villages were so few and small that it would be impossible for all the company to find a lodging. Nevertheless I wished to be present chiefly to please Zaira, who wanted to be seen with me on such an occasion. The review was to last three days; there were to be fireworks, and a mine was to be exploded besides the evolutions of the troops. I went in my travelling carriage, which would serve me for a lodging if I could get nothing better.

We arrived at the appointed place at eight o'clock in the morning; the evolutions lasted till noon. When they were over we went towards a tavern and had our meal served to us in the carriage, as all the rooms in the inn were full.

After dinner my coachman tried in vain to find me a lodging, so I disposed myself to sleep all night in the carriage; and so I did for the whole time of the review, and fared better than those who had spent so much money to be ill lodged. Melissino told me that the empress thought my idea a very sensible one. As I was the only person who had a sleeping carriage, which was quite a portable house in itself, I had numerous visitors, and Zaira was radiant to be able to do the honours.

I had a good deal of conversation during the review with Count Tott, brother of the nobleman who was employed at Constantinople, and known as Baron Tott. We had known each other at Paris, and afterwards at the Hague, where I had the pleasure of being of service to him. He had come to St. Petersburg with Madame de Soltikoff, whom he had met at Paris, and whose lover he was. He lived with her, went to Court, and was well received by everyone.

Two or three years after, the empress ordered him to leave St. Petersburg on account of the troubles in Poland. It was said that he kept up a correspondence with his brother, who was endeavouring to intercept the fleet under the command of Alexis Orloff. I never heard what became of him after he left Russia, where he obliged me with the loan of five hundred roubles, which I have not yet been able to return to him.

M. Maruzzi, by calling a Venetian merchant, and by birth a Greek, having left trade to live like a gentleman, came to St. Petersburg when I was there, and was presented at Court. He was a fine-looking man, and was admitted to all the great houses. The empress treated him with distinction because she had thoughts of making him her agent at Venice. He paid his court to the Countess Braun, but he had rivals there who were not afraid of him. He was rich enough, but did not know how to spend his money; and avarice is a sin which meets with no pity from the Russian ladies.

I went to Czarsko-Zelo, Peterhoff, and Cronstadt, for if you want to say you have been in a country you should see as much as possible of it. I wrote notes and memorandums on several questions with the hope of their procuring me a place in the civil service, and all my productions were laid before the empress but with no effect. In Russia they do not think much of foreigners unless they have specially summoned them; those who come of their own account rarely make much, and I suspect the Russians are right.

CHAPTER XXI

I See the Empress—My Conversations with Her—The Valville—I Leave Zaira—I Leave St. Petersburg and Arrive at Warsaw—The Princes Adam Czartoryski and Sulkowski—The King of Poland—Theatrical Intrigues —Branicki

I THOUGHT of leaving Russia at the beginning of the autumn, but I was told by MM. Panin and Alsuwieff that I ought not to go without having spoken to the empress.

"I should be sorry to do so," I replied, "but as I can't find anyone to present me to her, I must be resigned."

At last Panin told me to walk in a garden frequented by her majesty at an early hour, and he said that meeting me, as it were by chance, she would probably speak to me. I told him I should like him to be with her, and he accordingly named a day.

I repaired to the garden, and as I walked about I marvelled at the statuary it contained, all the statues being made of the worst stone, and executed in the worst possible taste. The names cut beneath them gave the whole the air of a practical joke. A weeping statue was Democritus; another, with grinning mouth, was labelled Heraclitus; an old man with a long beard was Sappho; and an old woman, Avicenna; and so on.

As I was smiling at this extraordinary collection, I saw the czarina, preceded by Count Gregorius Orloff, and followed by two ladies, approaching. Count Panin was on her left hand. I stood by the hedge to let her pass, but as soon as she came up to me she asked, smilingly, if I had been interested in the statues. I replied, following her steps, that I presumed they had been placed there to impose on fools, or to excite the laughter of those acquainted with history.

"From what I can make out," she replied, "the secret of the matter is that my worthy aunt was imposed on, and indeed she did not trouble herself much about such trifles. But I hope you have seen other things in Russia less ridiculous than these statues?"

I entertained the sovereign for more than an hour with my remarks on the things of note I had seen in St. Petersburg. The conversation happened to turn on the King of Prussia, and I sang his praises; but I censured his terrible habit of always interrupting the person whom he was addressing. Catherine smiled and asked me to tell her about the conversation I had had with this monarch, and I did so to the best of my ability. She was then kind enough to say that she had never seen me at the *Courtag,* which was a vocal and instrumental concert given at the palace, and open to all. I told her that I had only attended once, as I was so unfortunate as not to have a taste for music. At this she turned to Panin, and said smilingly that she knew someone else who had the same misfortune. If the reader remembers what I heard her say about music as she was leaving the opera, he will pronounce my speech to have been a very courtier-like one, and I confess it was; but who can resist making such speeches to a monarch, and above all, a monarch in petticoats?

The czarina turned from me to speak to M. Bezkoi, who had just come up, and as M. Panin left the garden I did so too, delighted with the honour I had had.

The empress, who was a woman of moderate height and yet of a majestic appearance, thoroughly understood the art of making herself loved. She was not beautiful, but yet she was sure of pleasing by her geniality and her wit, and also by that exquisite tact which made one forget the awfulness of the sovereign in the gentleness of the woman.

A few days after, Count Panin told me that the empress had twice asked after me, and that this was a sure sign I had pleased her. He advised me to look out for another opportunity of meeting her, and said that for the future she would always tell me to approach whenever she saw me, and that if I wanted some employment she might possible do something for me.

Though I did not know what employ I could ask for in that disagreeable country, I was glad to hear that I could have easy access to the Court. With that idea I walked in the garden every day, and here follows my second conversation with the empress:

She saw me at a distance and sent an officer to fetch me into her presence. As everybody was talking of the tournament, which had to be postponed on account of the bad weather, she asked me if this kind of entertainment could be given at Venice. I told her some amusing stories on the subject of shows and spectacles, and in this relation I remarked that the Venetian climate was more pleasant than the Russian, for at Venice fine days were the rule, while at St. Petersburg they were the exception, though the year is younger there than anywhere else.

"Yes," she said, "in your country it is eleven days older."

"Would it not be worthy of your majesty to put Russia on an equality with the rest of the world in this respect, by adopting the Gregorian calendar? All the Protestants have done so, and England, who adopted it fourteen years ago, has already gained several millions. All Europe is astonished that the old style should be suffered to exist in a country where the sovereign is the head of the Church, and whose capital contains an academy of science. It is thought that Peter the Great, who made the year begin in January, would have also abolished the old style if he had not been afraid of offending England, which then kept trade and commerce alive throughout your vast empire."

"You know," she replied, with a sly smile, "that Peter the Great was not exactly a learned man."

"He was more than a man of learning, the immortal Peter was a genius of the first order. Instinct supplied the place of science with him; his judgment was always in the right. His vast genius, his firm resolve, prevented him from making mistakes, and helped him to destroy all those abuses which threatened to oppose his great designs."

Her majesty seemed to have heard me with great interest, and was about to reply when she noticed two ladies whom she summoned to her presence. To me she said,——

"I shall be delighted to reply to you at another time," and then turned towards the ladies.

The time came in eight or ten days, when I was beginning to think she had had enough of me, for she had seen me without summoning me to speak to her.

She began by saying what I desired should be done was done already. "All the letters sent to foreign countries and all the important State records are marked with both dates."

"But I must point out to your majesty that by the

end of the century the difference will be of twelve days,
not eleven."

"Not at all; we have seen to that. The last year
of this century will not be counted as a leap year. It
is fortunate that the difference is one of eleven days,
for as that is the number which is added every year
to the epact our epacts are almost the same. As to the
celebration of Easter, that is a different question. Your
equinox is on March the 21st, ours on the 10th, and
the astronomers say we are both wrong; sometimes it
is we who are wrong and sometimes you, as the equinox
varies. You know you are not even in agreement with
the Jews, whose calculation is said to be perfectly ac-
curate; and, in fine, this difference in the time of cele-
brating Easter does not disturb in any way public order
or the progress of the Government."

"Your majesty's words fill me with admiration, but
the Festival of Christmas——"

"I suppose you are going to say that we do not celebrate Christmas in the winter solstice as should properly
be done. We know it, but it seems to me a matter of
no account. I would rather bear with this small mistake than grievously afflict vast numbers of my subjects
by depriving them of their birthdays. If I did so, there
would be no open complaints uttered, as that is not the
fashion in Russia; but they would say in secret that I
was an Atheist, and that I disputed the infallibility of
the Council of Nice. You may think such complaints
matter for laughter, but I do not, for I have much more
agreeable motives for amusement."

The czarina was delighted to mark my surprise. I
did not doubt for a moment that she had made a special
study of the whole subject. M. Alsuwieff told me, a
few days after, that she had very possibly read a little

pamphlet on the subject, the statements of which exactly coincided with her own. He took care to add, however, that it was very possible her highness was profoundly learned on the matter, but this was merely a courtier's phrase.

What she said was spoken modestly and energetically, and her good humour and pleasant smile remained unmoved throughout. She exercised a constant self-control over herself, and herein appeared the greatness of her character, for nothing is more difficult. Her demeanour, so different from that of the Prussian king, shewed her to be the greater sovereign of the two; her frank geniality always gave her the advantage, while the short, curt manners of the king often exposed him to being made a dupe. In an examination of the life of Frederick the Great, one cannot help paying a deserved tribute to his courage, but at the same time one feels that if it had not been for repeated turns of good fortune he must have succumbed, whereas Catherine was little indebted to the favours of the blind deity. She succeeded in enterprises which, before her time, would have been pronounced impossibilities, and it seemed her aim to make men look upon her achievements as of small account.

I read in one of our modern journals, those monuments of editorial self-conceit, that Catherine the Great died happily as she had lived. Everybody knows that she died suddenly on her close stool. By calling such a death happy, the journalist hints that it is the death he himself would wish for. Everyone to his taste, and we can only hope that the editor may obtain his wish; but who told this silly fellow that Catherine desired such a death? If he regards such a wish as natural to a person of her profound genius I would ask who told him that men of genius consider a sudden death to be a happy one? Is it because that is his opinion, and are we to conclude that he is therefore a person of genius? To come to the truth we should have to interrogate the late empress, and ask her some such question as——

"Are you well pleased to have died suddenly?"

She would probably reply:

"What a foolish question! Such might be the wish of one driven to despair, or of someone suffering from a long and grievous malady. Such was not my position, for I enjoyed the blessings of happiness and good health; no worse fate could have happened to me. My sudden death prevented me from concluding several designs which I might have brought to a successful issue if God had granted me the warning of a slight illness. But it was not so; I had to set out on the long journey at a moment's notice, without the time to make any preparations. Is my death any the happier from my not foreseeing it? Do you think me such a coward as to dread the approach of what is common to all? I tell you that I should have accounted myself happy if I had had a respite of but a day. Then I should not complain of the Divine justice."

"Does your highness accuse God of injustice, then?"

"What boots it, since I am a lost soul? Do you expect the damned to acknowledge the justice of the decree which has consigned them to eternal woe?"

"No doubt it is a difficult matter, but I should have thought that a sense of the justice of your doom would have mitigated the pains of it."

"Perhaps so, but a damned soul must be without consolation for ever."

"In spite of that there are some philosophers who call you happy in your death by virtue of its suddenness."

"Not philosophers, but fools, for in its suddenness was the pain and woe."

"Well said; but may I ask your highness if you admit the possibility of a happy eternity after an unhappy death, or of an unhappy doom after a happy death?"

"Such suppositions are inconceivable. The happiness of futurity lies in the ecstasy of the soul in feeling freed from the trammels of matter, and unhappiness is the doom of a soul which was full of remorse at the moment it left the body. But enough, for my punishment forbids my farther speech."

"Tell me, at least, what is the nature of your punishment?"

"An everlasting weariness. Farewell."

After this long and fanciful digression the reader will no doubt be obliged by my returning to this world.

Count Panin told me that in a few days the empress would leave for her country house, and I determined to have an interview with her, foreseeing that it would be for the last time.

I had been in the garden for a few minutes when heavy rain began to fall, and I was going to leave, when the empress summoned me into an apartment on the ground floor of the palace, where she was walking up and down with Gregorovitch and a maid of honour.

"I had forgotten to ask you," she said, graciously, "if you believe the new calculation of the calendar to be exempt from error?"

"No, your majesty; but the error is so minute that it will not produce any sensible effect for the space of nine or ten thousand years."

"I thought so; and in my opinion Pope Gregory should not have acknowledged any mistake at all. The Pope, however, had much less difficulty in carrying out his reform than I should have with my subjects, who are too fond of their ancient usages and customs."

"Nevertheless, I am sure your majesty would meet with obedience."

"No doubt, but imagine the grief of my clergy in not being able to celebrate the numerous saints' days, which would fall on the eleven days to be suppressed. You have only one saint for each day, but we have a dozen at least. I may remark also that all ancient states and kingdoms are attached to their ancient laws. I have heard that your Republic of Venice begins the year in March, and that seems to me, as it were, a monument and memorial of its antiquity—and indeed the year begins more naturally in March than in January —but does not this usage cause some confusion?"

"None at all, your majesty. The letters M V, which we adjoin to all dates in January and February, render all mistakes impossible."

"Venice is also noteworthy for its peculiar system of heraldry, by the amusing form under which it portrays its patron saint, and by the five Latin words with which the Evangelist is invoked, in which, as I am told, there is a grammatical blunder which has become respectable by its long standing. But is it true that you do not distinguish between the day and night hours?"

"It is, your majesty, and what is more we reckon the day from the beginning of the night."

"Such is the force of custom, which makes us admire what other nations think ridiculous. You see no inconvenience in your division of the day, which strikes me as most inconvenient."

"You would only have to look at your watch, and you would not need to listen for the cannon shot which announces the close of day."

"Yes, but for this one advantage you have over us, we have two over you. We know that at twelve o'clock it is either mid-day or midnight."

The czarina spoke to me about the fondness of the Venetians for games of chance, and asked if the Genoa Lottery had been established there.

"I have been asked," she added, "to allow the lottery to be established in my own dominions; but I should never permit it except on the condition that no stake should be below a rouble, and then the poor people would not be able to risk their money in it."

I replied to this discreet observation with a profound inclination of the head, and thus ended my last interview with the famous empress who reigned thirty-five years without committing a single mistake of any importance. The historian will always place her amongst great sovereigns, though the moralist will always consider her, and rightly, as one of the most notable of dissolute women.

A few days before I left I gave an entertainment to my friends at Catherinhoff, winding up with a fine display of fireworks, a present from my friend Melissino. My supper for thirty was exquisite, and my ball a brilliant one. In spite of the tenuity of my purse I felt obliged to give my friends this mark of my gratitude for the kindness they had lavished on me.

I left Russia with the actress Valville, and I must here tell the reader how I came to make her acquaintance.

I happened to go to the French play, and to find myself seated next to an extremely pretty lady who was unknown to me. I occasionally addressed an observation to her referring to the play or actors, and I was immensely delighted with her spirited answers. Her expression charmed me, and I took the liberty of asking her if she were a Russian.

"No, thank God!" she replied, "I am a Parisian, and an actress by occupation. My name is Valville; but I don't wonder I am unknown to you, for I have been only a month here, and have played but once."

"How is that?"

"Because I was so unfortunate as to fail to win the czarina's favour. However, as I was engaged for a year, she has kindly ordered that my salary of a hundred roubles shall be paid monthly. At the end of the year I shall get my passport and go."

"I am sure the empress thinks she is doing you a favour in paying you for nothing."

"Very likely; but she does not remember that I am forgetting how to act all this time."

"You ought to tell her that."

"I only wish she would give me an audience."

"That is unnecessary. Of course, you have a lover."

"No, I haven't."

"It's incredible to me!"

"They say the incredible often happens."

"I am very glad to hear it myself."

I took her address, and sent her the following note the next day:

"Madam,—I should like to begin an intrigue with you. You have inspired me with feelings that will make me unhappy unless you reciprocate them. I beg to take the liberty of asking myself to sup with you, but please tell me how much it will cost me. I am obliged to leave for Warsaw in the course of a month, and I shall be happy to offer you a place in my travelling carriage. I shall be able to get you a passport. The bearer of this has orders to wait, and I hope your answer will be as plainly worded as my question."

In two hours I received this reply:

"Sir,—As I have the knack of putting an end to an intrigue when it has ceased to amuse me, I have no hesitation in accepting your proposal. As to the sentiments with which you say I have inspired you, I will do my best to share them, and to make you happy. Your supper shall be ready, and later on we will settle the price of the dessert. I shall be delighted to accept the place in your carriage if you can obtain my expenses to Paris as well as my passport. And finally, I hope you will find my plain speaking on a match with yours. Good bye, till the evening."

I found my new friend in a comfortable lodging, and we accosted each other as if we had been old acquaintances.

"I shall be delighted to travel with you," said she, "but I don't think you will be able to get my passport."

"I have no doubt as to my success," I replied, "if you will present to the empress the petition I shall draft for you."

"I will surely do so," said she, giving me writing materials.

I wrote out the following petition:

"Your Majesty,—I venture to remind your highness that my enforced idleness is making me forget my art, which I have not yet learnt thoroughly. Your majesty's generosity is therefore doing me an injury, and your majesty would do me a great benefit in giving me permission to leave St. Petersburg."

"Nothing more than that?"

"Not a word."

"You say nothing about the passport, and nothing about the journey-money. I am not a rich woman."

"Do you only present this petition; and, unless I am very much mistaken, you will have, not only your journey-money, but also your year's salary."

"Oh, that would be too much!"

"Not at all. You do not know Catherine, but I do. Have this copied, and present it in person."

"I will copy it out myself, for I can write a good enough hand. Indeed, it almost seems as if I had composed it; it is exactly my style. I believe you are a better actor than I am, and from this evening I shall call myself your pupil. Come, let us have some supper, that you may give me my first lesson."

After a delicate supper, seasoned by pleasant and witty talk, Madame Valville granted me all I could desire. I went downstairs for a moment to send away my coachman and to instruct him what he was to say to Zaira, whom I had forewarned that I was going to Cronstadt, and might not return till the next day. My coachman was a Ukrainian on whose fidelity I could rely, but I knew that it would be necessary for me to be off with the old love before I was on with the new.

Madame Valville was like most young Frenchwomen of her class; she had charms which she wished to turn to account, and a passable education; her ambition was to be kept by one man, and the title of mistress was more pleasing in her ears than that of wife.

In the intervals of four amorous combats she told me enough of her life for me to divine what it had been. Clerval, the actor, had been gathering together a company of actors at Paris, and making her acquaintance by chance and finding her to be intelligent, he assured her that she was a born actress, though she had never suspected it. The idea had dazzled her, and she had signed the agreement. She started from Paris with six other actors and actresses, of whom she was the only one that had never played.

"I thought," she said, "it was like what is done at Paris, where a girl goes into the chorus or the ballet without having learnt to sing or dance. What else could I think, after an actor like Clerval had assured me I had a talent for acting and had offered me a good engagement? All he required of me was that I should learn by heart and repeat certain passages which I rehearsed in his presence. He said I made a capital soubrette, and he certainly could not have been trying to deceive me, but the fact is he was deceived himself. A fortnight after my arrival I made my first appearance, and my reception was not a flattering one."

"Perhaps you were nervous?"

"Nervous? not in the least. Clerval said that if I could have put on the appearance of nervousness the empress, who is kindness itself, would certainly have encouraged me."

I left her the next morning after I had seen her copy out the petition. She wrote a very good hand.

"I shall present it to-day," said she.

I wished her good luck, and arranged to sup with her again on the day I meant to part with Zaira.

All French girls who sacrifice to Venus are in the same style as the Valville; they are entirely without passion or love, but they are pleasant and caressing. They have only one object; and that is their own profit. They make and unmake an intrigue with a smiling face and without the slightest difficulty. It is their system, and if it be not absolutely the best it is certainly the most convenient.

When I got home I found Zaira submissive but sad, which annoyed me more than anger would have done, for I loved her. However, it was time to bring the matter to an end, and to make up my mind to endure the pain of parting.

Rinaldi, the architect, a man of seventy, but still vigorous and sensual, was in love with her, and he had hinted to me several times that he would be only too happy to take her over and to pay double the sum I had given for her. My answer had been that I could only give her to a man she liked, and that I meant to make her a present of the hundred roubles I had given for her. Rinaldi did not like this answer, as he had not very strong hopes of the girl taking a fancy to him; however, he did not despair.

He happened to call on me on the very morning on which I had determined to give her up, and as he spoke Russian perfectly he gave Zaira to understand how much he loved her. Her answer was that he must apply to me, as my will was law to her, but that she neither liked nor disliked anyone else. The old man could not obtain any more positive reply and left us with but feeble hopes, but commending himself to my good offices.

When he had gone, I asked Zaira whether she would not like me to leave her to the worthy man, who would treat her as his own daughter.

She was just going to reply when I was handed a note from Madame Valville, asking me to call on her, as she had a piece of news to give me. I ordered the carriage immediately, telling Zaira that I should not be long.

"Very good," she replied, "I will give you a plain answer when you come back."

I found Madame Valville in a high state of delight.

"Long live the petition!" she exclaimed, as soon as she saw me. "I waited for the empress to come out of her private chapel. I respectfully presented my petition, which she read as she walked along, and then told me with a kindly smile to wait a moment. I waited, and her majesty returned me the petition initialled in her own hand, and bade me take it to M. Ghelagin. This gentleman gave me an excellent reception, and told me that the sovereign hand ordered him to give me my passport, my salary for a year, and a hundred ducats for the journey. The money will be forwarded in a fortnight, as my name will have to be sent to the Gazette."

Madame Valville was very grateful, and we fixed the day of our departure. Three or four days later I sent in my name to the Gazette.

I had promised Zaira to come back, so telling my new love that I would come and live with her as soon as I had placed the young Russian in good hands, I went home, feeling rather curious to hear Zaira's determination.

After Zaira had supped with me in perfect good humour, she asked if M. Rinaldi would pay me back the money I had given for her. I said he would, and she went on,——

"It seems to me that I am worth more than I was, for I have all your presents, and I know Italian."

"You are right, dear, but I don't want it to be said that I have made a profit on you; besides, I intend to make you a present of the hundred roubles."

"As you are going to make me such a handsome present, why not send me back to my father's house? That would be still more generous. If M. Rinaldi really loves me, he can come and talk it over with my father. You have no objection to his paying me whatever sum I like to mention."

"Not at all. On the contrary, I shall be very glad to serve your family, and all the more as Rinaldi is a rich man."

"Very good; you will be always dear to me in my memory. You shall take me to my home to-morrow; and now let us go to bed."

Thus it was that I parted with this charming girl, who made me live soberly all the time I was at St. Petersburg. Zinowieff told me that if I had liked to deposit a small sum as security I could have taken her with me; but I had thought the matter over, and it seemed to me that as Zaira grew more beautiful and charming I should end by becoming a perfect slave to her. Possibly, however, I should not have looked into matters so closely if I had not been in love with Madame Valville.

Zaira spent the next morning in gathering together her belongings, now laughing and now weeping, and every time that she left her packing to give me a kiss I could not resist weeping myself. When I restored her to her father, the whole family fell on their knees around me. Alas for poor human nature! thus it is degraded by the iron heel of oppression. Zaira looked oddly in the humble cottage, where one large mattress served for the entire family.

Rinaldi took everything in good part. He told me that since the daughter would make no objection he had no fear of the father doing so. He went to the house the next day, but he did not get the girl till I had left St. Petersburg. He kept her for the remainder of his days, and behaved very handsomely to her.

After this melancholy separation Madame Valville

became my sole mistress, and we left the Russian capital in the course of a few weeks. I took an Armenian merchant into my service; he had lent me a hundred ducats, and cooked very well in the Eastern style. I had a letter from the Polish resident to Prince Augustus Sulkowski, and another from the English ambassador for Prince Adam Czartoryski.

The day after we left St. Petersburg we stopped at Koporie to dine; we had taken with us some choice viands and excellent wines. Two days later we met the famous chapel-master, Galuppi or Buranelli, who was on his way to St. Petersburg with two friends and an artiste. He did not know me, and was astonished to find a Venetian dinner awaiting him at the inn, as also to hear a greeting in his mother tongue. As soon as I had pronounced my name he embraced me with exclamations of surprise and joy.

The roads were heavy with rain, so we were a week in getting to Riga, and when we arrived I was sorry to hear that Prince Charles was not there. From Riga, we were four days before getting to Konigsberg, where Madame Valville, who was expected at Berlin, had to leave me. I left her my Armenian, to whom she gladly paid the hundred ducats I owed him. I saw her again two years later, and shall speak of the meeting in due time.

We separated like good friends, without any sadness. We spent the night at Klein Roop, near Riga, and she offered to give me her diamonds, her jewels, and all that she possessed. We were staying with the Countess Lowenwald, to whom I had a letter from the Princess Dolgorouki. This lady had in her house, in the capacity of governess, the pretty English woman whom I had known as Campioni's wife. She told me that her husband was at Warsaw, and that he was living with

Villiers. She gave me a letter for him, and I promised to make him send her some money, and I kept my word. Little Betty was as charming as ever, but her mother seemed quite jealous of her and treated her ill.

When I reached Konigsberg I sold my travelling carriage and took a place in a coach for Warsaw. We were four in all, and my companions only spoke German and Polish, so that I had a dreadfully tedious journey. At Warsaw I went to live with Villiers, where I hoped to meet Campioni.

It was not long before I saw him, and found him well in health and in comfortable quarters. He kept a dancing school, and had a good many pupils. He was delighted to have news of Fanny and his children. He sent them some money, but had no thoughts of having them at Warsaw, as Fanny wished. He assured me she was not his wife.

He told me that Tomatis, the manager of the comic opera, had made a fortune, and had in his company a Milanese dancer named Catai, who enchanted all the town by her charms rather than her talent. Games of chance were permitted, but he warned me that Warsaw was full of card-sharpers. A Veronese named Giropoldi, who lived with an officer from Lorrain called Bachelier, held a bank at faro at her house, where a dancer, who had been the mistress of the famous Afflisio at Vienna, brought customers.

Major Sadir, whom I have mentioned before, kept another gaming-house, in company with his mistress, who came from Saxony. The Baron de St. Héleine was also in Warsaw, but his principal occupation was to contract debts which he did not mean to pay. He also lived in Villier's house with his pretty and virtuous young wife, who would have nothing to say to us. Campioni told me of some other adventurers, whose names I was very glad to know that I might the better avoid them.

The day after my arrival I hired a man and a carriage, the latter being an absolute necessity at Warsaw, where in my time, at all events, it was impossible to go on foot. I reached the capital of Poland at the end of October, 1765.

My first call was on Prince Adam Czartoryski, Lieutenant of Podolia, for whom I had an introduction. I found him before a table covered with papers, surrounded by forty or fifty persons, in an immense library which he had made into his bedroom. He was married to a very pretty woman, but had not yet had a child by her because she was too thin for his taste.

He read the long letter I gave him, and said in elegant French that he had a very high opinion of the writer of the letter; but that as he was very busy just then he hoped I would come to supper with him if I had nothing better to do.

I drove off to Prince Sulkouski, who had just been appointed ambassador to the Court of Louis XV. The prince was the elder of four brothers and a man of great understanding, but a theorist in the style of the Abbé St. Pierre. He read the letter, and said he wanted to have a long talk with me; but that being obliged to go out he would be obliged if I would come and dine with him at four o'clock. I accepted the invitation.

I then went to a merchant named Schempinski, who was to pay me fifty ducats a month on Papanelopulo's order. My man told me that there was a public rehearsal of a new opera at the theatre, and I accordingly spent three hours there, knowing none and unknown to all. All the actresses were pretty, but especially the

Catai, who did not know the first elements of dancing.
She was greatly applauded, above all by Prince Repnin,
the Russian ambassador, who seemed a person of the
greatest consequence.

Prince Sulkouski kept me at table for four mortal
hours, talking on every subject except those with which
I happened to be acquainted. His strong points were
politics and commerce, and as he found my mind a mere
void on these subjects, he shone all the more, and took
quite a fancy to me, as I believe, because he found me
such a capital listener.

About nine o'clock, *having nothing better to do* (a
favourite phrase with the Polish noblemen), I went to
Prince Adam, who after pronouncing my name introduced me to the company. There were present Monseigneur Krasinski, the Prince-Bishop of Warmia, the
Chief Prothonotary Rzewuski, whom I had known at
St. Petersburg, the Palatin Oginski, General Roniker,
and two others whose barbarous names I have forgotten.
The last person to whom he introduced me was his
wife, with whom I was very pleased. A few moments
after a fine-looking gentleman came into the room, and
everybody stood up. Prince Adam pronounced my
name, and turning to me said, coolly,——

"That's the king."

This method of introducing a stranger to a sovereign
prince was assuredly not an overwhelming one, but it
was nevertheless a surprise; and I found that an excess
of simplicity may be as confusing as the other extreme.
At first I thought the prince might be making a fool of
me; but I quickly put aside the idea, and stepped forward and was about to kneel, but his majesty gave me
his hand to kiss with exquisite grace, and as he was
about to address me, Prince Adam shewed him the let-

ter of the English ambassador, who was well known to the king. The king read it, still standing, and began to ask me questions about the Czarina and the Court, appearing to take great interest in my replies.

When supper was announced the king continued to talk, and led me into the supper-room, and made me sit down at his right hand. Everybody ate heartily except the king, who appeared to have no appetite, and myself, who had no right to have any appetite, even if I had not dined well with Prince Sulkouski, for I saw the whole table hushed to listen to my replies to the king's questions.

After supper the king began to comment very graciously on my answers. His majesty spoke simply but with great elegance. As he was leaving he told me he should always be delighted to see me at his Court, and Prince Adam said that if I liked to be introduced to his father, I had only to call at eleven o'clock the next morning.

The King of Poland was of a medium height, but well made. His face was not a handsome one, but it was kindly and intelligent. He was rather short-sighted, and his features in repose bore a somewhat melancholy expression; but in speaking, the whole face seemed to light up. All he said was seasoned by a pleasant wit.

I was well enough pleased with this interview, and returned to my inn, where I found Campioni seated amongst several guests of either sex, and after staying with them for half an hour I went to bed.

At eleven o'clock the next day I was presented to the great Russian Paladin. He was in his dressing-gown, surrounded by his gentlemen in the national costume. He was standing up and conversing with his followers in a kindly but grave manner. As soon as his son Adam mentioned my name, he unbent and gave me a most kindly yet dignified welcome. His manners were not awful, nor did they inspire one with familiarity, and I thought him likely to be a good judge of character. When I told him that I had only gone to Russia to amuse myself and see good company, he immediately concluded that my aims in coming to Poland were of the same kind, and he told me that he could introduce me to a large circle. He added that he should be glad to see me to dinner and supper whenever I had no other engagements.

He went behind a screen to complete his toilette, and soon appeared in the uniform of his regiment, with a fair peruke in the style of the late King Augustus II. He made a collective bow to everyone, and went to see his wife, who was recovering from a disease which would have proved fatal if it had not been for the skill of Reimann, a pupil of the great Boerhaave. The lady came of the now extinct family of Enoff, whose immense wealth she brought to her husband. When he married her he abandoned the Maltese Order, of which he had been a knight. He won his bride by a duel with pistols on horseback. The lady had promised that her hand should be the conqueror's guerdon, and the prince was so fortunate as to kill his rival. Of this marriage there issued Prince Adam and a daughter, now a widow, and known under the name of Lubomirska, but formerly under that of Strasnikowa, that being the title of the office her husband held in the royal army.

It was this prince palatine and his brother, the High Chancellor of Lithuania, who first brought about the Polish troubles. The two brothers were discontented with their position at the Court where Count Brühl was supreme, and put themselves at the head of the plot for dethroning the king, and for placing on the throne, under Russian protection, their young nephew, who had originally gone to St. Petersburg as an attaché at the embassy, and afterwards succeeded in winning the favour of Catherine, then Grand Duchess, but soon to become empress.

This young man was Stanislas Poniatowski, son of Constance Czartoryski and the celebrated Poniatowski, the friend of Charles XII. As luck would have it, a revolution was unnecessary to place him on the throne, for the king died in 1763, and gave place to Prince Poniatowski, who was chosen king on the 6th of September, 1764, under the title of Stanislas Augustus I. He had reigned two years at the time of my visit; and I found Warsaw in a state of gaiety, for a diet was to be held and everyone wished to know how it was that Catherine had given the Poles a native king.

At dinner-time I went to the paladin's and found three tables, at each of which there were places for thirty, and this was the usual number entertained by the prince. The luxury of the Court paled before that of the paladin's house. Prince Adam said to me,——

"Chevalier, your place will always be at my father's table."

This was a great honour, and I felt it. The prince introduced me to his handsome sister, and to several palatins and starosts. I did not fail to call on all these great personages, so in the course of a fortnight I found myself a welcome guest in all the best houses.

My purse was too lean to allow of my playing or consoling myself with a theatrical beauty, so I fell back on the library of Monseigneur Zalewski, the Bishop of Kiowia, for whom I had taken a great liking. I spent almost all my mornings with him, and it was from this prelate that I learnt all the intrigues and complots by which the ancient Polish constitution, of which the bishop was a great admirer, had been overturned. Unhappily, his firmness was of no avail, and a few months after I left Warsaw the Russian tyrants arrested him and he was exiled to Siberia.

I lived calmly and peaceably, and still look back upon those days with pleasure. I spent my afternoons with the paladin playing tressette—an Italian game of which he was very fond, and which I played well enough for the paladin to like to have me as a partner.

In spite of my sobriety and economy I found myself in debt three months after my arrival, and I did not know where to turn for help. The fifty ducats per month, which were sent me from Venice, were insufficient, for the money I had to spend on my carriage, my lodging, my servant, and my dress brought me down to the lowest ebb, and I did not care to appeal to anyone. But fortune had a surprise in store for me, and hitherto she had never left me.

Madame Schmit, whom the king for good reasons of his own had accommodated with apartments in the palace, asked me one evening to sup with her, telling me that the king would be of the party. I accepted the invitation, and I was delighted to find the delightful Bishop Kraswiski, the Abbé Guigiotti, and two or three other amateurs of Italian literature. The king, whose knowledge of literature was extensive, began to tell anecdotes of classical writers, quoting manuscript authorities which reduced me to silence, and which were possibly invented by him. Everyone talked except myself, and as I had had no dinner I ate like an ogre, only replying by monosyllables when politeness obliged me to say something. The conversation turned on Horace, and everyone gave his opinion on the great materialist's philosophy, and the Abbé Guigiotti obliged me to speak by saying that unless I agreed with him I should not keep silence.

"If you take my silence for consent to your extravagant eulogium of Horace," I said, "you are mistaken; for in my opinion the *nec cum venari volet poemata panges,* of which you think so much, is to my mind a satire devoid of delicacy."

"Satire and delicacy are hard to combine."

"Not for Horace, who succeeded in pleasing the great Augustus, and rendering him immortal as the protector of learned men. Indeed other sovereigns seem to vie with him by taking his name and even by disguising it."

The king (who had taken the name of Augustus himself) looked grave and said,——

"What sovereigns have adopted a disguised form of the name Augustus?"

"The first king of Sweden, who called himself Gustavus, which is only an anagram of Augustus."

"That is a very amusing idea, and worth more than all the tales we have told. Where did you find that?"

"In a manuscript at Wolfenbuttel."

The king laughed loudly, though he himself had been citing manuscripts. But he returned to the charge and said,——

"Can you cite any passage of Horace (not in manuscript) where he shews his talent for delicacy and satire?"

"Sir, I could quote several passages, but here is one which seems to me very good: *Coram rege,* says the poet, *sua de paupertate tacentes, plus quan pocentes ferent.*"

"True indeed," said the king, with a smile.

Madame Schmit, who did not know Latin, and inherited curiosity from her mother, and eventually from Eve, asked the bishop what it meant, and he thus translated it:

"They that speak not of their necessities in the presence of a king, gain more than they that are ever asking."

The lady remarked that she saw nothing satirical in this.

After this it was my turn to be silent again; but the king began to talk about Ariosto, and expressed a desire to read it with me. I replied with an inclination of the head, and Horace's words: *Tempora quæram.*

Next morning, as I was coming out from mass, the generous and unfortunate Stanislas Augustus gave me his hand to kiss, and at the same time slid a roll of money into my hand, saying,——

"Thank no one but Horace, and don't tell anyone about it."

The roll contained two hundred ducats, and I immediately paid off my debts. Since then I went almost every morning to the king's closet, where he was always glad to see his courtiers, but there was no more said about reading Ariosto. He knew Italian, but not enough to speak it, and still less to appreciate the beauties of the great poet. When I think of this worthy prince, and of the great qualities he possessed as a man, I cannot understand how he came to commit so many errors as a king. Perhaps the least of them all was that he allowed himself to survive his country. As he could not find a friend to kill him, I think he should have killed himself. But indeed he had no need to ask a friend to do him this service; he should have imitated the great Kosciuszko, and entered into life eternal by the sword of a Russian.

The carnival was a brilliant one. All Europe seemed to have assembled at Warsaw to see the happy being whom fortune had so unexpectedly raised to a throne, but after seeing him all were agreed that, in his case at all events, the deity had been neither blind nor foolish. Perhaps, however, he liked shewing himself rather too much. I have detected him in some distress on his being informed that there was such a thing as a stranger in Warsaw who had not seen him. No one had any need of an introduction, for his Court was, as all Courts should be, open to everyone, and when he noticed a strange face he was the first to speak.

Here I must set down an event which took place towards the end of January. It was, in fact, a dream; and, as I think I have confessed before, superstition had always some hold on me.

I dreamt I was at a banquet, and one of the guests threw a bottle at my face, that the blood poured forth, that I ran my sword through my enemy's body, and jumped into a carriage, and rode away.

Prince Charles of Courland came to Warsaw, and asked me to dine with him at Prince Poninski's, the same that became so notorious, and was afterwards proscribed and shamefully dishonoured. His was a hospitable house, and he was surrounded by his agreeable family. I had never called on him, as he was not a *persona grata* to the king or his relations.

In the course of the dinner a bottle of champagne burst, and a piece of broken glass struck me just below the eye. It cut a vein, and the blood gushed over my face, over my clothes, and even over the cloth. Everybody rose, my wound was bound up, the cloth was changed, and the dinner went on merrily. I was surprised at the likeness between my dream and this incident, while I congratulated myself on the happy difference between them. However, it all came true after a few months.

Madame Binetti, whom I had last seen in London, arrived at Warsaw with her husband and Pic the dancer. She had a letter of introduction to the king's brother, who was a general in the Austrian service, and then resided at Warsaw. I heard that the day they came, when I was at supper at the palatin's. The king was present, and said he should like to keep them in Warsaw for a week and see them dance, if a thousand ducats could do it.

I went to see Madame Binetti and to give her the good news the next morning. She was very much surprised to meet me in Warsaw, and still more so at the news I gave her. She called Pic who seemed undecided, but as we were talking it over, Prince Poniatowski came in to acquaint them with his majesty's wishes, and the offer was accepted. In three days Pic arranged a ballet; the costumes, the scenery, the music, the dancers —all were ready, and Tomatis put it on handsomely to please his generous master. The couple gave such satisfaction that they were engaged for a year. The Catai was furious, as Madame Binetti threw her completely into the shade, and, worse still, drew away her lovers. Tomatis, who was under the Catai's influence, made things so unpleasant for Madame Binetti that the two dancers became deadly enemies.

In ten or twelve days Madame Binetti was settled in a well-furnished house; her plate was simple but good, her cellar full of excellent wine, her cook an artist, and her adorers numerous, amongst them being Mosz-ciuski and Branicki, the king's friends.

The pit was divided into two parties, for the Catai was resolved to make a stand against the new comer, though her talents were not to be compared to Madame Binetti's. She danced in the first ballet, and her rival in the second. Those who applauded the first greeted the second in dead silence, and *vice versâ*. I had great obligations towards Madame Binetti, but my duty also drew me towards the Catai, who numbered in her party all the Czartoryskis and their following, Prince Lubomirski, and other powerful nobles. It was plain that I could not desert to Madame Binetti without earning the contempt of the other party.

Madame Binetti reproached me bitterly, and I laid the case plainly before her. She agreed that I could not do otherwise, but begged me to stay away from the theatre in future, telling me that she had got a rod in pickle for Tomatis which would make him repent of his impertinence. She called me her oldest friend; and indeed I was very fond of her, and cared nothing for the Catai despite her prettiness.

Xavier Branicki, the royal Postoli, Knight of the White Eagle, Colonel of Uhlans, the king's friend, was the chief adorer of Madame Binetti. The lady probably confided her displeasure to him, and begged him to take vengeance on the manager, who had committed so many offences against her. Count Branicki in his turn probably promised to avenge her quarrel, and, if no opportunity of doing so arose, to create an opportunity. At least, this is the way in which affairs of this kind are usually managed, and I can find no better explanation for what happened. Nevertheless, the way in which the Pole took vengeance was very original and extraordinary.

On the 20th of February Branicki went to the opera, and, contrary to his custom, went to the Catai's dressing-room, and began to pay his court to the actress, Tomatis being present. Both he and the actress concluded that Branicki had had a quarrel with her rival, and though she did not much care to place him in the number of her adorers, she yet gave him a good reception, for she knew it would be dangerous to despise his suit openly.

When the Catai had completed her toilet, the gallant postoli offered her his arm to take her to her carriage, which was at the door. Tomatis followed, and I too was there, awaiting my carriage. Madame Catai came down, the carriage-door was opened, she stepped in, and Branicki got in after her, telling the astonished Tomatis to follow them in the other carriage. Tomatis replied that he meant to ride in his own carriage, and begged the colonel to get out. Branicki paid no attention, and told the coachman to drive on. Tomatis forbade him to stir, and the man, of course, obeyed his master. The gallant postoli was therefore obliged to get down, but he bade his hussar give Tomatis a box on the ear, and this order was so promptly and vigorously obeyed that the unfortunate man was on the ground before he had time to recollect that he had a sword. He got up eventually and drove off, but he could eat no supper, no doubt because he had a blow to digest. I was to have supped with him, but after this scene I had really not the face to go. I went home in a melancholy and reflective mood, wondering whether the whole had been concerted; but I concluded that this was impossible, as neither Branicki nor Binetti could have foreseen the impoliteness and cowardice of Tomatis.

In the next chapter the reader will see how tragically the matter ended.

CHAPTER XXII

*My Duel with Branicki—My Journey to Leopol and
Return to Warsaw—I Receive the Order to Leave—
My Departure with the Unknown One*

O N REFLECTION I concluded that Branicki had
not done an ungentlemanly thing in getting into
Tomatis's carriage; he had merely behaved with im-
petuosity, as if he were the Catai's lover. It also appeared to me that, considering the affront he had received from the jealous Italian, the box on the ear was
a very moderate form of vengeance. A blow is bad,
of course, but not so bad as death; and Branicki might
very well have run his sword through the manager's
body. Certainly, if Branicki had killed him he would
have been stigmatised as an assassin, for though Tomatis had a sword the Polish officer's servants would never
have allowed him to draw it, nevertheless I could not
help thinking that Tomatis should have tried to take
the servant's life, even at the risk of his own. He wanted
no more courage for that than in ordering the king's
favourite to come out of the carriage. He might have
foreseen that the Polish noble would be stung to the
quick, and would surely attempt to take speedy vengeance.

The next day the encounter was the subject of all
conversations. Tomatis remained indoors for a week,
calling for vengeance in vain. The king told him he
could do nothing for him, as Branicki maintained he

had only given insult for insult. I saw Tomatis, who told me in confidence that he could easily take vengeance, but that it would cost him too dear. He had spent forty thousand ducats on the two ballets, and if he had avenged himself he would have lost it nearly all, as he would be obliged to leave the kingdom. The only consolation he had was that his great friends were kinder to him than ever, and the king himself honoured him with peculiar attention. Madame Binetti was triumphant. When I saw her she condoled with me ironically on the mishap that had befallen my friend. She wearied me; but I could not guess that Branicki had only acted at her instigation, and still less that she had a grudge against me. Indeed, if I had known it, I should only have laughed at her, for I had nothing to dread from her bravo's dagger. I had never seen him nor spoken to him; he could have no opportunity for attacking me. He was never with the king in the morning and never went to the palatin's to supper, being an unpopular character with the Polish nobility. This Branicki was said to have been originally a Cossack, Branecki by name. He became the king's favorite and assumed the name of Branicki, pretending to be of the same family as the illustrious marshal of that name who was still alive; but he, far from recognizing the pretender, ordered his shield to be broken up and buried with him as the last of the race. However that may be, Branicki was the tool of the Russian party, the determined enemy of those who withstood Catherine's design of Russianising the ancient Polish constitution. The king liked him out of habit, and because he had peculiar obligations to him.

The life I lived was really exemplary. I indulged neither in love affairs nor gaming. I worked for the king, hoping to become his secretary. I paid my court to the princess-palatine, who liked my company, and I played *tressette* with the palatin himself.

On the 4th of March, St. Casimir's Eve, there was a banquet at Court to which I had the honour to be invited. Casimir was the name of the king's eldest brother, who held the office of grand chamberlain. After dinner the king asked me if I intended going to the theatre, where a Polish play was to be given for the first time. Everybody was interested in this novelty, but it was a matter of indifference to me as I did not understand the language, and I told the king as much.

"Never mind," said he, "come in my box."

This was too flattering an invitation to be refused, so I obeyed the royal command and stood behind the king's chair. After the second act a ballet was given, and the dancing of Madame Caracci, a Piedmontese, so pleased his majesty that he went to the unusual pains of clapping her.

I only knew the dancer by sight, for I had never spoken to her. She had some talents. Her principal admirer was Count Poninski, who was always reproaching me when I dined with him for visiting the other dancers to the exclusion of Madame Caracci. I thought of his reproach at the time, and determined to pay her a visit after the ballet to congratulate her on her performance and the king's applause. On my way I passed by Madame Binetti's dressing-room, and seeing the door open I stayed a moment. Count Branicki came up, and I left with a bow and passed on to Madame Caracci's dressing-room. She was astonished to see me, and began with kindly reproaches for my neglect; to which I replied with compliments, and then giving her a kiss I promised to come and see her.

Just as I embraced her who should enter but Branicki, whom I had left a moment before with Madame Binetti. He had clearly followed me in the hopes of picking a quarrel. He was accompanied by Bininski, his lieutenant-colonel. As soon as he appeared, politeness made me stand up and turn to go, but he stopped me.

"It seems to me I have come at a bad time; it looks as if you loved this lady."

"Certainly, my lord; does not your excellency consider her as worthy of love?"

"Quite so; but as it happens I love her too, and I am not the man to bear any rivals."

"As I know that, I shall love her no more."

"Then you give her up?"

"With all my heart; for everyone must yield to such a noble as you are."

"Very good; but I call a man that yields a coward."

"Isn't that rather a strong expression?"

As I uttered these words I looked proudly at him and touched the hilt of my sword. Three or four officers were present and witnessed what passed.

I had hardly gone four paces from the dressing-room when I heard myself called "Venetian coward." In spite of my rage I restrained myself, and turned back saying, coolly and firmly, that perhaps a Venetian coward might kill a brave Pole outside the theatre; and without awaiting a reply I left the building by the chief staircase.

I waited vainly outside the theatre for a quarter of an hour with my sword in my hand, for I was not afraid of losing forty thousand ducats like Tomatis. At last, half perishing with cold, I called my carriage and drove to the palatin's, where the king was to sup.

The cold and loneliness began to cool my brain, and

I congratulated myself on my self-restraint in not drawing my sword in the actress's dressing-room; and I felt
glad that Branicki had not followed me down the stairs,
for his friend Bininski had a sabre, and I should probably have been assassinated.

Although the Poles are polite enough, there is still a
good deal of the old leaven in them. They are still
Dacians and Samaritans at dinner, in war, and in friendship, as they call it, but which is often a burden hardly
to be borne. They can never understand that a man
may be sufficient company for himself, and that it is
not right to descend on him in a troop and ask him to
give them dinner.

I made up my mind that Madame Binetti had excited
Branicki to follow me, and possibly to treat me as he
had treated Tomatis. I had not received a blow certainly, but I had been called a coward. I had no choice
but to demand satisfaction, but I also determined to
be studiously moderate throughout. In this frame of
mind I got down at the palatin's, resolved to tell the
whole story to the king, leaving to his majesty the task
of compelling his favourite to give me satisfaction.

As soon as the palatin saw me, he reproached me in
a friendly manner for keeping him waiting, and we sat
down to tressette. I was his partner, and committed
several blunders. When it came to losing a second game
he said,——

"Where is your head to-night?"

"My lord, it is four leagues away."

"A respectable man ought to have his head in the
game, and not at a distance of four leagues."

With these words the prince threw down his cards and
began to walk up and down the room. I was rather
startled, but I got up and stood by the fire, waiting for

the king. But after I had waited thus for half an hour a chamberlain came from the palace, and announced that his majesty could not do himself the honour of supping with my lord that night.

This was a blow for me, but I concealed my disappointment. Supper was served, and I sat down as usual at the left hand of the palatin, who was annoyed with me, and shewed it. We were eighteen at table, and for once I had no appetite. About the middle of the supper Prince Gaspard Lubomirski came in, and chanced to sit down opposite me. As soon as he saw me he condoled with me in a loud voice for what had happened.

"I am sorry for you," said he, "but Branicki was drunk, and you really shouldn't count what he said as an insult."

"What has happened?" became at once the general question. I held my tongue, and when they asked Lubomirski he replied that as I kept silence it was his duty to do the same.

Thereupon the palatin, speaking in his friendliest manner, said to me,——

"What has taken place between you and Branicki?"

"I will tell you the whole story, my lord, in private after supper."

The conversation became indifferent, and after the meal was over the palatin took up his stand by the small door by which he was accustomed to leave the room, and there I told him the whole story. He sighed, condoled with me, and added,——

"You had good reasons for being absent-minded at cards."

"May I presume to ask your excellency's advice?"

"I never give advice in these affairs, in which you must do everything or nothing."

The palatin shook me by the hand, and I went home and slept for six hours. As soon as I awoke I sat up in bed, and my first thought was *everything or nothing.* I soon rejected the latter alternative, and I saw that I must demand a duel to the death. If Branicki refused to fight I should be compelled to kill him, even if I were to lose my head for it.

Such was my determination; to write to him proposing a duel at four leagues from Warsaw, this being the limit of the starostia, in which duelling was forbidden on pain of death. I wrote as follows, for I have kept the rough draft of the letter to this day:

"Warsaw,

"*March 5th,* 1766.　5 A.M.

"My Lord,—Yesterday evening your excellency insulted me with a light heart, without my having given you any cause or reason for doing so. This seems to indicate that you hate me, and would gladly efface me from the land of the living. I both can and will oblige you in this matter. Be kind enough, therefore, to drive me in your carriage to a place where my death will not subject your lordship to the vengeance of the law, in case you obtain the victory, and where I shall enjoy the same advantage if God give me grace to kill your lordship. I should not make this proposal unless I believe your lordship to be of a noble disposition.

"I have the honour to be, etc."

I sent this letter an hour before day-break to Branicki's lodging in the palace. My messenger had orders to give the letter into the count's own hands, to wait for him to rise, and also for an answer.

In half an hour I received the following answer:

"Sir,—I accept your proposal, and shall be glad if

you will have the kindness to inform me when I shall have the honour of seeing you.

"I remain, sir, etc."

I answered this immediately, informing him I would call on him the next day, at six o'clock in the morning.

Shortly after, I received a second letter, in which he said that I might choose the arms and place, but that our differences must be settled in the course of the day.

I sent him the measure of my sword, which was thirty-two inches long, telling him he might choose any place beyond the ban. In reply, I had the following:

"Sir,—You will greatly oblige me by coming now. I have sent my carriage.

"I have the honour to be, etc."

I replied that I had business all the day, and that as I had made up my mind not to call upon him, except for the purpose of fighting, I begged him not to be offended if I took the liberty of sending back his carriage.

An hour later Branicki called in person, leaving his suite at the door. He came into the room, requested some gentlemen who were talking with me to leave us alone, locked the door after them, and then sat down on my bed. I did not understand what all this meant so I took up my pistols.

"Don't be afraid," said he, "I am not come to assassinate you, but merely to say that I accept your proposal, on condition only that the duel shall take place to-day. If not, never."

"It is out of the question. I have letters to write, and some business to do for the king."

"That will do afterwards. In all probability you will not fall, and if you do I am sure the king will forgive you. Besides, a dead man need fear no reproaches."

"I want to make my will."

"Come, come, you needn't be afraid of dying; it will be time enough for you to make your will in fifty years."

"But why should your excellency not wait till to-morrow?"

"I don't want to be caught."

"You have nothing of the kind to fear from me."

"I daresay, but unless we make haste the king will have us both arrested."

"How can he, unless you have told him about our quarrel?"

"Ah, you don't understand! Well, I am quite willing to give you satisfaction, but it must be to-day or never."

"Very good. This duel is too dear to my heart for me to leave you any pretext for avoiding it. Call for me after dinner, for I shall want all my strength."

"Certainly. For my part I like a good supper after, better than a good dinner before."

"Everyone to his taste."

"True. By the way, why did you send me the length of your sword? I intend to fight with pistols, for I never use swords with unknown persons."

"What do you mean? I beg of you to refrain from insulting me in my own house. I do not intend to fight with pistols, and you cannot compel me to do so, for I have your letter giving me the choice of weapons."

"Strictly speaking, no doubt you are in the right; but I am sure you are too polite not to give way, when I assure you that you will lay me under a great obligation by doing so. Very often the first shot is a miss, and if that is the case with both of us, I promise to fight with swords as long as you like. Will you oblige me in the matter?"

"Yes, for I like your way of asking, though, in my

opinion, a pistol duel is a barbarous affair. I accept, but on the following conditions: You must bring two pistols, charge them in my presence, and give me the choice. If the first shot is a miss, we will fight with swords till the first blood or to the death, whichever you prefer. Call for me at three o'clock, and choose some place where we shall be secure from the law."

"Very good. You are a good fellow, allow me to embrace you. Give me your word of honour not to say a word about it to anyone, for if you did we should be arrested immediately."

"You need not be afraid of my talking; the project is too dear to me."

"Good. Farewell till three o'clock."

As soon as the brave braggart had left me, I placed the papers I was doing for the king apart, and went to Campioni, in whom I had great confidence.

"Take this packet to the king," I said, "if I happen to be killed. You may guess, perhaps, what is going to happen, but do not say a word to anyone, or you will have me for your bitterest enemy, as it would mean loss of honour to me."

"I understand. You may reckon on my discretion, and I hope the affair may be ended honourably and prosperously for you. But take a piece of friendly advice—don't spare your opponent, were it the king himself, for it might cost you your life. I know that by experience."

"I will not forget. Farewell."

We kissed each other, and I ordered an excellent dinner, for I had no mind to be sent to Pluto fasting. Campioni came in to dinner at one o'clock, and at dessert I had a visit from two young counts, with their tutor, Bertrand, a kindly Swiss. They were witnesses to my cheerfulness and the excellent appetite with which I ate. At half-past two I dismissed my company, and stood at the window to be ready to go down directly Branicki's carriage appeared. He drove up in a travelling carriage and six; two grooms, leading saddle-horses, went in front, followed by his two aide-de-camps and two hussars. Behind his carriage stood four servants. I hastened to descend, and found my enemy was accompanied by a lieutenant-general and an armed footman. The door was opened, the general gave me his place, and I ordered my servants not to follow me but to await my orders at the house.

"You might want them," said Branicki; "they had better come along."

"If I had as many as you, I would certainly agree to your proposition; but as it is I shall do still better without any at all. If need be, your excellency will see that I am tended by your own servants."

He gave me his hand, and assured me they should wait on me before himself.

I sat down, and we went off.

It would have been absurd if I had asked where we were going, so I held my tongue, for at such moments a man should take heed to his words. Branicki was silent, and I thought the best thing I could do would be to engage him in a trivial conversation.

"Does your excellency intend spending the spring at Warsaw?"

"I had thought of doing so, but you may possibly send me to pass the spring somewhere else."

"Oh, I hope not!"

"Have you seen any military service?"

"Yes; but may I ask why your excellency asks me the question, for——"

"I had no particular reason; it was only for the sake of saying something."

We had driven about half an hour when the carriage stopped at the door of a large garden. We got down and, following the postoli, reached a green arbour which, by the way, was not at all green on that 5th of March. In it was a stone table on which the footman placed two pistols, a foot and half long, with a powder flask and scales. He weighed the powder, loaded them equally, and laid them down crosswise on the table.

This done, Branicki said boldly,——

"Choose your weapon, sir."

At this the general called out,——

"Is this a duel, sir?"

"Yes."

"You cannot fight here; you are within the ban."

"No matter."

"It does matter; and I, at all events, refuse to be a witness. I am on guard at the castle, and you have taken me by surprise."

"Be quiet; I will answer for everything. I owe this gentleman satisfaction, and I mean to give it him here."

"M. Casanova," said the general, "you cannot fight here."

"Then why have I been brought here? I shall defend myself wherever I am attacked."

"Lay the whole matter before the king, and you shall have my voice in your favour."

"I am quite willing to do so, general, if his excellency will say that he regrets what passed between us last night."

Branicki looked fiercely at me, and said wrathfully that he had come to fight and not to parley.

"General," said I, "you can bear witness that I have done all in my power to avoid this duel."

The general went away with his head between his hands, and throwing off my cloak I took the first pistol that came to my hand. Branicki took the other, and said that he would guarantee upon his honour that my weapon was a good one.

"I am going to try its goodness on your head," I answered.

He turned pale at this, threw his sword to one of his servants, and bared his throat, and I was obliged, to my sorrow, to follow his example, for my sword was the only weapon I had, with the exception of the pistol. I bared my chest also, and stepped back five or six paces, and he did the same.

As soon as we had taken up our positions I took off my hat with my left hand, and begged him to fire first.

Instead of doing so immediately he lost two or three seconds in sighting, aiming, and covering his head by raising the weapon before it. I was not in a position to let him kill me at his ease, so I suddenly aimed and fired on him just as he fired on me. That I did so is evident, as all the witnesses were unanimous in saying that they only heard one report. I felt I was wounded in my left hand, and so put it into my pocket, and I ran towards my enemy who had fallen. All of a sudden, as I knelt beside him, three bare swords were flourished over my head, and three noble assassins prepared to cut me down beside their master. Fortunately, Branicki had not lost consciousness or the power of speaking, and he cried out in a voice of thunder,——

"Scoundrels! have some respect for a man of honour."

This seemed to petrify them. I put my right hand

under the pistoli's armpit, while the general helped him on the other side, and thus we took him to the inn, which happened to be near at hand.

Branicki stooped as he walked, and gazed at me curiously, apparently wondering where all the blood on my clothes came from.

When we got to the inn, Branicki laid himself down in an arm-chair. We unbottoned his clothes and lifted up his shirt, and he could see himself that he was dangerously wounded. My ball had entered his body by the seventh rib on the right hand, and had gone out by the second false rib on the left. The two wounds were ten inches apart, and the case was of an alarming nature, as the intestines must have been pierced. Branicki spoke to me in a weak voice,——

"You have killed me, so make haste away, as you are in danger of the gibbet. The duel was fought in the ban, and I am a high court officer, and a Knight of the White Eagle. So lose no time, and if you have not enough money take my purse."

I picked up the purse which had fallen out, and put it back in his pocket, thanking him, and saying it would be useless to me, for if I were guilty I was content to lose my head. "I hope," I added, "that your wound will not be mortal, and I am deeply grieved at your obliging me to fight."

With these words I kissed him on his brow and left the inn, seeing neither horses nor carriage, nor servant. They had all gone off for doctor, surgeon, priest, and the friends and relatives of the wounded man.

I was alone and without any weapon, in the midst of a snow-covered country, my hand was wounded, and I had not the slightest idea which was the way to Warsaw.

I took the road which seemed most likely, and after I I had gone some distance I met a peasant with an empty sleigh.

"Warszawa?" I cried, shewing him a ducat.

He understood me, and lifted a coarse mat, with which he covered me when I got into the sleigh, and then set off at a gallop.

All at once Biniski, Branicki's bosom-friend, came galloping furiously along the road with his bare sword in his hand. He was evidently running after me. Happily he did not glance at the wretched sleigh in which I was, or else he would undoubtedly have murdered me. I got at last to Warsaw, and went to the house of Prince Adam Czartoryski to beg him to shelter me, but there was nobody there. Without delay I determined to seek refuge in the Convent of the Recollets, which was handy.

I rang at the door of the monastery, and the porter seeing me covered with blood hastened to shut the door, guessing the object of my visit. But I did not give him the time to do so, but honouring him with a hearty kick forced my way in. His cries attracted a troop of frightened monks. I demanded sanctuary, and threatened them with vengeance if they refused to grant it. One of their number spoke to me, and I was taken to a little den which looked more like a dungeon than anything else. I offered no resistance, feeling sure that they would change their tune before very long. I asked them to send for my servants, and when they came I sent for a doctor and Campioni. Before the surgeon could come the Palatin of Polduchia was announced. I had never had the honour of speaking to him, but after hearing the history of my duel he was so kind as to give me all the particulars of a duel he had fought in his youthful days. Soon after came the Palatin of Kalisch, Prince Jablenowski, Prince

Sanguska, and the Palatin of Wilna, who all joined in a chorus of abuse of the monks who had lodged me so scurvily. The poor religious excused themselves by saying that I had ill-treated their porter, which made my noble friends laugh; but I did not laugh, for my wound was very painful. However I was immediately moved into two of their best guest-rooms.

The ball had pierced my hand by the metacarpus under the index finger, and had broken the first phalanges. Its force had been arrested by a metal button on my waistcoat, and it had only inflicted a slight wound on my stomach close to the navel. However, there it was and it had to be extracted, for it pained me extremely. An empiric named Gendron, the first surgeon my servants had found, made an opening on the opposite side of my hand which doubled the wound. While he was performing this painful operation I told the story of the duel to the company, concealing the anguish I was enduring. What a power vanity exercises on the moral and physical forces! If I had been alone I should probably have fainted.

As soon as the empiric Gendron was gone, the palatin's surgeon came in and took charge of the case, calling Gendron a low fellow. At the same time Prince Lubomirski, the husband of the palatin's daughter, arrived, and gave us all a surprise by recounting the strange occurrences which had happened after the duel. Bininski came to where Branicki was lying, and seeing his wound rode off furiously on horseback, swearing to strike me dead wherever he found me. He fancied I would be with Tomatis, and went to his house. He found Tomatis with his mistress, Prince Lubomirski, and Count Moszczinski, but no Casanova was visible. He asked where I was, and on Tomatis replying that he did not know he discharged a pistol at his head. At this dastardly action Count Moszczincki seized him and tried to throw him out of the window, but the madman got loose with three cuts of his sabre, one of which slashed the count on the face and knocked out three of his teeth.

"After this exploit," Prince Lubomirski continued, "he seized me by the throat and held a pistol to my head, threatening to blow out my brains if I did not take him in safety to the court where his horse was, so that he might get away from the house without any attack being made on him by Tomatis's servants; and I did so immediately. Moszczinski is in the doctor's hands, and will be laid up for some time.

"As soon as it was reported that Branicki was killed, his Uhlans began to ride about the town swearing to avenge their colonel, and to slaughter you. It is very fortunate that you took refuge here.

"The chief marshal has had the monastery surrounded by two hundred dragoons, ostensibly to prevent your escape, but in reality to defend you from Branicki's soldiers.

"The doctors say that the postoli is in great danger if the ball has wounded the intestines, but if not they answer for his recovery. His fate will be known to-morrow. He now lies at the lord chamberlain's, not daring to have himself carried to his apartments at the palace. The king has been to see him, and the general who was present told his majesty that the only thing that saved your life was your threat to aim at Branicki's head. This frightened him, and to keep your ball from his head he stood in such an awkward position that he missed your vital parts. Otherwise he would undoubtedly have shot you through the heart, for he can split a bullet into two halves by firing against the blade of a knife. It was also a lucky thing for you that you escaped Bininski, who never thought of looking for you in the wretched sleigh."

"My lord, the most fortunate thing for me is that I did not kill my man outright. Otherwise I should have been cut to pieces just as I went to his help by three of his servants, who stood over me with drawn swords. However, the postoli ordered them to leave me alone.

"I am sorry for what has happened to your highness and Count Moszczinski; and if Tomatis was not killed by the madman it is only because the pistol was only charged with powder."

"That's what I think, for no one heard the bullet; but it was a mere chance."

"Quite so."

Just then an officer of the palatin's came to me with a note from his master, which ran as follows:

"Read what the king says to me, and sleep well."

The king's note was thus conceived:

"Branicki, my dear uncle, is dangerous wounded. My surgeons are doing all they can for him, but I have not forgotten Casanova. You may assure him that he is pardoned, even if Branicki should die."

I kissed the letter gratefully, and shewed it to my visitors, who lauded this generous man truly worthy of being a king.

After this pleasant news I felt in need of rest, and my lords left me. As soon as they were gone, Campioni, who had come in before and had stood in the background, came up to me and gave me back the packet of papers, and with tears of joy congratulated me on the happy issue of the duel.

Next day I had shoals of visitors, and many of the chiefs of the party opposed to Branicki sent me purses full of gold. The persons who brought the money on behalf of such a lord or lady, said that being a foreigner I might be in need of money, and that was their excuse for the liberty they had taken. I thanked and refused them all, and sent back at least four thousand ducats, and was very proud of having done so. Campioni thought it was absurd, and he was right, for I repented afterwards of what I had done. The only present I accepted was a dinner for four persons, which Prince Adam Czartoryski sent me in every day, though the doctor would not let me enjoy it, he being a great believer in diet.

The wound in my stomach was progressing favourably, but on the fourth day the surgeons said my hand was becoming gangrened, and they agreed that the only remedy was amputation. I saw this announced in the *Court Gazette* the next morning, but as I had other views on the matter I haughed heartily at the paragraph. The sheet was printed at night, after the king had placed his initials to the copy. In the morning several persons came to condole with me, but I received their sympathy with great irreverence. I merely laughed at Count Clary, who said I would surely submit to the operation; and just as he uttered the words the three surgeons came in together.

"Well, gentlemen," said I, "you have mustered in great strength; why is this?"

My ordinary surgeon replied that he wished to have the opinion of the other two before proceeding to amputation, and they would require to look at the wound.

The dressing was lifted and gangrene was declared to be undoubtedly present, and execution was ordered that evening. The butchers gave me the news with radiant faces, and assured me I need not be afraid as the operation would certainly prove efficacious.

"Gentlemen," I replied, "you seem to have a great many solid scientific reasons for cutting off my hand; but one thing you have not got, and that is my consent. My hand is my own, and I am going to keep it."

"Sir, it is certainly gangrened; by to-morrow the arm will begin to mortify, and then you will have to lose your arm."

"Very good; if that prove so you shall cut off my arm, but I happen to know something of gangrene, and there is none about me."

"You cannot know as much about it as we do."

"Possibly; but as far as I can make out, you know nothing at all."

"That's rather a strong expression."

"I don't care whether it be strong or weak; you can go now."

In a couple of hours everyone whom the surgeons had told of my obstinacy came pestering me. Even the prince-palatin wrote to me that the king was extremely surprised at my lack of courage. This stung me to the quick, and I wrote the king a long letter, half in earnest and half in jest, in which I laughed at the ignorance of the surgeons, and at the simplicity of those who took whatever they said for gospel truth. I added that as an arm without a hand would be quite as useless as no arm at all, I meant to wait till it was necessary to cut off the arm.

My letter was read at Court, and people wondered how a man with gangrene could write a long letter of four pages. Lubomirski told me kindly that I was mistaken in laughing at my friends, for the three best surgeons in Warsaw could not be mistaken in such a simple case.

"My lord, they are not deceived themselves, but they want to deceive me."

"Why should they?"

"To make themselves agreeable to Branicki, who is in a dangerous state, and might possibly get better if he heard that my hand had been taken off."

"Really that seems an incredible idea to me!"

"What will your highness say on the day when I am proved to be right?"

"I shall say you are deserving of the highest praise, but the day must first come."

"We shall see this evening, and I give you my word that if any gangrene has attacked the arm, I will have it cut off to-morrow morning."

Four surgeons came to see me. My arm was pronounced to be highly ædematous, and of a livid colour up to the elbow; but when the lint was taken off the wound I could see for myself that it was progressing admirably. However, I concealed my delight. Prince Augustus Sulkowski and the Abbé Gouvel were present; the latter being attached to the palatin's court. The judgment of the surgeons was that the arm was gangrened, and must be amputated by the next morning at latest.

I was tired of arguing with these rascals, so I told them to bring their instruments, and that I would submit to the operation. At this they went way in high glee, to tell the news at the Court, to Branicki, to the palatin, and so forth. I merely gave my servants orders to send them away when they came.

I can dwell no more on this matter, though it is interesting enough to me. However, the reader will no doubt be obliged to me by my simply saying that a French surgeon in Prince Sulkowski's household took charge of the case in defiance of professional etiquette, and cured me perfectly, so I have my hand and my arm to this day.

On Easter Day I went to mass with my arm in a sling. My cure had only lasted three weeks, but I was not able to put the hand to any active employment for eighteen months afterwards. Everyone was obliged to congratulate me on having held out against the amputation, and the general consent declared the surgeons grossly ignorant, while I was satisfied with thinking them very great knaves.

I must here set down an incident which happened three days after the duel.

I was told that a Jesuit father from the bishop of the diocese wanted to speak to me in private, and I had him shewn in, and asked him what he wanted.

"I have come from my lord-bishop," said he, "to absolve you from the ecclesiastical censure, which you have incurred by duelling."

"I am always delighted to receive absolution, father, but only after I have confessed my guilt. In the present case I have nothing to confess; I was attacked, and I defended myself. Pray thank my lord for his kindness. If you like to absolve me without confession, I shall be much obliged."

"If you do not confess, I cannot give you absolution, but you can do this: ask me to absolve you, supposing you have fought a duel."

"Certainly; I shall be glad if you will absolve me, supposing I have fought a duel."

The delightful Jesuit gave me absolution in similar terms. He was like his brethren—never at a loss when a loophole of any kind is required.

Three days before I left the monastery, that is on

Holy Thursday, the marshal withdrew my guard. After I had been to mass on Easter Day, I went to Court, and as I kissed the king's hand, he asked me (as had been arranged) why I wore my arm in a sling. I said I had been suffering from a rheum, and he replied, with a meaning smile,——

"Take care not to catch another."

After my visit to the king, I called on Branicki, who had made daily enquiries afer my health, and had sent me back my sword. He was condemned to stay in bed for six weeks longer at least, for the wad of my pistol had got into the wound, and in extracting it the opening had to be enlarged, which retarded his recovery. The king had just appointed him chief huntsman, not so exalted an office as chamberlain, but a more lucrative one. It was said he had got the place because he was such a good shot; but if that were the reason I had a better claim to it, for I had proved the better shot—for one day at all events.

I entered an enormous ante-room in which stood officers, footmen, pages, and lacqueys, all gazing at me with the greatest astonishment. I asked if my lord was to be seen, and begged the door-keeper to send in my name. He did not answer, but sighed, and went into his master's room. Directly after, he came out and begged me, with a profound bow, to step in.

Branicki, who was dressed in a magnificent gown and supported by pillows and cushions, greeted me by taking off his nightcap. He was as pale as death.

"I have come here, my lord," I began, "to offer you my service, and to assure you how I regret that I did not pass over a few trifling words of yours."

"You have no reason to reproach yourself, M. Casanova."

"Your excellency is very kind. I am also come to say that by fighting with me you have done me an honour which completely swallows up all offence, and I trust that you will give me your protection for the future."

"I confess I insulted you, but you will allow that I have paid for it. As to my friends, I openly say that they are my enemies unless they treat you with respect. Bininski has been cashiered, and his nobility taken from him; he is well served. As to my protection you have no need of it, the king esteems you highly, like myself, and all men of honour. Sit down; we will be friends. A cup of chocolate for this gentleman. You seem to have got over your wound completely."

"Quite so, my lord, except as to the use of my fingers, and that will take some time."

"You were quite right to withstand those rascally surgeons, and you had good reason for your opinion that the fools thought to please me by rendering you one-handed. They judged my heart by their own. I congratulate you on the preservation of your hand, but I have not been able to make out how my ball could have wounded you in the hand after striking your stomach."

Just then the chocolate was brought, and the chamberlain came in and looked at me with a smile. In five minutes the room was full of lords and ladies who had heard I was with Branicki, and wanted to know how we were getting on. I could see that they did not expect to find us on such good terms, and were agreeably surprised. Branicki asked the question which had been interrupted by the chocolate and the visitors over again.

"Your excellency will allow me to assume the position I was in as I received your fire."

"Pray do so."

I rose and placed myself in the position, and he said he understood how it was.

A lady said,——

"You should have put your hand behind your body."

"Excuse me, madam, but I thought it better to put my body behind my hand."

This sally made Branicki laugh, but his sister said to me,——

"You wanted to kill my brother, for you aimed at his head."

"God forbid, madam! my interest lay in keeping him alive to defend me from his friends."

"But you said you were going to fire at his head."

"That's a mere figure of speech, just as one says, 'I'll blow your brains out.' The skilled duellist, however, always aims at the middle of the body; the head does not offer a large enough surface."

"Yes," said Branicki, "your tactics were superior to mine, and I am obliged to you for the lesson you gave me."

"Your excellency gave me a lesson in heroism of far greater value."

"You must have had a great deal of practice with the pistol," continued his sister.

"Not at all, madam, I regard the weapon with detestation. This unlucky shot was my first; but I have always known a straight line, and my hand has always been steady."

"That's all one wants," said Branicki. "I have those advantages myself, and I am only too well pleased that I did not aim so well as usual."

"Your ball broke my first phalanges. Here it is you see, flattened by my bone. Allow me to return it to you."

"I am sorry to say I can't return yours, which I suppose remains on the field of battle."

"You seem to be getting better, thank God!"

"The wound is healing painfully. If I had imitated you I should no longer be in the land of the living; I am told you made an excellent dinner?"

"Yes, my lord, I was afraid I might never have another chance of dining again."

"If I had dined, your ball would have pierced my intestines; but being empty it yielded to the bullet, and let it pass by harmlessly."

I heard afterwards that on the day of the duel Branicki had gone to confession and mass, and had communicated. The priest could not refuse him absolution, if he said that honour obliged him to fight; for this was in accordance with the ancient laws of chivalry. As for me I only addressed these words to God:

"Lord, if my enemy kill me, I shall be damned; deign, therefore, to preserve me from death. Amen."

After a long and pleasant conversation I took leave of the hero to visit the high constable, Count Bielinski, brother of Countess Salmor. He was a very old man, but the sovereign administrator of justice in Poland. I had never spoken to him, but he had defended me from Branicki's Uhlans, and had made out my pardon, so I felt bound to go and thank him.

I sent in my name, and the worthy old man greeted me with——

"What can I do for you?"

"I have come to kiss the hand of the kindly man that signed my pardon, and to promise your excellency to be more discreet in future."

"I advise you to be more discreet indeed. As for your pardon, thank the king; for if he had not requested me especially to grant it you, I should have had you beheaded."

"In spite of the extenuating circumstances, my lord?"

"What circumstances? Did you or did you not fight a duel."

"That is not a proper way of putting it; I was obliged to defend myself. You might have charged me with fighting a duel if Branicki had taken me outside the ban, as I requested, but as it was he took me where he willed and made me fight. Under these circumstances I am sure your excellency would have spared my head."

"I really can't say. The king requested that you should be pardoned, and that shews he believes you to be deserving of pardon; I congratulate you on his good will. I shall be pleased if you will dine with me to-morrow."

"My lord, I am delighted to accept your invitation."

The illustrious old constable was a man of great intelligence. He had been a bosom-friend of the celebrated Poniatowski, the king's father. We had a good deal of conversation together at dinner the next day.

"What a comfort it would have been to your excellency's friend," said I, "if he could have lived to see his son crowned King of Poland."

"He would never have consented."

The vehemence with which he pronounced these words gave me a deep insight into his feelings. He was of the Saxon party. The same day, that is on Easter Day, I dined at the palatin's.

"Political reasons," said he, "prevented me from visiting you at the monastery; but you must not think I had forgotten you, for you were constantly in my thoughts. I am going to lodge you here, for my wife is very fond of your society; but the rooms will not be ready for another six weeks."

"I shall take the opportunity, my lord, of paying a visit to the Palatin of Kiowia, who has honoured me with an invitation to come and see him."

"Who gave you the invitation?"

"Count Brühl, who is at Dresden; his wife is daughter of the palatin."

"This journey is an excellent idea, for this duel of yours has made you innumerable enemies, and I only hope you will have to fight no more duels. I give you fair warning; be on your guard, and never go on foot, especially at night."

I spent a fortnight in going out to dinner and supper every day. I had become the fashion, and wherever I went I had to tell the duel story over again. I was rather tired of it myself, but the wish to please and my own self-love were too strong to be resisted. The king was nearly always present, but feigned not to hear me. However, he once asked me if I had been insulted by a patrician in Venice, whether I should have called him out immediately.

"No, sire, for his patrician pride would have prevented his complying, and I should have had my pains for my trouble."

"Then what would you have done?"

"Sire, I should have contained myself, though if a noble Venetian were to insult me in a foreign country he would have to give me satisfaction."

I called on Prince Moszczinski, and Madame Binetti happened to be there; the moment she saw me she made her escape.

"What has she against me?" I asked the count.

"She is afraid of you, because she was the cause of the duel, and now Branicki who was her lover will have nothing more to say to her. She hoped he would serve you as he served Tomatis, and instead of that you almost killed her bravo. She lays the fault on him for having accepted your challenge, but he has resolved to have done with her."

This Count Moszczinski was both good-hearted and quick-witted, and so generous that he ruined himself by making presents. His wounds were beginning to heal, but though I was the indirect cause of his mishap, far from bearing malice against me he had become my friend.

The person whom I should have expected to be most grateful to me for the duel was Tomatis, but on the contrary he hated the sight of me and hardly concealed his feelings. I was the living reproach of his cowardice; my wounded hand seemed to shew him that he had loved his money more than his honour. I am sure he would have preferred Branicki to have killed me, for then he would have become an object of general execration, and Tomatis would have been received with less contempt in the great houses he still frequented.

I resolved to pay a visit to the discontented party who had only recognized the new king on compulsion, and some of whom had not recognized him at all; so I set out with my true friend Campioni and one servant.

Prince Charles of Courland had started for Venice, where I had given him letters for my illustrious friends who would make his visit a pleasant one. The English ambassador who had given me an introduction to Prince Adam had just arrived at Warsaw. I dined with him at the prince's house, and the king signified his wish to be of the party. I heard a good deal of conversation about Madame de Geoffrin, an old sweetheart of the king's whom he had just summoned to Warsaw. The Polish monarch, of whom I cannot speak in too favourable terms, was yet weak enough to listen to the slanderous reports against me, and refused to make my fortune. I had the pleasure of convincing him that he was mistaken, but I will speak of this later on.

I arrived at Leopol the sixth day after I had left Warsaw, having stopped a couple of days at Prince Zamoiski's; he had forty thousand ducats a-year, but also —the falling sickness.

"I would give all my goods," said he, "to be cured."

I pitied his young wife. She was very fond of him, and yet had to deny him, for his disease always came on him in moments of amorous excitement. She had the bitter task of constantly refusing him, and even of running away if he pressed her hard. This great nobleman, who died soon after, lodged me in a splendid room utterly devoid of furniture. This is the Polish custom; one is supposed to bring one's furniture with one.

At Leopol I put up at an hotel, but I soon had to move from thence to take up my abode with the famous Kaminska, the deadly foe of Branicki, the king, and all that party. She was very rich, but she has since been ruined by conspiracies. She entertained me sumptuously for a week, but the visit was agreeable to neither side, as she could only speak Polish and German. From Leopol I proceeded to a small town, the name of which I forget (the Polish names are very crabbed) to take an introduction from Prince Lubomirski to Joseph Rzewuski, a little old man who wore a long beard as a sign of mourning for the innovations that were being introduced into his country. He was rich, learned, superstitiously religious, and polite exceedingly. I stayed with him for three days. He was the commander of a stronghold containing a garrison of five hundred men.

On the first day, as I was in his room with some other officers, about eleven o'clock in the morning, another officer came in, whispered to Rzewuski, and then came up to me and whispered in my ear, *"Venice and St. Mark."*

"St. Mark," I answered aloud, "is the patron saint and protector of Venice;" and everybody began to laugh.

It dawned upon me that *"Venice and St. Mark"* was the watchword, and I began to apologize profusely, and the word was changed.

The old commander spoke to me with great politeness. He never went to Court, but he had resolved on going to the Diet to oppose the Russian party with all his might. The poor man, a Pole of the true old leaven, was one of the four whom Repnin arrested and sent to Siberia.

After taking leave of this brave patriot, I went to Christianpol, where lived the famous palatin Potocki, who had been one of the lovers of the empress Anna Ivanovna. He had founded the town in which he lived and called it after his own name. This nobleman, still a fine man, kept a splendid court. He honoured Count Brühl by keeping me at his house for a fortnight, and sending me out every day with his doctor, the famous Styrneus, the sworn foe of Van Swieten, a still more famous physician. Although Styrneus was undoubtedly a learned man, I thought him somewhat extravagant and empirical. His system was that of Asclepiades, considered as exploded since the time of the great Boerhaave; nevertheless, he effected wonderful cures.

In the evenings I was always with the palatin and his court. Play was not heavy, and I always won, which was fortunate and indeed necessary for me. After an extremely agreeable visit to the palatin I returned to Leopol, where I amused myself for a week with a pretty girl who afterwards so captivated Count Potocki, starost of Sniatin, that he married her. This is purity of blood with a vengeance in your noble families!

Leaving Leopol I went to Palavia, a splendid palace on the Vistula, eighteen leagues distant from Warsaw. It belonged to the prince palatin, who had built it himself.

Howsoever magnificent an abode may be, a lonely man will weary of it unless he has the solace of books or of some great idea. I had neither, and boredom soon made itself felt.

A pretty peasant girl came into my room, and finding her to my taste I tried to make her understand me without the use of speech, but she resisted and shouted so loudly that the door-keeper came up, and asked me, coolly,——

"If you like the girl, why don't you go the proper way to work?"

"What way is that?"

"Speak to her father, who is at hand, and arrange the matter amicably."

"I don't know Polish. Will you carry the thing through?"

"Certainly. I suppose you will give fifty florins?"

"You are laughing at me. I will give a hundred willingly, provided she is a maid and is as submissive as a lamb."

No doubt the arrangement was made without difficulty, for our hymen took place the same evening, but no sooner was the operation completed than the poor lamb fled away in hot haste, which made me suspect that her father had used rather forcible persuasion with her. I would not have allowed this had I been aware of it.

The next morning several girls were offered to me, but the faces of all of them were covered.

"Where is the girl?" said I. "I want to see her face."

"Never mind about the face, if the rest is all right."

"The face is the essential part for me," I replied, "and the rest I look upon as an accessory."

He did not understand this. However, they were uncovered, but none of their faces excited my desires.

As a rule, the Polish women are ugly; a beauty is a miracle, and a pretty woman a rare exception. At the end of a week of feasting and weariness, I returned to Warsaw.

In this manner I saw Podolia and Volkynia, which were rebaptized a few years later by the names of Galicia and Lodomeria, for they are now part of the Austrian Empire. It is said, however, that they are more prosperous than they ever were before.

At Warsaw I found Madame Geoffrin the object of universal admiration; and everybody was remarking with what simplicity she was dressed. As for myself, I was received not coldly, but positively rudely. People said to my face,——

"We did not expect to see you here again. Why did you come back?"

"To pay my debts."

This behaviour astonished and disgusted me. The prince-palatin even seemed quite changed towards me. I was still invited to dinner, but no one spoke to me. However, Prince Adam's sister asked me very kindly to come and sup with her, and I accepted the invitation with delight. I found myself seated opposite the king, who did not speak one word to me the whole time. He had never behaved to me thus before.

The next day I dined with the Countess Oginski, and in the course of dinner the countess asked where the king had supper the night before; nobody seemed to know, and I did not answer. Just as we were rising, General Roniker came in, and the question was repeated.

"At Princess Strasnikowa's," said the general, "and M. Casanova was there."

"Then why did you not answer my question?" said the countess to me.

"Because I am very sorry to have been there. His majesty neither spoke to me nor looked at me. I see I am in disgrace, but for the life of me I know not why."

On leaving the house I went to call on Prince Augustus Sulkowski, who welcomed me as of old, but told me that I had made a mistake in returning to Warsaw as public opinion was against me.

"What have I done?"

"Nothing; but the Poles are always inconstant and changeable. *Sarmatarum virtus veluti extra ipsos.* This inconstancy will cost us dear sooner or later. Your fortune was made, but you missed the turn of the tide, and I advise you to go."

"I will certainly do so, but it seems to me rather hard."

When I got home my servant gave me a letter which some unknown person had left at my door. I opened it and found it to be anonymous, but I could see it came from a well-wisher. The writer said that the slanderers had got the ears of the king, and that I was no longer a *persona grata* at Court, as he had been assured that the Parisians had burnt me in effigy for my absconding

with the lottery money, and that I had been a strolling
player in Italy and little better than a vagabond.

Such calumnies are easy to utter but hard to refute
in a foreign country. At all Courts hatred, born of
envy, is ever at work. I might have despised the slan-
ders and left the country, but I had contracted debts and
had not sufficient money to pay them and my expenses
to Portugal, where I thought I might do something.

I no longer saw any company, with the exception of
Campioni, who seemed more distressed than myself. I
wrote to Venice and everywhere else, where there was a
chance of my getting funds; but one day the general,
who had been present at the duel, called on me, and told
me (though he seemed ashamed of his task) that the
king requested me to leave the ban in the course of a
week.

Such a piece of insolence made my blood boil, and I
informed the general that he might tell the king that I
did not feel inclined to obey such an unjust order, and
that if I left I would let all the world know that I had
been compelled to do so by brute force.

"I cannot take such a message as that," said the general, kindly. "I shall simply tell the king that I have
executed his orders, and no more; but of course you
must follow your own judgment."

In the excess of my indignation I wrote to the king
that I could not obey his orders and keep my honour.
I said in my letter,——

"My creditors, sire, will forgive me for leaving Poland
without paying my debts, when they learn that I have
only done so because your majesty gave me no choice."

I was thinking how I could ensure this letter reach-
ing the king, when who should arrive but Count Moszczinski. I told him what had happened, and asked if

he could suggest any means of delivering the letter.

"Give it to me," said he; "I will place it in the king's hands."

As soon as he had gone I went out to take the air, and called on Prince Sulkowski, who was not at all astonished at my news. As if to sweeten the bitter pill I had to swallow, he told me how the Empress of Austria had ordered him to leave Vienna in twenty-four hours, merely because he had complimented the Archduchess Christina on behalf of Prince Louis of Wurtemberg.

The next day Count Moszczinski brought me a present of a thousand ducats from the king, who said that my leaving Warsaw would probably be the means of preserving my life, as in that city I was exposed to danger which I could not expect to escape eventually.

This referred to five or six challenges I had received, and to which I had not even taken the trouble to reply. My enemies might possibly assassinate me, and the king did not care to be constantly anxious on my account. Count Moszczinski added that the order to leave carried no dishonour with it, considering by whom it had been delivered, and the delay it gave me to make my preparations.

The consequence of all this was that I not only gave my word to go, but that I begged the count to thank his majesty for his kindness, and the interest he had been pleased to take in me.

When I gave in, the generous Moszczinski embraced me, begged me to write to him, and accept a present of a travelling carriage as a token of his friendship. He informed me that Madame Binetti's husband had gone off with his wife's maid, taking with him her diamonds, jewels, linen, and even her silver plate, leaving her to the tender mercies of the dancer, Pic. Her admirers had clubbed together to make up to her for what her husband had stolen. I also heard that the king's sister had arrived at Warsaw from Bialistock, and it was hoped that her husband would follow her. This husband was the real Count Branicki, and the Branicki, or rather Branecki, or Bragnecki, who had fought with me, was no relation to him whatever.

The following day I paid my debts, which amounted to about two hundred ducats, and I made preparations for starting for Breslau, the day after, with Count Clary, each of us having his own carriage. Clary was one of those men to whom lying has become a sort of second nature; whenever such an one opens his mouth, you may safely say to him, "You have lied, or you are going to lie." If they could feel their own degradation, they would be much to be pitied, for by their own fault at last no one will believe them even when by chance they speak the truth. This Count Clary, who was not one of the Clarys of Teplitz, could neither go to his own country nor to Vienna, because he had deserted the army on the eve of a battle. He was lame, but he walked so adroitly that his defect did not appear. If this had been the only truth he concealed, it would have been well, for it was a piece of deception that hurt no one. He died miserably in Venice.

We reached Breslau in perfect safety, and without experiencing any adventures. Campioni, who had accompanied me as far as Wurtemburg, returned, but rejoined me at Vienna in the course of seven months. Count Clary had left Breslau, and I thought I would make the acquaintance of the Abbé Bastiani, a celebrated Venetian, whose fortune had been made by the King of Prussia. He was canon of the cathedral, and received me cordially; in fact, each mutually desired the other's acquaintance. He was a fine well-made man, fair-complexioned, and at least six feet high. He was also witty, learned, eloquent, and gifted with a persuasive voice; his cook was an artist, his library full of choice volumes, and his cellar a very good one. He was well lodged on the ground floor, and on the first floor he accommodated a lady, of whose children he was very fond, possibly because he was their father. Although a great admirer of the fair sex, his tastes were by no means exclusive, and he did not despise love of the Greek or philosophic kind. I could see that he entertained a passion for a young priest whom I met at his table. This young abbé was Count di Cavalcano and Bastiani seemed to adore him, if fiery glances signified anything; but the innocent young man did not seem to understand, and I suppose Bastiani did not like to lower his dignity by declaring his love. The canon shewed me all the letters he had received from the King of Prussia before he had been made canon. He was the son of a tailor at Venice, and became a friar, but having committed some peccadillo which got him into trouble, he was fortunate enough to be able to make his escape. He fled to The Hague, and there met Tron, the Venetian ambassador, who lent him a hundred ducats with which he made his way to Berlin and favour with the king. Such are the ways by which men arrive at fortune! *Sequere deum!*

On the event of my departure from Breslau I went to pay a call on a baroness for whom I had a letter of introduction from her son, who was an officer of the Polish Court. I sent up my name and was asked to wait a few moments, as the baroness was dressing. I sat down beside a pretty girl, who was neatly dressed in a mantle with a hood. I asked her if she were waiting for the baroness like myself.

"Yes, sir," she replied, "I have come to offer myself as governess for her three daughters."

"What! Governess at your age?"

"Alas! sir, age has nothing to do with necessity. I have neither father nor mother. My brother is a poor lieutenant who cannot help me; what can I do? I can only get a livelihood by turning my good education to account."

"What will your salary be?"

"Fifty wretched crowns, enough to buy my dresses."

"It's very little."

"It is as much as people give."

"Where are you living now?"

"With a poor aunt, where I can scarce earn enough bread to keep me alive by sewing from morning till night."

"If you liked to become my governess instead of becoming a children's governess, I would give you fifty crowns, not per year, but per month."

"Your governess? Governess to your family, you mean, I suppose?"

"I have no family; I am a bachelor, and I spend my time in travelling. I leave at five o'clock to-morrow morning for Dresden, and if you like to come with me there is a place for you in my carriage. I am staying at such an inn. Come there with your trunk, and we will start together."

"You are joking; besides, I don't know you."

"I am not jesting; and we should get to know each other perfectly well in twenty-four hours; that is ample time."

My serious air convinced the girl that I was not laughing at her; but she was still very much astonished, while I was very much astonished to find I had gone so far when I had only intended to joke. In trying to win over the girl I had won over myself. It seemed to me a rare adventure, and I was delighted to see that she was giving it her serious attention by the side-glances she kept casting in my direction to see if I was laughing at her. I began to think that fate had brought us together that I might become the architect of her fortune. I had no doubt whatever as to her goodness or her feelings for me, for she completely infatuated my judgment. To put the finishing stroke on the affair I drew out two ducats and gave them her as an earnest of her first month's wages. She took them timidly, but seemed convinced that I was not imposing on her.

By this time the baroness was ready, and she welcomed me very kindly; but I said I could not accept her invitation to dine with her the following day, as I was leaving at day-break. I replied to all the questions that a fond mother makes concerning her son, and then took leave of the worthy lady. As I went out I noticed that the would-be governess had disappeared. The rest of the day I spent with the canon, making good cheer, playing ombre, drinking hard, and talking about girls or literature. The next day my carriage came to the door at the time I had arranged, and I went off without thinking of the girl I had met at the baroness's. But we had not gone two hundred paces when the postillion stopped, a bundle of linen whirled through the window into the carriage, and the governess got in. I gave her a hearty welcome by embracing her, and made her sit down beside me, and so we drove off.

In the ensuing chapter the reader will become more fully acquainted with my fresh conquest. In the meantime let him imagine me rolling peacefully along the Dresden road.

CHAPTER XXIII

My Arrival at Dresden with Maton—She Makes Me a Present—Leipzig—Castelbajac—Schwerin—Return to Dresden and Departure—I Arrive at Vienna—Pocchini's Vengeance

WHEN I saw myself in the carriage with this pretty girl, who had fallen on me as if from the clouds, I imagined I was intended to shape her destiny. Her tutelary genius must have placed her in my hands, for I felt inclined to do her all the good that lay in my power. But for myself; was it a piece of good or ill luck for me? I formed the question, but felt that time alone could give the answer. I knew that I was still living in my old style, while I was beginning to feel that I was no longer a young man.

I was sure that my new companion could not have abandoned herself to me in this manner, without having made up her mind to be complaisant; but this was not enough for me, it was my humour to be loved. This was my chief aim, everything else was only fleeting enjoyment, and as I had not had a love affair since I parted with Zaira, I hoped most fervently that the present adventure would prove to be one.

Before long I learnt that my companion's name was Maton; this at least was her surname, and I did not feel any curiosity to know the name of the he or she saint whom her godmothers had constituted her patron at the baptismal font. I asked her if she could write French as well as she spoke it, and she shewed me a letter by way of sample. It assured me that she had received an excellent education, and this fact increased my pleasure in the conquest I had made. She said she had left Breslau without telling her aunt or her cousin that she was going, perhaps never to return.

"How about your belongings?"

"Belongings? They were not worth the trouble of gathering together. All I have is included in that small package, which contains a chemise, a pair of stockings, some handkerchiefs, and a few nick-nacks."

"What will your lover say?"

"Alas! I haven't got one to say anything."

"I cannot credit that."

"I have had two lovers; the first one was a rascal, who took advantage of my innocence to seduce me, and then left me when I ceased to present any novelty for him; my second was an honest man, but a poor lieutenant with no prospects of getting on. He has not abandoned me, but his regiment was ordered to Stetin, and since then——"

"And since then?"

"We were too poor to write to one another, so we had to suffer in silence."

This pathetic history seemed to bear the marks of truth; and I thought it very possible that Maton had only come with me to make her fortune or to do rather better than she had been doing, which would not be difficult. She was twenty-five years old, and as she had never been out of Breslau before, she would doubtless be delighted to see what the world was like at Dresden. I could not help feeling that I had been a fool to burden myself with the girl, who would most likely cost me a lot of money; but still I found my conduct excusable, as the chances were a hundred to one against her accepting the proposal I had been foolish enough to make. In short, I resolved to enjoy the pleasure of having a pretty girl all to myself, and I determined not to do anything during the journey, being anxious to see whether her moral qualities would plead as strongly with me as her physical beauty undoubtedly did. At nightfall I stopped, wishing to spend the night at the posting-station. Maton, who had been very hungry all day, but had not dared to tell me so, ate with an amazing and pleasing appetite; but not being accustomed to wine, she would have fallen asleep at table, if I had not begged her to retire. She begged my pardon, assuring me she would not let such a thing occur again. I smiled by way of reply, and stayed at the table, not looking to see whether she undressed or went to bed in her clothes. I went to bed myself soon after, and at five o'clock was up again to order the coffee, and to see that the horses were put in. Maton was lying on her bed with all her clothes on, fast asleep, and perspiring with the heat. I woke her, telling her that another time she must sleep more comfortably, as such heats were injurious to health.

She got up and left the room, no doubt to wash, for she returned looking fresh and gay, and bade me good day, and asked me if I would like to give her a kiss.

"I shall be delighted," I replied; and, after kissing her, I made her hurry over the breakfast, as I wished to reach Dresden that evening. However, I could not manage it, my carriage broke down, and took five hours to mend, so I had to sleep at another posting station. Maton undressed this time, but I had the firmness not to look at her.

When I reached Dresden I put up at the "Hotel de Saxe," taking the whole of the first floor. My mother was in the country, and I paid her a visit, much to her delight; we made quite an affecting picture, with my arm in a sling. I also saw my brother John and his wife Thérèse, Roland, and a Roman girl whom I had known before him, and who made much of me. I also saw my sister, and I then went with my brother to pay my suit to Count Brühl and to his wife, the daughter of the palatin of Kiowia, who was delighted to hear news of her family. I was welcomed everywhere, and everywhere I had to tell the story of my duel. I confess that very little pressing was required, for I was very proud of it.

At this period the States were assembled in Dresden, and Prince Xavier, uncle of the Elector, was regent during his minority.

The same evening I went to the opera-house, where faro was played. I played, but prudently, for my capital only consisted of eighteen hundred ducats.

When I came back we had a good supper, and Maton pleased me both by her appetite and amiability. When we had finished I affectionately asked her if she would like to share my bed, and she replied as tenderly that she was wholly mine. And so, after passing a voluptuous night, we rose in the morning the best friends in the world.

I spent the whole morning in furnishing her toilette. A good many people called on me, and wanted to be presented to Maton; but my answer was that, as she was only my housekeeper, and not my wife, I could not have the pleasure of introducing her. In the same way I had instructed her that she was not to let anyone in when I was away. She was working in her room on the linen I had provided for her, aided in her task by a seamstress. Nevertheless, I did not want to make her a slave, so I occasionally took her into the pleasant suburbs of Dresden, where she was at liberty to speak to any of my acquaintances we might meet.

This reserve of mine which lasted for the fortnight we stayed in Dresden was mortifying for all the young officers in the place, and especially for the Comte de Bellegarde, who was not accustomed to being denied any girl to whom he chose to take a fancy. He was a fine young fellow, of great boldness and even impudence, and one day he came into our room and asked me to give him a dinner just as Maton and myself were sitting down to table. I could not refuse him, and I could not request Maton to leave the room, so from the beginning to the end of the meal he showered his military jokes and attentions on her, though he was perfectly polite the whole time. Maton behaved very well; she was not prudish, nor did she forget the respect she owed to me and indeed to herself.

I was accustomed to take a siesta every day after dinner, so half an hour after the conclusion of the meal I stated the fact and begged him to leave us. He asked smilingly if the lady took a siesta too, and I replied that we usually took it together. This made him take up his hat and cane, and as he did so he asked us both to dine with him the next day. I replied that I never took Maton out anywhere, but that he would be welcome to come and take pot-luck with us every day if he liked.

This refusal exhausted his resources, and he took his leave if not angrily, at least very coldly.

My mother returned to her town apartments, which were opposite to mine, and the next day when I was calling on her I noticed the *erker* (a sort of grating in the Spanish fashion) which indicated my rooms in the hotel. I happened to look in that direction and I saw

Maton at the window standing up and talking to M. de Bellegarde, who was at a neighbouring window. This window belonged to a room which adjoined my suite of rooms, but did not belong to it. This discovery amused me. I knew what I was about, and did not fear to be made a cuckold in spite of myself. I was sure I had not been observed, and I was not going to allow any trespassers. I was jealous, in fact; but the jealousy was of the mind, not the heart.

I came in to dinner in the highest spirits, and Maton was as gay as myself. I led the conversation up to Bellegarde, and said I believed him to be in love with her.

"Oh, he is like all officers with girls; but I don't think he is more in love with me than any other girl."

"Oh, but didn't he come to call on me this morning?"

"Certainly not; and if he had come the maid would have told him you were out."

"Did you not notice him walking up and down under the windows?"

"No."

This was enough for me; I knew they had laid a plot together. Maton was deceiving me, and I should be cheated in twenty-four hours unless I took care. At my age such treason should not have astonished me, but my vanity would not allow me to admit the fact.

I dissembled my feelings and caressed the traitress, and then leaving the house I went to the theatre where I played with some success and returned home while the second act was in progress; it was still daylight. The waiter was at the door, and I asked him whether there were any rooms besides those which I occupied on the first floor.

"Yes, two rooms, both looking on the street."

"Tell the landlord that I will take them both."

"They were taken yesterday evening."

"By whom?"

"By a Swiss officer, who is entertaining a party of friends to supper here this evening."

I said no more lest I should awaken suspicion; but I felt sure that Bellegarde could easily obtain access to my rooms from his. Indeed, there was a door leading to the room where Maton slept with her maid when I did not care to have her in my room. The door was bolted on her side, but as she was in the plot there was not much security in this.

I went upstairs softly, and finding Maton on the balcony, I said, after some indifferent conversation, that I should like to change rooms.

"You shall have my room," I said, "and I will have yours; I can read there, and see the people going by."

She thought it a very good idea, and added that it would serve us both if I would allow her to sit there when I was out.

This reply shewed me that Maton was an old hand, and that I had better give her up if I did not wish to be duped.

I changed the rooms, and we supped pleasantly together, laughing and talking, and in spite of all her craft Maton did not notice any change in me.

I remained alone in my new room, and soon heard the voices of Bellegarde and his merry companions. I went on to the balcony, but the curtains of Bellegarde's room were drawn, as if to assure me that there was no complot. However, I was not so easily deceived, and I found afterwards that Mercury had warned Jupiter that Amphytrion had changed his room.

Next day, a severe headache, a thing from which I

seldom suffer, kept me to the house all day. I had myself let blood, and my worthy mother, who came to keep me company, dined with Maton. My mother had taken a weakness for the girl, and had often asked me to let her come and see her, but I had the good sense to refuse this request. The next day I was still far from well, and took medicine, and in the evening, to my horror, I found myself attacked by a fearful disease. This must be a present from Maton, for I had not known anyone else since leaving Leopol. I spent a troubled night, rage and indignation being my principal emotions; and next morning, coming upon Maton suddenly, I found everything in the most disgusting state. The wretched creature confessed she had been infected for the last six months, but that she had hoped not to give it me, as she had washed herself carefully whenever she thought I was going to have to do with her.

"Wretch, you have poisoned me; but nobody shall know it, as it is by my own fault, and I am ashamed of it. Get up, and you shall see how generous I can be."

She got up, and I had all the linen I had given her packed into a trunk. This done, I told my man to take a small room for her at another inn. His errand was soon over, and I then told Maton to go immediately, as I had done with her. I gave her fifty crowns, and made her sign a receipt specifying the reason why I had sent her away, and acknowledging that she had no further claim upon me. The conditions were humiliating, and she wished me to soften them down, but she soon gave in when I told her that unless she signed I would turn her into the streets as naked as when I found her.

"What am I to do here? I don't know anyone."

"If you like to return to Breslau I will pay your expenses there."

She made no answer, so I sent her away bag and baggage, and merely turned my back on her when she went down on her knees to excite my compassion.

I got rid of her without the slightest feeling of pity, for from what she had done to me and from what she was preparing to do I considered her as a mere monster, who would sooner or later have cost me my life.

I left the inn the following day, and I took a furnished apartment on the first floor of the house where my mother lived for six months, and proceeded about my cure. Everyone asked me what I had done with my housekeeper, and I said that having no further need of her services I had sent her away.

A week afterwards my brother John came to tell me that Bellegarde and five or six of his friends were on the sick list; Maton had certainly lost no time.

"I am sorry for them, but it's their own fault; why didn't they take more care?"

"But the girl came to Dresden with you."

"Yes, and I sent her about her business. It was enough for me to keep them off while she was under my charge. Tell them that if they complain of me they are wrong, and still more wrong to publish their shame. Let them learn discretion and get themselves cured in secrecy, if they do not want sensible men to laugh at them. Don't you think I am right?"

"The adventure is not a very honourable one for you."

"I know it, and that's why I say nothing; I am not such a fool as to proclaim my shame from the housetops. These friends of yours must be simpletons indeed; they must have known that I had good reasons for sending the girl away, and should consequently have been on their guard. They deserve what they got, and I hope it may be a lesson to them."

"They are all astonished at your being well."

"You may comfort them by saying that I have been as badly treated as they, but that I have held my tongue, not wishing to pass for a simpleton."

Poor John saw he had been a simpleton himself and departed in silence. I put myself under a severe diet, and by the middle of August my health was re-established.

About this time, Prince Adam Czartoryski's sister came to Dresden, lodging with Count Brühl. I had the honour of paying my court to her, and I heard from her own mouth that her royal cousin had had the weakness to let himself be imposed on by calumnies about me. I told her that I was of Ariosto's opinion—that all the virtues are nothing worth unless they are covered with the veil of constancy.

"You saw yourself when I supped with you, how his majesty completely ignored me. Your highness will be going to Paris next year; you will meet me there and you can write to the king that if I had been burnt in effigy I should not venture to shew myself."

The September fair being a great occasion at Leipzig, I went there to regain my size by eating larks, for which Leipzig is justly famous. I had played a cautious but a winning game at Dresden, the result of which had been the gain of some hundreds of ducats, so I was able to start for Leipzig with a letter of credit for three thousand crowns on the banker Hohman, an intelligent old man of upwards of eighty. It was of him I heard that the hair of the Empress of Russia, which looked a dark brown or even black, had been originally quite fair. The old banker had seen her at Stettin every day between her seventh and tenth years, and told me that even then they had begun to comb her hair with lead combs, and to rub a certain composition into it. From an early age Catherine had been looked upon as the future bride of the Duke of Holstein, afterwards the hapless Peter III. The Russians are fair as a rule, and so it was thought fit that the reigning family should be dark.

Here I will note down a pleasant adventure I had at Leipzig. The Princess of Aremberg had arrived from Vienna, and was staying at the same hotel as myself. She took a fancy to go to the fair incognito, and as she had a large suite she dressed up one of her maids as the princess, and mingled with her following. I suppose my readers to be aware that this princess was witty and beautiful, and that she was the favourite mistress of the Emperor Francis the First.

I heard of his masquerade, and leaving my hotel at the same time I followed her till she stopped at a stall, and then going up to her and addressing her as one would any other maid, I asked if that (pointing at the false princess) were really the famous Princess of Aremberg.

"Certainly," she replied.

"I can scarcely believe it, for she is not pretty, and she has not the look nor the manners of a princess."

"Perhaps you are not a good judge of princesses."

"I have seen enough of them anyhow, and to prove that I am a good judge I say that it is you who ought to be the princess; I would willingly give a hundred ducats to spend the night with you."

"A hundred ducats! What would you do if I were to take you at your word?"

"Try me. I lodge at the same hotel as you, and if you can contrive ways and means, I will give you the money in advance, but not till I am sure of my prize, for I don't like being taken in."

"Very good. Say not a word to anyone, but try to

speak with me either before or after supper. If you are brave enough to face certain risks, we will spend the night together."

"What is your name?"

"Caroline."

I felt certain it would come to nothing, but I was glad to have amused the princess, and to have let her know that I appreciated her beauties, and I resolved to go on with the part I was playing.

About supper-time I began a promenade near the princess's apartments, stopping every now and then in front of the room where her women were sitting, till one of them came out to ask me if I wanted anything.

"I want to speak for a moment to one of your companions to whom I had the pleasure of talking at the fair."

"You mean Caroline, I expect?"

"Yes."

"She is waiting on the princess, but she will be out in half an hour."

I spent this half hour in my own room, and then returned to dance attendance. Before long the same maid to whom I had spoken came up to me and told me to wait in a closet which she shewed me, telling me that Caroline would be there before long. I went into the closet, which was small, dark, and uncomfortable. I was soon joined by a woman. This time I was sure it was the real Caroline, but I said nothing.

She came in, took my hand, and told me that if I would wait there she would come to me as soon as her mistress was in bed.

"Without any light?"

"Of course, or else the people of the house would notice it, and I should not like that."

"I cannot do anything without light, charming Caroline; and besides, this closet is not a very nice place to pass five or six hours. There is another alternative, the first room above is mine. I shall be alone, and I swear to you that no one shall come in; come up and make me happy; I have got the hundred ducats here."

"Impossible! I dare not go upstairs for a million ducats."

"So much the worse for you, as I am not going to stay in this hole which has only a chair in it, if you offer me a million and a half. Farewell, sweet Caroline."

"Wait a moment; let me go out first."

The sly puss went out quickly enough, but I was as sharp as she, and trod on the tail of her dress so that she could not shut the door after her. So we went out together, and I left her at the door, saying,——

"Good night, Caroline, you see it was no use."

I went to bed well pleased with the incident. The princess, it was plain, had intended to make me pass the night in the hole of a closet, as a punishment for having dared to ask the mistress of an emperor to sleep with me for a hundred crowns.

Two days later, as I was buying a pair of lace cuffs, the princess came into the shop with Count Zinzendorf, whom I had known at Paris twelve years before. Just as I was making way for the lady the count recognized me, and asked me if I knew anything about the Casanova that had fought the duel at Warsaw.

"Alas! count, I am that Casanova, and here is my arm still in a sling."

"I congratulate you, my dear fellow; I should like to hear about it."

With these words he introduced me to the princess, asking her if she had heard of the duel.

"Yes; I heard something about it in the papers. So this is the hero of the tale. Delighted to make your acquaintance."

The princess spoke with great kindness, but with the cool politeness of the Court. She did not give me the slightest sign of recognition, and of course I imitated her in her reserve.

I visited the count in the afternoon, and he begged me to come and see the princess, who would be delighted to hear the account of my duel from my own lips, and I followed him to her apartment with pleasure. The princess listened to my narrative in stately sort, and her women never looked at me. She went away the day after, and the story went no farther.

Towards the end of the fair I received a very unexpected visit from the fair Madame Castelbajac. I was just sitting down to table to eat a dozen larks, when she made her appearance.

"What, madam, you here!"

"Yes, to my sorrow. I have been here for the last three weeks, and have seen you several times, but you have always avoided us."

"Who are 'us'?"

"Schwerin and myself."

"Schwerin is here, is he?"

"Yes; and in prison on account of a forged bill. I am sure I do not know what they will do to the poor wretch. He would have been wise to have fled, but it seems as if he wanted to get hanged."

"And you have been with him ever since you left England? that is, three years ago."

"Exactly. Our occupation is robbing, cheating, and escaping from one land to another. Never was a woman so unhappy as I."

"For how much is the forged bill?"

"For three hundred crowns. Do a generous action M. Casanova, and let bygones be bygones; deliver the poor wretch from the gallows and me from death, for if he is hanged I shall kill myself."

"Indeed, madam, he may hang for me, for he did his best to send me to the gallows with his forged bills; but I confess I pity you. So much, indeed, that I invite you to come to Dresden with me the day after to-morrow, and I promise to give you three hundred crowns as soon as Schwerin has undergone the extreme penalty of the law. I can't understand how a woman like you can have fallen in love with a man that has neither face, nor talents, nor wit, nor fortune, for all that he has to boast of is his name of Schwerin."

"I confess, to my shame, that I never loved him. Ever since the other rogue, Castelbajac—who, by the way, was never married to me—made me know him, I have only lived with him by force, though his tears and his despairs have excited my compassion. If destiny had given me an honest man in his stead, I would have forsaken him long ago, for sooner or later he will be the death of me."

"Where do you live?"

"Nowhere. I have been turned out into the street with nothing but the clothes on my back. Have compassion on me."

With these words the hapless woman threw herself at my knees and burst into tears. I was much affected. The waiter of the inn stood staring with amazement till I told him to go out. I may safely say that this woman was one of the most handsome in France; she was probably about twenty-six years old. She had been the wife of a druggist of Montpellier, and had been so unfortunate as to let Castelbajac seduce her. At London her beauty had produced no impression on me, my heart was anothers; nevertheless, she was made to seduce the heart of man.

I raised her from her knees, and said I felt inclined to help her, but that in the first place she must calm herself, and in the second share my supper. The waiter brought another bed and put it in my room, without receiving any orders to do so; this made me feel inclined to laugh.

The appetite with which the poor woman ate, despite her sorrow, reminded me of the matron of Ephesus. When supper was over I gave her her choice: she might either stay in Leipzig and fare as best she might, or I would reclaim her effects, take her with me to Dresden, and pay her a hundred gold ducats as soon as I could be certain that she would not give the money to the wretch who had reduced her to such an extremity. She did not ask much time for reflection. She said that it would be no good for her to stay in Leipzig, for she could do nothing for the wretched Schwerin or even keep herself for a day, for she had not got a farthing. She would have to beg or to become a prostitute, and she could not make up her mind to either course.

"Indeed," she concluded, "if you were to give me the hundred ducats this moment, and I used them to free Schwerin, I should be no better off than before; so I accept your generous offer thankfully."

I embraced her, promised to get back what her landlord had seized for rent, and then begged her to go to bed, as she was in need of rest.

"I see," she answered, "that either out of liking or for politeness' sake you will ask me for those favours which I should be only too happy to grant, but if I allowed that it would be a bad return indeed for your kindness. Look at my linen, and behold in what a state that unhappy wretch has left me!"

I saw that I ran the risk of being infected again, and thanked her for warning me of the danger I ran. In spite of her faults she was a woman of feeling, and had an excellent heart, and from these good qualitites of hers proceeded all her misfortunes.

The next morning I arranged for the redemption of her effects, which cost me sixty crowns of Saxony, and in the afternoon the poor woman saw herself once more in possession of her belongings, which she had thought never to see again. She seemed profoundly grateful, and deplored her state, which hindered her from proving the warmth of her feelings.

Such is the way of women: a grateful woman has only one way of shewing her gratitude, and that is to surrender herself without reserve. A man is different, but we are differently constituted; a man is made to give and a woman to receive.

The next day, a short while before we left, the broker I had employed in the redemption of the lady's effects, told me that the banker, whom Schwerin had cheated, was going to send an express to Berlin, to enquire whether the king would object to Count Schwerin's being proceeded against with the utmost rigour of the law.

"Alas!" cried his late mistress, "that's what he was most afraid of. It's all up with him. The King of Prussia will pay his debts, but he will end his days at Spandau. Why didn't they put him there before I ever knew him?"

She left Leipzig with me, and our appearance at Dresden caused a good deal of surprise. She was not a mere girl, like Maton; she had a good appearance, and a modest yet distinguished manner. I called her Countess Blasin, and introduced her to my mother and relations, and put her in my best room. I summoned the doctor who had treated me, and made him swear not to disclose the countess's state, but to tell everyone that he came to see me. I took her to the theatre, and it was my humour to have her regarded as a person of distinction. Good treatment soon restored her to health, and by the end of November she believed herself in a state to reward me for my kindness.

The wedding was a secret one, but none the less pleasant; and as if by way of wedding present the next day I heard that the King of Prussia had paid Schwerin's debts, and had had him brought to Berlin under a strong escort. If he is alive, the rascal is at Spandau to this day.

The time had come for me to pay her the hundred ducats. I told her frankly that I was obliged to go to Portugal, and that I could not make my appearance there in company with a pretty woman without failing in my project. I added that my means would not allow me to pay double expenses for so long a journey.

She had received too many proofs of my love to think for a moment that I had got tired of her, and wanted to be on with some other woman. She told me that she owed everything to me, while I owed nothing to her; and that all she asked of me was to enable her to return to Montpellier.

"I have relations there," said she, "who will be glad to see me, and I hope that my husband will let me return to him. I am the Prodigal Son, and I hope to find in him the forgiving father."

I told her I would do my utmost to send her home in safety and comfort.

Towards the middle of December I left Dresden with Madame Blasin. My purse only contained four hundred ducats, for I had had a run of bad luck at play; and the journey to Leipzig had cost me altogether three hundred ducats. I told my mistress nothing of all this, for my only thought was how to please her.

We stayed a short while at Prague, and reached Vienna on Christmas Day. We put up at the "Red Bull," the Countess Blasin (who had been transformed into a milliner) in one room, and I in another, so that we might pass for strangers while continuing our intimacy.

The next morning, as we were taking coffee together, two individuals came into the room, and asked the rude question,——

"Who are you, madam?"

"My name is Blasin."

"Who is this gentleman?"

"You had better ask him."

"What are you doing at Vienna?"

"Taking coffee. I should have thought you could have seen that for yourselves."

"If the gentleman is not your husband, you will leave the town within twenty-four hours."

"The gentleman is my friend, and not my husband; and I shall leave Vienna exactly when I choose, unless you make me go away by force."

"Very good. We are aware, sir, that you have a separate room, but that makes no difference."

Thereupon one of the policemen entered my room, I following him.

"What do you want here?" said I.

"I am looking at your bed, and I can see you have not slept in it. That's enough."

"The devil! What business have you here at all, and who authorizes such disgraceful proceedings?"

He made no reply, but returned to Madame Blasin's room, where they both ordered her to leave Vienna in the course of twenty-four hours, and then they both left us.

"Dress yourself," said I to her, and tell the French ambassador the whole story. Tell him that you are a milliner, Blasin by name, and that all you want is to go from here to Strasburg, and from there to Montpellier."

While she was dressing I ordered a carriage and a servant to be in attendance. She returned in an hour's time, and said the ambassador had assured her that she would be left alone, and need not leave Vienna till she thought fit. I took her to mass in triumph, and then, as the weather was bad, we spent the rest of the day in eating and drinking and sitting by the fire.

At eight o'clock in the evening the landlord came up and said very politely that he had been ordered by the police to give the lady a room at some distance from mine, and that he was obliged to obey.

"I am quite ready to change my room," said Madame Blasin, with a smile.

"Is the lady to sup alone?" I asked.

"I have received no instructions on that point."

"Then I will sup with her, and I hope you will treat us well."

"You shall be well served, sir."

In spite of the detestable and tyrannical police we spent the last four days and nights together in the closest intimacy. When she left I wanted her to take fifty louis; but she would only have thirty, saying that she could travel to Montpellier on that sum, and have money in her pocket when she got there. Our parting was an affecting one. She wrote to me from Strasburg, and we shall hear of her again when I describe my visit to Montpellier.

The first day of the year 1767 I took an apartment in the house of a certain Mr. Schroder, and I took letters of introduction to Madame de Salmor and Madame de Stahremberg. I then called on the elder Calsabigi, who was in the service of Prince Kaunitz.

This Calsabigi, whose whole body was one mass of eruption, always worked in bed, and the minister, his master, went to see him almost every day. I went constantly to the theatre, where Madame Vestris was dancing. On January the 7th or 8th, I saw the empress dowager come to the theatre dressed in black; she was received with applause, as this was the first appearance she had made since the death of her husband. At Vienna I met the Comte de la Perouse, who was trying to induce the empress to give him half a million of florins, which Charles VI. owed his father. Through him I made the acquaintance of the Spaniard Las Casas, a man of intelligence, and, what is a rare thing in a Spaniard, free from prejudices. I also met at the count's house the Venetian Uccelli, with whom I had been at St. Cyprian's College at Muran; he was, at the time of which I write, secretary to the ambassador, Polo Renieri. This gentleman had a great esteem for me, but my affair with the State Inquisitors prevented him from receiving me. My friend Campioni arrived at this date from Warsaw; he had passed through Cracovia. I accommodated him in my apartment with great pleasure. He had an engagement at London, but to my great delight he was able to spend a couple of months with me.

Prince Charles of Courland, who had been at Venice

and had been well received by M. de Bragadin and my
other friends, had been in Vienna and had left it a
fortnight before my arrival to return to Venice. Prince
Charles wrote to tell me that there was no bounds to
the care and kindness of my Venetian friends, and that
he would be grateful to me for all his days.

I lived very quietly at Vienna; my health was good,
and I thought of nothing but my journey to Portugal,
which I intended to take place in the spring. I saw no
company of any kind, whether good or ill. I often
called on Calsabigi, who made a parade of his Atheism,
and slandered my friend Metastasio, who dispised him.
Calsabigi knew it and laughed at him; he was a profound
politician and the right hand of Prince Kaunitz.

One day after dinner, as I was sitting at table with
my friend Campioni, a pretty little girl, between twelve
and thirteen, as I should imagine, came into my room
with mingled boldness and fear, and made me a low bow.
I asked her what she wanted, and she replied in Latin
verse to the effect that her mother was in the next
room, and that if I liked she would come in. I replied
in Latin prose that I did not care about seeing her mother,
telling her my reasons with great plainness. She replied
with four Latin lines, but as they were not to the point
I could see that she had learnt them by heart, and repeated them like a parrot. She went on—still in
Latin verse—to tell me that her mother must come in or
else the authorities might think I was abusing her.

This last phrase was uttered with all the directness
of the Latin style. It made me burst out laughing,
and I felt inclined to explain to her what she had said
in her own language. The little slut told me she was
a Venetian, and this putting me at my ease I told her
that the authorities would never suspect her of doing

such a thing as she was too young. At this the girl seemed to reflect a moment, and then recited some verses from the *Priapeia* to the effect that unripe fruit is often more piquant than that which is ripe. This was enough to set me on fire, and Campioni, seeing that he was not wanted, went back to his room.

I drew her gently to me and asked her if her father was at Vienna. She said yes, and instead of repulsing my caresses she proceeded to accompany my actions with the recital of erotic verses. I sent her away with a fee of two ducats, but before she went she gave me her address written in German with four Latin verses beneath, stating that her bedfellow would find her either Hebe or Ganymede, according to his liking.

I could not help admiring the ingenuity of her father, who thus contrived to make a living out of his daughters. She was a pretty girl enough, but at Vienna pretty girls are so common that they often have to starve in spite of their charms. The Latin verses had been thrown in as an attraction in this case, but I did not think she would find it very remunerative in Vienna.

Next evening my evil genius made me go and seek her out at the address she had given me. Although I was forty-two years old, in spite of the experience I had had, I was so foolish as to go alone. The girl saw me coming from the window, and guessing that I was looking for her, she came down and shewed me in. I went in, I went upstairs, and when I found myself in the presence of the wretch Pocchini my blood froze in my veins. A feeling of false shame prevented my retracing my steps, as it might have looked as if I had been afraid. In the same room were his pretended wife, Catina, two Sclavonic-looking assassins, and the decoy-duck. I saw that this was not a laughing matter, so I dissembled to the best of my ability, and made up my mind to leave the place in five minutes' time.

Pocchini, swearing and blaspheming, began to reproach me with the manner in which I had treated him in England, and said that his time had come, and that my life was in his hands. One of the two Sclavs broke in, and said we must make friends, and so made me sit down, opened a bottle, and said we must drink together. I tried to put as good a face upon it as I could, but I begged to be excused, on which Pocchini swore that I was afraid of having to pay for the bottle of wine.

"You are mistaken," said I; "I am quite ready to pay."

I put my hand in my pocket to take out a ducat without drawing out my purse, but the Sclav told me I need not be afraid, as I was amongst honest people. Again shame made me yield, and as I had some difficulty in extracting my purse, the Sclav kindly did it for me. Pocchini immediately snatched it from his hands, and said he should keep it as part compensation for all I had made him endure.

I saw that it was a concerted scheme, and said with a smile that he could do as he liked, and so I rose to leave them. The Sclav said we must embrace each other, and on my declaring that to be unnecessary, he and his comrade drew their sabres, and I thought myself undone. Without more ado, I hastened to embrace them. To my astonishment they let me go, and I went home in a grievous state, and not knowing what else to do went to bed.

the best of my ability, and made up my mind to take
the place in five minutes' time.

"Possibly," swearing and blaspheming, began to reproach me with the manner in which I had treated him
in England, and said that his time had come, and that
my life was in his hands. One of the two pistols broke in
and said we must make friends, and so made the sit-
down opened a bottle, and said we must drink together.
I tried to put an end at once upon it as I could, but I
begged to be excused, on which Pocchini swore that I
was afraid of having to pay for the bottle of wine.

"Not so quickly," said I, "I am quite ready to
pay."

I put my hand in my pocket to take out a dozen with
out drawing out my purse, but this Seller told me I had
not to afford as I was amongst honest people. Again
their madness yield, and as I had some difficulty in
rescuing all safe, the seller liberty paid it for me
Pocchini busied to snatching it from his hands and
said he should have it to part compensation for all I
had made him endure.

I saw that it was a concerted scheme and did this
while that he could do as he liked, and as I was to
leave them. The seller said we must remain each man
all on my imagining that he had a dimension we had the
company drink their supper call I decide in my pre-
dons. Without more ado I hastened to embrace from
Pocchini demanded that the two rascals and I were home
in a desperate state, and on leaving the place we read
all at last.